UNOBTRUSIVE MEASURES

Nonreactive Research in the Social Sciences

UNOBTRUSIVE MEASURES

Nonreactive Research in the Social Sciences

EUGENE J. WEBB
Stanford University

DONALD T. CAMPBELL
RICHARD D. SCHWARTZ
LEE SECHREST
Northwestern University

RAND McNALLY & COMPANY • CHICAGO

Rand McNally Sociology Series

Edgar F. Borgatta, *Advisory Editor*

Seventh Printing, 1971

Preface

This monograph has had a series of working titles, and we should identify them for the benefit of our friends who shared early drafts. To some, this is *The Bullfighter's Beard* — a provocative, if uncommunicative, title drawn from the observation that toreros' beards are longer on the day of the fight than on any other day. No one seems to know if the torero's beard really grows faster that day because of anxiety or if he simply stands further away from the blade, shaking razor in hand. Either way, there were not enough American aficionados to get the point, so we added ... *and Other Nonreactive Measures*.

This title lasted for a while, but the occasionally bizarre content of the material shifted the working title to *Oddball Research, Oddball Measures*, and the like. Most of our friends have known the manuscript under one of the "oddball" labels, and it is only a fear of librarians that has caused us to drop it. In this day of explicit indexing, we feared that the book would nestle on a shelf between *Notes for the T Quarterback* and *Putting Hints for Beginning Golfers*. As much as we might enjoy the company of an Arnold Palmer, we prefer it outside the library. A widely circulated version used the non-title *Other Measures*. The list of titles we have specifically decided *not* to use is even longer and less descriptively adequate.

In presenting these novel methods, we have purposely avoided consideration of the ethical issues which they raise. We have done so because we feel that this is a matter for separate consideration. Some readers will find none of the methods objectionable, others may find virtually all of them open to question. Each school is welcome to use this compilation to buttress its position — either to illustrate the harmless ingenuity of social scientists or to marshal a parade of horribles. Although the authors vary in moral boiling points, we are all between these positions. Some of the methods described strike us as possibly unethical; their inclusion is not intended as a warrant for their use. But we vary among ourselves in criteria and application. We do not feel able at this point to prepare a compelling ethical resolution of these complex issues. Nonetheless, we recognize the need of such a resolution and hope that our compilation will, among other things, stimulate and expedite thoughtful debate on these matters.

Perhaps the most extreme position on this matter has been stated by Edward Shils (1959). He asserts that all social science activity should be disciplined by careful attention to the problem of privacy. He would rule out any "observations of private behavior, however technically feasible, without the explicit and fully informed permission of the person to be approved." His concern on this issue would lead him to recommend that questionnaire and interview studies be sharply limited by ethical considerations. Among the practices he deplores are (1) the simulation of warmth by the interviewer to insure rapport and (2) giving the appearance of agreement to answers on controversial questions to encourage the expression of unpopular attitudes.

He would have the interviewer not only avoid such practices but also disclose, presumably in advance, his purpose in asking the question. This disclosure should include not only a statement of the researcher's "personal goal, e.g., to complete a thesis" but also his "cognitive intention." Groups or types of questions "ought to be justified by the explanation of what the answers will contribute to the clarification of the problem being investigated." Even the technique of participant observation seems to Shils "morally obnoxious . . . manipulation" unless the observer discloses at the outset his intention of conducting a social scientific investigation.

Most social scientists would find this position too extreme. If it were adopted, it would add enormously to the problems of reactivity with which this monograph is primarily concerned. Nevertheless, Shils' position specifies some of the dangers to the citizen and social science of an unconscionable invasion of privacy. Few would deny that social scientists can go too far in intruding on privacy. Recording deliberations in a jury room or hiding under beds to record pillow talk are techniques which have led to moral revulsion on the part of large numbers of professionals. Manipulations aimed at the arousal of anxiety or extreme aggression could conceivably produce lasting damage to the psychological health of experimental subjects.

What is needed is a set of criteria by which various research techniques can be appraised morally. Each of the social sciences has attempted to develop a code of ethics for guidance in these matters. So far, however, these have suffered from the absence of a careful analysis of the problem. We need a specification of the multiple interests potentially threatened by social science research: the privacy of the individual, his freedom from manipulation, the protection of the aura of trust on which the society depends, and, by no means least in importance, the good reputation of social science.

The multiple methods presented here may do more than raise these questions for discussion. They may provide alternatives by which ethical criteria can be met without impinging on important interests of the research subjects. Some of the methods described here, such as the use of archival records and trace measures, may serve to avoid the problems of invasion of privacy by permitting the researcher to gain valuable information without ever identifying the individual actors or in any way manipulating them. If ethical considerations lead us to avoid participant observation, interviews, or eavesdropping in given circumstances, the novel methods described in this monograph may be of value not only in improving and supplementing our information but also in permitting ethically scrupulous social scientists to do their work effectively and to sleep better at night.

We received notable aid from the following of our associates: Howard S. Becker, James H. Crouse, Kay C. Kujala, Irene E. Nolte, Michael L. Ray, Jerry R. Salancik, Carole R. Siegman, Gerald Solomon, and Susan H. Stocking. The acute eye and sensitive pen of Rand McNally's Lucia Boyden we bow before.

This study was supported in part by Project C-998, Contract 3-20-001, with the Media Research Branch, Office of Education, U. S. Department of Health, Education and Welfare, under provisions of Title VII of the National Defense Education Act.

Grateful acknowledgment is made to the following for permission to use copyrighted material:
American Journal of Psychology; Annual Review of Psycho-

logy; Atheneum Publishers; Basic Books; Cambridge University Press; Criterion Books; Doubleday; Free Press of Glencoe and Macmillan; Harcourt, Brace and World; Holt, Rinehart and Winston; *Human Organization* and the Society for Applied Anthropology; Little, Brown and Company; *Public Opinion Quarterly;* Oxford University Press; Simon & Schuster; *Speech Monographs* and the Speech Association of America; University of Chicago, Graduate School of Business; and Yale University Press.

The errors which have penetrated the perimeter of our friends we acknowledge. Surely every reader will think of studies which could have been included, yet were heinously omitted. If such studies are sent to the senior author, at Northwestern, an amended bibliography will be prepared and distributed — either in another edition of this book or separately.

E.J.W.
D.T.C.
R.D.S.
L.S.

Evanston, Illinois
June, 1965

To the memory of Sir Francis Galton

Table of Contents

UNOBTRUSIVE MEASURES

Nonreactive Research in the Social Sciences

CHAPTER 1

Approximations to Knowledge

This survey directs attention to social science research data *not* obtained by interview or questionnaire. Some may think this exclusion does not leave much. It does. Many innovations in research method are to be found scattered throughout the social science literature. Their use, however, is unsystematic, their importance understated. Our review of this material is intended to broaden the social scientist's currently narrow range of utilized methodologies and to encourage creative and opportunistic exploitation of unique measurement possibilities.

Today, the dominant mass of social science research is based upon interviews and questionnaires. We lament this overdependence upon a single, fallible method. Interviews and questionnaires intrude as a foreign element into the social setting they would describe, they create as well as measure attitudes, they elicit atypical roles and responses, they are limited to those who are accessible and will cooperate, and the responses obtained are produced in part by dimensions of individual differences irrelevant to the topic at hand.

But the principal objection is that they are used alone. No research method is without bias. Interviews and questionnaires must be supplemented by methods testing the same social science variables but having *different* methodological weaknesses.

In sampling the range of alternative approaches, we examine their weaknesses, too. The flaws are serious and give insight into why we do depend so much upon the interview. But the issue is not choosing among individual methods. Rather it is the necessity for a multiple operationism, a collection of methods combined to avoid

1

sharing the same weaknesses. The goal of this monograph is not to replace the interview but to supplement and cross-validate it with measures that do not require the cooperation of a respondent and that do not themselves contaminate the response.

Here are some samples of the kinds of methods we will be surveying in Chapters 2 through 6 of this monograph:

The floor tiles around the hatching-chick exhibit at Chicago's Museum of Science and Industry must be replaced every six weeks. Tiles in other parts of the museum need not be replaced for years. The selective erosion of tiles, indexed by the replacement rate, is a measure of the relative popularity of exhibits.

The accretion rate is another measure. One investigator wanted to learn the level of whisky consumption in a town which was officially "dry." He did so by counting empty bottles in ashcans.

The degree of fear induced by a ghost-story-telling session can be measured by noting the shrinking diameter of a circle of seated children.

Chinese jade dealers have used the pupil dilation of their customers as a measure of the client's interest in particular stones, and Darwin in 1872 noted this same variable as an index of fear.

Library withdrawals were used to demonstrate the effect of the introduction of television into a community. Fiction titles dropped, nonfiction titles were unaffected.

The role of rate of interaction in managerial recruitment is shown by the overrepresentation of baseball managers who were infielders or catchers (high-interaction positions) during their playing days.

Sir Francis Galton employed surveying hardware to estimate the bodily dimensions of African women whose language he did not speak.

The child's interest in Christmas was demonstrated by distortions in the size of Santa Claus drawings.

Racial attitudes in two colleges were compared by noting the degree of clustering of Negroes and whites in lecture halls.

These methods have been grouped into chapters by the characteristic of the data: physical traces, archives, observations.

Before making a detailed examination of such methods, it is well to present a closer argument for the use of multiple methods and to present a methodological framework within which both the traditional and the more novel methods can be evaluated.

The reader may skip directly to Sherlock Holmes and the opening of Chapter 2 if he elects, infer the criteria in a piece of detection himself, and then return for a validity check.

OPERATIONISM AND MULTIPLE OPERATIONS

The social sciences are just emerging from a period in which the precision of carefully specified operations was confused with operationism by definitional fiat — an effort now increasingly recognized as an unworkable model for science. We wish to retain and augment the precision without bowing to the fiat.

The mistaken belief in the operational definition of theoretical terms has permitted social scientists a complacent and self-defeating dependence upon single classes of measurement — usually the interview or questionnaire. Yet the operational implication of the inevitable theoretical complexity of every measure is exactly opposite: it calls for a multiple operationism, that is, for multiple measures which are hypothesized to share in the theoretically relevant components but have different patterns of irrelevant components (e.g., Garner, 1954; Garner, Hake, & Eriksen, 1956; Campbell & Fiske, 1959; Campbell, 1960; Humphreys, 1960).

Once a proposition has been confirmed by two or more independent measurement processes, the uncertainty of its interpretation is greatly reduced. The most persuasive evidence comes through a triangulation of measurement processes. If a proposition can survive the onslaught of a series of imperfect measures, with all their irrelevant error, confidence should be placed in it. Of course, this confidence is increased by minimizing error in each instrument and by a reasonable belief in the different and divergent effects of the sources of error.

A consideration of the laws of physics, as they are seen in that science's measuring instruments, demonstrates that no theoretical parameter is ever measured independently of other physical parameters and other physical laws. Thus, a typical galvanometer responds in its operational measurement of voltage not only according to the laws of electricity but also to the laws of gravitation, inertia, and friction. By reducing the mass of the galvanometer needle, by orienting the needle's motion at right angles to gravity, by setting the needle's axis in jeweled bearings, by counterweighting the needle point, and by other refinements, the instrument designer attempts to minimize the most important of the irrelevant physical forces for his measurement purposes. As a result, the galvanometer reading may reflect, *almost* purely, the single parameter of voltage (or amperage, etc.).

Yet from a theoretical point of view, the movement of the needle is always a complex product of many physical forces and laws. The adequacy with which the needle measures the conceptually defined variable is a matter for investigation; the operation itself is not the ultimate basis for defining the variable. Excellent illustrations of the specific imperfections of measuring instruments are provided by Wilson (1952).

Starting with this example from physics and the construction of meters, we can see that no meter ever perfectly measures a single theoretical parameter; all series of meter readings are imperfect estimates of the theoretical parameters they are intended to measure.

Truisms perhaps, yet they belie the mistaken concept of the "operational definition" of theoretical constructs which continues to be popular in the social sciences. The inappropriateness is accentuated in the social sciences because we have no measuring devices as carefully compensated to control all irrelevancies as is the galvanometer. There simply are no social science devices designed with so perfect a knowledge of all the major relevant sources of variation. In physics, the instruments we think of as "definitional" reflect magnificently successful theoretical achievements and themselves embody classical experiments in their very operation. In the social sciences, our measures lack such control. They tap multiple processes and sources of variance of which we are as yet unaware. At such a stage of development, the theoretical impurity and factorial complexity of every measure are not niceties for pedantic quibbling but are overwhelmingly and centrally relevant in all measurement applications which involve inference and generalization.

Efforts in the social sciences at multiple confirmation often yield disappointing and inconsistent results. Awkward to write up and difficult to publish, such results confirm the gravity of the problem and the risk of false confidence that comes with dependence upon single methods (Vidich & Shapiro, 1955; Campbell, 1957; Campbell & McCormack, 1957; Campbell & Fiske, 1959; Kendall, 1963; Cook & Selltiz, 1964). When multiple operations provide consistent results, the possibility of slippage between conceptual definition and operational specification is diminished greatly.

This is not to suggest that all components of a multimethod approach should be weighted equally. Prosser (1964) has observed: "... but there is still no man who would not accept dog tracks in the mud against the sworn testimony of a hundred eye-witnesses that no dog had passed by" (p. 216). Components ideally should be weighted according to the amount of extraneous variation each is known to have and, taken in combination, according to their independence from similar sources of bias.

INTERPRETABLE COMPARISONS AND PLAUSIBLE RIVAL HYPOTHESES

In this monograph we deal with methods of measurement appropriate to a wide range of social science studies. Some of these studies are comparisons of a single group or unit at two or more points in time; others compare several groups or units at one time; others purport to measure but a single unit at a single point in time; and, to close the circle, some compare several groups at two or more points in time. In this discussion, we assume that the goal of the social scientist is always to achieve interpretable comparisons, and that the goal of methodology is to rule out those plausible rival hypotheses which make comparisons ambiguous and tentative.

Often it seems that absolute measurement *is* involved, and that a social instance is being described in its splendid isolation, not for comparative purposes. But a closer look shows that absolute, isolated measurement is meaningless. In all useful measurement, an implicit comparison exists when an explicit one is not visible. "Absolute" measurement is a convenient fiction and usually is nothing more than a shorthand summary in settings where plausible rival hypotheses are either unimportant or so few, specific, and well known as to be taken into account habitually. Thus, when we report a length "absolutely" in meters or feet, we immediately imply comparisons with numerous familiar objects of known length, as well as comparisons with a standard preserved in some Paris or Washington sanctuary.

If measurement is regarded always as a comparison, there are three classes of approaches which have come to be used in achieving interpretable comparisons. First, and most satisfactory, is experimental design. Through deliberate randomization, the *ceteris* of the pious *ceteris paribus* prayer can be made *paribus*. This may require randomization of respondents, occasions, or stimulus objects. In any event, the randomization strips of plausibility many of the otherwise available explanations of the difference in question. It is a sad truth that randomized experimental design is possible for only a portion of the settings in which social scientists make measurements and seek interpretable comparisons. The number of opportunities for its use may not be staggering, but, where possible, experimental design should by all means be exploited. Many more opportunities exist than are used.

Second, a quite different and historically isolated tradition of comparison is that of index numbers. Here, sources of variance known to be irrelevant are controlled by transformations of raw data and weighted aggregates. This is analogous to the compensated and counterbalanced meters of physical science which also control irrelevant sources of variance. The goal of this old and currently neglected social science tradition is to provide measures for meaningful comparisons across wide spans of time and social space. Real wages, intelligence quotients, and net reproductive rates are examples, but an effort in this direction is made even when a percentage, a per capita, or an annual rate is computed. Index numbers cannot be used uncritically because the imperfect knowledge of the laws invoked in any such measurement situation precludes computing any effective all-purpose measures.

Furthermore, the use of complex compensated indices in the assurance that they measure what they are devised for has in many instances proved quite misleading. A notable example is found in the definitional confusion surrounding the labor force concept (Jaffe & Stewart, 1951; W. E. Moore, 1953). Often a relationship established between an over-all index and external variables is found due to only one component of the index. Cronbach (1958) has described this problem well in his discussion of dyadic scores of interpersonal perception. In the older methodological literature, the problem is raised under the term *index correlations* (e.g., Stouffer, 1934; Guilford, 1954; Campbell, 1955).

Despite these limitations, the problem of index numbers, which once loomed large in sociology and economics, deserves to be reactivated and integrated into modern social science methodology. The tradition is relevant in two ways for the problems of this monograph. Many of the sources of data suggested here, particularly secondary records, require a transformation of the raw data if they are to be interpretable in any but truly experimental situations. Such transformations should be performed with the wisdom accumulated within the older tradition, as well as with a regard for the precautionary literature just cited. Properly done, such transformations often improve interpretability even if they fall far short of some ideal (cf. Bernstein, 1935).

A second value of the literature on index numbers lies in an examination of the types of irrelevant variation which the index computation sought to exclude. The construction of index numbers is usually a response to criticisms of less sophisticated indices. They thus embody a summary of the often unrecorded criticisms of prior measures. In the criticisms and the corrections are clues to implicit or explicit plausible rival interpretations of differences, the viable threats to valid interpretation.

Take so simple a measure as an index on unemployment or of retail sales. The gross number of the unemployed or the gross total dollar level of sales is useless if one wants to make comparisons within a single year. Some of the objections to the gross figures are reflected in the seasonal corrections applied to time-series data. If we look at only the last quarter of the year, we can see that the effect of weather must be considered. Systematically, winter depresses the number of employed construction workers, for example, and increases the unemployment level. Less systematically, spells of bad weather keep people in their homes and reduce the amount of retail shopping. Both periodic and aperiodic elements of the weather should be considered if one wants a more stable and interpretable measure of unemployment or sales. So, too, our custom of giving gifts at Christmas spurs December sales, as does the coinciding custom of Christmas bonuses to employees. All of these are accounted for, crudely, by a correction applied to the gross levels for either December or the final quarter of the year.

Some of these sources of invalidity are too specific to a single setting to be generalized usefully; others are too obvious to be catalogued. But some contribute to a general enumeration of re-current threats to valid interpretation in social science measures.

The technical problems of index-number construction are heroic. "The index number should give *consistent* results for different base periods and also with its counterpart price or quantity index. No reasonably simple formula satisfies both of these consistency requirements" (Ekelblad, 1962, p. 726). The consistency problem is usually met by substituting a geometric mean for an arithmetic one, but then other problems arise. With complex indices of many components, there is the issue of getting an index that will yield consistent scores across all the different levels and times of the components.

In his important work on economic cycles, Hansen (1921) wrote, "Here is a heterogeneous group of statistical series all of which are related in a causal way, somehow or another, to the cycle of prosperity and depression" (p. 21). The search for a metric to relate these different components consistently, to be able to reverse factors without chaos, makes index construction a difficult task. But the payoff is great, and the best approximation to solving both the base-reversal and factor-reversal issues is a weighted aggregate with time-averaged weights. For good introductory state-ments of these and other index-number issues, see Yule & Kendall (1950), Zeisel (1957), and Ekelblad (1962). More detailed treat-ments can be found in Mitchell (1921), Fisher (1923), Mills (1927), and Mudgett (1951).

The third general approach to comparison may be called that of "plausible rival hypotheses." It is the most general and least formal of the three and is applicable to the other two. Given a comparison which a social scientist wishes to interpret, this ap-proach asks what other plausible interpretations are allowed by the research setting and the measurement processes. The more of these, and the more plausible each is, the less validly interpretable is the comparison. Platt (1964) and Hafner and Presswood (1965) have discussed this approach with a focus in the physical sciences.

A social scientist may reduce the number of plausible rival hypotheses in many ways. Experimental methods and adequate indices serve as useful devices for eliminating some rival interpretations. A checklist of commonly relevant threats to validity may point to other ways of limiting the number of viable alternative hypotheses. For some major threats, it is often possible to provide supplementary analyses or to assemble additional data which can rule out a source of possible invalidity.

Backstopping the individual scientist is the critical reaction of his fellow scientists. Where he misses a plausible rival hypothesis, he can expect his colleagues to propose alternative interpretations. This resource is available even in disciplines which are not avowedly scientific. J. H. Wigmore, a distinguished legal scholar, showed an awareness of the criteria of other plausible explanations of data:

> If the potential defect of Inductive Evidence is that the fact offered as the basis of the conclusion may be open to one or more other explanations or inferences, the failure to exclude a single other rational inference would be, from the standpoint of *Proof*, a fatal defect; and yet, if only that single other inference were open, there might still be an extremely high degree of probability for the Inference desired.... The provisional test, then, from the point of view valuing the Inference, would be something like this: *Does the evidentiary fact point to the desired conclusion ... as the inference ... most plausible or most natural out of the various ones that are conceivable?* [1937, p. 25].

The culture of science seeks, however, to systematize the production of rival plausible hypotheses and to extend them to every generalization proposed. While this may be implicit in a field such as law, scientific epistemology requires that the original and competing hypotheses be explicitly and generally stated.

Such a commitment could lead to rampant uncertainty unless some criterion of plausibility were adopted before the rival hypothesis was taken as a serious alternative. Accordingly, each rival hypothesis is a threat only if we can give it the status of a law at least as creditable as the law we seek to demonstrate. If it falls short of that credibility, it is not thereby "plausible" and can be ignored.

In some logical sense, even in a "true" experimental comparison, an infinite number of potential laws could predict this result. We do not let this logical state of affairs prevent us from interpreting the results. Instead, uncertainty comes only from those unexcluded hypotheses to which we, in the current state of our science, are willing to give the status of established laws: these are the plausible rival hypotheses. While the north-south orientation of planaria may have something to do with conditioning, no interview studies report on the directional orientation of interviewer and interviewee. And they should not.

For those plausible rival hypotheses to which we give the status of laws, the conditions under which they would explain our obtained result also imply specific outcomes for other sets of data. Tests in other settings, attempting to verify these laws, may enable us to rule them out. In a similar fashion, the theory we seek to test has many implications other than that involved in the specific comparison, and the exploration of these is likewise demanded. The more numerous and complex the manifestations of the law, the fewer singular plausible rival hypotheses are available, and the more parsimony favors the law under study.

Our longing is for data that prove and certify theory, but such is not to be our lot. Some comfort may come from the observation that this is not an existential predicament unique to social science. The replacement of Newtonian theory by relativity and quantum mechanics shows us that even the best of physical science experimentation probes theory rather than proves it. Modern philosophies of science as presented by Popper (1935; 1959; 1962), Quine (1953), Hanson (1958), Kuhn (1962), and Campbell (1965), make this point clear.

INTERNAL AND EXTERNAL VALIDITY

Before discussing a list of some common sources of invalidity, a distinction must be drawn between internal and external validity. *Internal validity* asks whether a difference exists at all in any given comparison. It asks whether or not an apparent difference can be explained away as some measurement artifact. For true experiments, this question is usually not salient, but even there, the happy vagaries of random sample selection occasionally delude one and spuriously produce the appearance of a difference where in fact none exists. For the rival hypothesis of chance, we fortunately have an elaborated theoretical model which evaluates its plausibility. A p-value describes the darkness of the ever present shadow of doubt. But for index-number comparisons not embedded in a formal experiment, and for the plausible-rival-hypothesis strategy more generally, the threats to internal validity — the argument that even the appearance of a difference is spurious — is a serious problem and the one that has first priority.

External validity is the problem of interpreting the difference, the problem of generalization. To what other populations, occasions, stimulus objects, and measures may the obtained results be applied? The distinction between internal and external validity can be illustrated in two uses of randomization. When the experimentalist in psychology randomly assigns a sample of persons into two or more experimental groups, he is concerned entirely with internal validity — with making it implausible that the luck of the draw produced the resulting differences. When a sociologist carefully randomizes the selection of respondents so that his sample represents a larger population, representativeness or external validity is involved.

The psychologist may be extremely confident that a difference is traceable to an experimental treatment, but whether it would hold up with another set of subjects or in a different setting may be quite equivocal. He has achieved internal validity by his random assignment but not addressed the external validity issue by the chance allocation of subjects.

The sociologist, similarly, has not met all the validity concerns by simply drawing a random sample. Conceding that he has taken a necessary step toward achieving external validity and generalization of his differences, the internal validity problem remains.

Random assignment is only one method of reaching toward internal validity. Experimental-design control, exclusive of randomization, is another. Consider the case of a pretest-posttest field experiment on the effect of a persuasive communication. Randomly choosing those who participate, the social scientist properly wards off some major threats to external validity. But we also know of other validity threats. The first interview in a two-stage study may set into motion attitude change and clarification processes which would otherwise not have occurred (e.g., Crespi, 1948). If such processes did occur, the comparison of a first and second measure on the same person is internally invalid, for the shift is a measurement-produced artifact.

Even when a measured control group is used, and a persuasive communication produces a greater change in an experimental group, the persuasive effect may be internally valid but externally invalid. There is the substantial risk that the effect occurs only with pretested populations and might be absent in populations lacking the pretest (cf. Schanck & Goodman, 1939; Hovland, Lumsdaine, & Sheffield, 1949; Solomon, 1949). For more extensive discussions of internal and external validity, see Campbell (1957) and Campbell and Stanley (1963).

The distinction between internal and external validity is often murky. In this work, we have considered the two classes of threat jointly, although occasionally detailing the risks separately. The reason for this is that the factors which are a risk for internal validity are often the same as those threatening external validity. While for one scientist the representative sampling of cities is a method to achieve generalization to the United States population, for another it may be an effort to give an internally valid comparison across cities.

Sources of Invalidity of Measures

In this section, we review frequent threats to the valid interpretation of a difference—common plausible rival hypotheses. They are broadly divided into three groups: error that may be traced to those being studied, error that comes from the investigator, and error associated with sampling imperfections. This section is the only one in which we draw illustrations mainly from the most popular methods of current social science. For that reason, particular attention is paid to those weaknesses which create the need for multiple and alternate methods.

In addition, some other criteria such as the efficiency of the research instrument are mentioned. These are independent of validity, but important for the practical research decisions which must be made.

Reactive Measurement Effect: Error from the Respondent

The most understated risk to valid interpretation is the error produced by the respondent. Even when he is well intentioned and cooperative, the research subject's knowledge that he is participating in a scholarly search may confound the investigator's data. Four classes of this error are discussed here: awareness of being tested, role selection, measurement as a change agent, and response sets.

1. The guinea pig effect—awareness of being tested. Selltiz and her associates (1959) make the observation:

> The measurement process used in the experiment may itself affect the outcome. If people feel that they are "guinea pigs" being experimented with, or if they feel that they are being "tested" and must make a good impression, or if the method of data collection suggests responses or stimulates an interest the subject did not previously feel, the measuring process may distort the experimental results [p. 97].

These effects have been called "reactive effect of measurement" and "reactive arrangement" bias (Campbell, 1957; Campbell & Stanley, 1963). It is important to note early that the awareness of testing need not, by itself, contaminate responses. It is a question of probabilities, but the probability of bias is high in any study in which a respondent is aware of his subject status.

Although the methods to be reviewed here do not involve "respondents," comparable reactive effects on the population may often occur. Consider, for example, a potentially nonreactive instrument such as the movie camera. If it is conspicuously placed, its lack of ability to talk to the subjects doesn't help us much. The visible presence of the camera undoubtedly changes behavior, and does so differentially depending upon the labeling involved. The response is likely to vary if the camera has printed on its side "Los Angeles Police Department" or "NBC" or "Foundation Project on Crowd Behavior." Similarly, an Englishman's presence at a wedding in Africa exerts a much more reactive effect on the proceedings than it would on the Sussex Downs.

A specific illustration may be of value. In the summer of 1952, some graduate students in the social sciences at the University of

Chicago were employed to observe the numbers of Negroes and whites in stores, restaurants, bars, theaters, and so on on a south side Chicago street intersecting the Negro-white boundary (East 63rd). This, presumably, should have been a nonreactive process, particularly at the predominantly white end of the street. No questions were asked, no persons stopped. Yet, in spite of this hopefully inconspicuous activity, two merchants were agitated and persistent enough to place calls to the university which somehow got through to the investigators; how many others tried and failed cannot be known. The two calls were from a store operator and the manager of a currency exchange, both of whom wanted assurance that this was some university nosiness and not a professional casing for subsequent robbery (Campbell & Mack, in preparation). An intrusion conspicuous enough to arouse such an energetic reaction may also have been conspicuous enough to change behavior; for observations other than simple enumerations the bias would have been great. But even with the simple act of nose-counting, there is the risk that the area would be differentially avoided. The research mistake was in providing observers with clipboards and log sheets, but their appearance might have been still more sinister had they operated Veeder counters with hands jammed in pockets.

The present monograph argues strongly for the use of archival records. Thinking, perhaps, of musty files of bound annual reports of some prior century, one might regard such a method as totally immune to reactive effects. However, were one to make use of precinct police blotters, going around to copy off data once each month, the quality and nature of the records would almost certainly change. In actual fact, archives are kept indifferently, as a low-priority task, by understaffed bureaucracies. Conscientiousness is often low because of the lack of utilization of the records. The presence of a user can revitalize the process — as well as create anxieties over potentially damaging data (Campbell, 1963a). When records are seen as sources of vulnerability, they may be altered systematically. Accounts thought likely to enter into tax audits are an obvious case (Schwartz, 1961), but administrative records (Blau, 1955) and criminal statistics (Kadish, 1964) are equally amenable to this source of distortion. The selective and wholesale rifling of records by ousted political administrations sets an example of potential reactive effects, self-consciousness, and dissembling on the part of archivists.

These reactive effects may threaten both internal and external validity, depending upon the conditions. If it seems plausible that the reactivity was equal in both measures of a comparison, then the threat is to external validity or generalizability, not to internal validity. If the reactive effect is plausibly differential, then it may generate a pseudo-difference. Thus, in a study (Campbell & McCormack, 1957) showing a reduction in authoritarian attitudes over the course of one year's military training, the initial testing was done in conjunction with an official testing program, while the subsequent testing was clearly under external university research auspices. As French (1955) pointed out in another connection, this difference provides a plausible reactive threat jeopardizing the conclusion that any reduction has taken place even for this one group, quite apart from the external validity problems of explanation and generalization. In many interview and questionnaire studies, increased or decreased rapport and increased awareness of the researcher's goals or decreased fear provide plausible alternative explanations of the apparent change recorded.

The common device of guaranteeing anonymity demonstrates concern for the reactive bias, but this concern may lead to validity threats. For example, some test constructors have collected normative data under conditions of anonymity, while the test is likely to be used with the respondent's name signed. Making a response public, or guaranteeing to hide one, will influence the nature of the response. This has been seen for persuasive communications, in the validity of reports of brands purchased, and for the level of antisocial responses. There is a clear link between awareness of being tested and the biases associated with a tendency to answer with socially desirable responses.

The considerations outlined above suggest that reactivity may be selectively troublesome within trials or tests of the experiment. Training trials may accommodate the subject to the task, but a practice effect may exist that either enhances or inhibits the reactive bias. Early responses may be contaminated, later ones not, or vice versa (Underwood, 1957).

Ultimately, the determination of reactive effect depends on validating studies — few examples of which are currently available.

Behavior observed under nonreactive conditions must be compared with corresponding behavior in which various potentially reactive conditions are introduced. Where no difference in direction of relationship occurs, the reactivity factor can be discounted.

In the absence of systematic data of this kind, we have little basis for determining what is and what is not reactive. Existing techniques consist of asking subjects in a posttest interview whether they were affected by the test, were aware of the deception in the experiment, and so forth. While these may sometimes demonstrate a method to be reactive, they may fail to detect many instances in which reactivity is a serious contaminant. Subjects who consciously dissemble during an experiment may do so afterward for the same reasons. And those who are unaware of the effects on them at the time of the research may hardly be counted on for valid reports afterwards.

The types of measures surveyed in this monograph have a double importance in overcoming reactivity. In the absence of validation for verbal measures, nonreactive techniques of the kind surveyed here provide ways of avoiding the serious problems faced by more conventional techniques. Given the limiting properties of these "other measures," however, their greatest utility may inhere in their capacity to provide validation for the more conventional measures.

2. Role selection.   Another way in which the respondent's awareness of the research process produces differential reaction involves not so much inaccuracy, defense, or dishonesty, but rather a specialized selection from among the many "true" selves or "proper" behaviors available in any respondent.

By singling out an individual to be tested (assuming that being tested is not a normal condition), the experimenter forces upon the subject a role-defining decision—What kind of a person should I be as I answer these questions or do these tasks? In many of the "natural" situations to which the findings are generalized, the subject may not be forced to define his role relative to the behavior. For other situations, he may. Validity decreases as the role assumed in the research setting varies from the usual role present in comparable behavior beyond the research setting. Orne and his colleagues have provided compelling demonstrations of the magnitude of this variable's effect (Orne, 1959; Orne, 1962; Orne & Scheibe, 1964; Orne & Evans, 1965). Orne has noted:

> The experimental situation is one which takes place within context of an explicit agreement of the subject to participate in a special form of social interaction known as "taking part in an experiment." Within the context of our culture the roles of subject and experimenter are well understood and carry with them well-defined mutual role expectations [1962, p. 777].

Looking at all the cues available to the respondent attempting to puzzle out an appropriate set of roles or behavior, Orne labeled the total of all such cues the "demand characteristics of the experimental situation." The recent study by Orne & Evans (1965) showed that the alleged antisocial effects induced by hypnosis can be accounted for by the demand characteristics of the research setting. Subjects who were not hypnotized engaged in "antisocial" activities as well as did those who were hypnotized. The behavior of those not hypnotized is traced to social cues that attend the experimental situation and are unrelated to the experimental variable.

The probability of this confounding role assumption varies from one research study to another, of course. The novelty of a test-taking role may be selectively biasing for subjects of different educational levels. Less familiar and comfortable with testing, those with little formal schooling are more likely to produce nonrepresentative behavior. The act of being tested is "more different." The same sort of distortion risk occurs when subject matter is unusual or novel. Subject matter with which the respondent is unfamiliar may produce uncertainty of which role to select. A role-playing choice is more likely with such new or unexpected material.

Lack of familiarity with tests or with testing materials can influence response in different ways. Responses may be depressed because of a lack of training with the materials. Or the response level may be distorted as the subject perceives himself in the rare role of expert.

Both unfamiliarity and "expertness" can influence the character as well as the level of response. It is common to find experimental procedures which augment the experting bias. The instruction which reads, "You have been selected as part of a scientifically selected sample ... it is important that you answer the questions ..." underlines in what a special situation and what a special person the respondent is. The empirical test of the experting hypothesis in field research is the extent of "don't know" replies. One should predict that a set of instructions stressing the importance of the respondent as a member of a "scientifically selected sample" will produce significantly fewer "don't knows" than an instruction set that does not stress the individual's importance.

Although the "special person" set of instructions may increase participation in the project, and thus reduce some concern on the sampling level, it concurrently increases the risk of reactive bias. In science as everywhere else, one seldom gets something for nothing. The critical question for the researcher must be whether or not the resultant sampling gain offsets the risk of deviation from "true" responses produced by the experting role.

Not only does interviewing result in role selection, but the problem or its analogues may exist for any measure. Thus, in a study utilizing conversation sampling with totally hidden microphones, each social setting elicits a different role selection. Conversation samples might thus differ between two cities, not because of any true differences, but rather because of subtle differences in role elicitation of the differing settings employed.

3. Measurement as change agent.   With all the respondent candor possible, and with complete role representativeness, there can still be an important class of reactive effects — those in which the initial measurement activity introduces real changes in what is being measured. The change may be real enough in these instances, but be invalidly attributed to any of the intervening events, and be invalidly generalized to other settings not involving a pretest. This process has been deliberately demonstrated by Schanck and Goodman (1939) in a classic study involving information-test taking as a disguised persuasive process. Research by Roper (cited by Crespi, 1948) shows that the well-established "preamble effect" (Cantril, 1944) is not merely a technical flaw in determining the response to the question at hand, but that it also creates attitudes which persist and which are measurable on subsequent unbiased questions. Crespi reports additional research of his own confirming that even for those who initially say "don't know," processes leading to opinion development are initiated.

The effect has been long established in the social sciences. In psychology, early research in transfer of training encountered the threat to internal validity called "practice effects": the exercise provided by the pretest accounted for the gain shown on the posttest. Such research led to the introduction of control groups in studies that had earlier neglected to include them. Similarly, research in intelligence testing showed that dependable gains in test-passing ability could be traced to experience with previous tests even where no knowledge of results had been provided. (See Cane & Heim, 1950, and Anastasi, 1958, pp. 190-191, for reviews of this literature.) Similar gains have been shown in personal "adjustment" scores (Windle, 1954).

While such effects are obviously limited to intrusive measurement methods such as this review seeks to avoid, the possibility of analogous artifacts must be considered. Suppose one were interested in measuring the weight of women in a secretarial pool, and their weights were to be the dependent variable in a study on the effects of a change from an all-female staff to one including men. One might for this purpose put free weight scales in the women's restroom, with an automatic recording device inside. However, the recurrent availability of knowledge of one's own weight in a semisocial situation would probably act as a greater change agent for weight than would any experimental treatment that might be under investigation. A floor-panel treadle would be better, recording weights without providing feedback to the participant, possibly disguised as an automatic door-opener.

4. Response sets. The critical literature on questionnaire methodology has demonstrated the presence of several irrelevant but lawful sources of variance. Most of these are probably applicable to interviews also, although this has been less elaborately demonstrated to date. Cronbach (1946) has summarized this literature, and evidence continues to show its importance (e.g., Jackson & Messick, 1957; Chapman & Bock, 1958).

Respondents will more frequently endorse a statement than disagree with its opposite (Sletto, 1937). This tendency differs widely and consistently among individuals, generating the reliable source of variance known as acquiescence response set. Rorer (1965) has recently entered a dissent from this point of view. He validly notes the evidence indicating that acquiescence or yea-saying is not a totally general personality trait elicitable by items of any content. He fails to note that, even so, the evidence clearly indicates the methodological problem that direction of wording lawfully enhances the correlation between two measures when shared, and depresses the correlation when running counter to the direction of the correlation of the content (Campbell, 1965b). Another idiosyncracy, dependably demonstrated over varied multiple-choice content, is the preference for strong statements versus moderate or indecisive ones. Sequences of questions asked in very similar format produce stereotyped responses, such as a tendency to endorse the righthand or the lefthand response, or to alternate in some simple fashion. Furthermore, decreasing attention produces reliable biases from the order of item presentation.

Response biases can occur not only for questionnaires or public opinion polls, but also for archival records such as votes (Bain & Hecock, 1957). Still more esoteric observational or erosion measures face similar problems. Take the example of a traffic study.

Suppose one wanted to obtain a nonreactive measure of the relative attractiveness of paintings in an art museum. He might employ an erosion method such as the relative degree of carpet or floor-tile wear in front of each painting. Or, more elaborately, he might install invisible photoelectric timers and counters. Such an approach must also take into account irrelevant habits which affect traffic flow. There is, for example, a general right-turn bias upon entering a building or room. When this is combined with time deadlines and fatigue (Do people drag their feet more by the time they get to the paintings on the left side of the building?), there probably is a predictably biased response tendency. The design of museums tends to be systematic, and this, too, can bias the measures. The placement of an exit door will consistently bias the traffic flow and thus confound any erosion measure unless it is controlled. (For imaginative and provocative observational studies on museum behavior see Robinson, 1928; Melton, 1933a; Melton, 1933b; Melton, 1935; Melton, 1936; Melton, Feldman, & Mason, 1936.)

Each of these four types of reactive error can be reduced by employing research measures which do not require the cooperation of the respondent and which are "blind" to him. Although we

urge more methodological research to make known the degree of
error that may be traced to reactivity, our inclination now is to urge
the use of compensating measures which do not contain the
reactive risk.

Error from the Investigator

To some degree, error from the investigator was implicit in the
reactive error effects. After all, the investigator is an important
source of cues to the respondent, and he helps to structure the
demand characteristics of the interview. However, in these previous points, interviewer character was unspecified. Here we deal
with effects that vary systematically with interviewer characteristics, and with instrument errors totally independent of respondents.

5. *Interviewer effects.* It is old news that the characteristics
of the interviewer can contribute a substantial amount of variance
to a set of findings. Interviewees respond differentially to visible
cues provided by the interviewer. Within any single study, this
variance can produce a spurious difference. The work of Katz
(1942) and Cantril (1944) early demonstrated the differential effect
of the race of the interviewer, and that bias has been more recently
shown by Athey and his associates (1960). Riesman and Ehrlich
(1961) reported that the age of the interviewer produced a bias,
with the number of "unacceptable" (to the experimenter) answers
higher when questions were posed by younger interviewers. Religion of the interviewer is a possible contaminant (Robinson &
Rohde, 1946; Hyman *et al.*, 1954), as is his social class (Riesman,
1956; Lenski & Leggett, 1960). Benney, Riesman, and Star (1956)
showed that one should consider not only main effects, but also
interactions. In their study of age and sex variables they report:
"Male interviewers obtain fewer responses than female, and few-
est of all from males, while female interviewers obtain their
highest responses from men, except for young women talking to
young men" (p. 143).

The evidence is overwhelming that a substantial number of
biases are introduced by the interviewer (see Hyman *et al.*, 1954;
Kahn & Cannell, 1957). Some of the major biases, such as race,
are easily controllable; other biases, such as the interaction of age

and sex, are less easily handled. If we heeded all the known biases, without considering our ignorance of major interactions, there could no longer be a simple survey. The understandable action by most researchers has been to ignore these biases and to assume them away. The biases are lawful and consistent, and all research employing face-to-face interviewing or questionnaire administration is subject to them. Rather than flee by assumptions, the experimenter may use alternative methodologies that let him flee by circumvention.

6. *Change in the research instrument.* The measuring (data-gathering) instrument is frequently an interviewer, whose characteristics, we have just shown, may alter responses. In panel studies, or those using the same interviewer at two or more points in time, it is essential to ask: To what degree is the interviewer or experimenter the same research instrument at all points of the research?

Just as a spring scale becomes fatigued with use, reading "heavier" a second time, an interviewer may also measure differently at different times. His skill may increase. He may be better able to establish rapport. He may have learned necessary vocabulary. He may loaf or become bored. He may have increasingly strong expectations of what a respondent "means" and code differently with practice. Some errors relate to recording accuracy, while others are linked to the nature of the interviewer's interpretation of what transpired. Either way, there is always the risk that the interviewer will be a variable filter over time and experience.

Even when the interviewer becomes more competent, there is potential trouble. Although we usually think of difficulty only when the instrument weakens, a difference in competence between two waves of interviewing, *either increasing or decreasing,* can yield spurious effects. The source of error is not limited to interviewers, and every class of measurement is vulnerable to wavering calibration. Suicides in Prussia jumped 20 per cent between 1882 and 1883. This clearly reflected a change in record-keeping, not a massive increase in depression. Until 1883 the records were kept by the police, but in that year the job was transferred to the civil service (Halbwachs, 1930; cited in Selltiz *et al.*, 1959). Archivists undoubtedly drift in recording standards, with occasional administrative reforms in conscientiousness altering the output of the "instrument" (Kitsuse & Cicourel, 1963).

Where human observers are used, they have fluctuating adaptation levels and response thresholds (Holmes, 1958; Campbell, 1961). Rosenthal, in an impressive series of commentary and research, has focused on errors traceable to the experimenter himself. Of particular interest is his work on the influence of early data returns upon analysis of subsequent data (Rosenthal *et al.*, 1963. See also Rosenthal, 1963; Rosenthal & Fode, 1963; Rosenthal & Lawson, 1963; Rosenthal, 1964; Kintz *et al.*, 1965).

Varieties of Sampling Error

Historically, social science has examined sampling errors as a problem in the selection of respondents. The person or group has been the critical unit, and our thinking has been focused on a universe of people. Often a sample of time or space can provide a practical substitute for a sample of persons. Novel methods should be examined for their potential in this regard. For example, a study of the viewing of bus advertisements used a time-stratified, random triggering of an automatic camera pointed out a window over the bus ad (Politz, 1959). One could similarly take a photographic sample of bus passengers modulated by door entries as counted by a photo cell. A photo could be taken one minute after the entry of every twentieth passenger. For some methods, such as the erosion methods, total population records are no more costly than partial ones. For some archives, temporal samples or agency samples are possible. For voting records, precincts may be sampled. But for any one method, the possibilities should be examined.

We look at sampling in this section from the point of view of restrictions on reaching people associated with various methods and the stability of populations over time and areas.

7. *Population restrictions.* In the public-opinion-polling tradition, one conceptualizes a "universe" from which a representative sample is drawn. This model gives little or no formal attention to the fact that only certain universes are possible for any given method. A method-respondent interaction exists — one that gives each method a different set of defining boundaries for its universe. One reason so little attention is given to this fact is that,

as methods go, public opinion polling is relatively unrestricted. Yet even here there is definite universe rigidity, with definite restrictions on the size and character of the population able to be sampled.

In the earliest days of polling, people were questioned in public places, probably excluding some 80 per cent of the total population. Shifting to in-home interviewing with quota controls and no callbacks still excluded some 60 per cent—perhaps 5 per cent unaccessible in homes under any conditions, 25 per cent not at home, 25 per cent refusals, and 5 per cent through interviewers' reluctance to approach homes of extreme wealth or poverty and a tendency to avoid fourth-floor walkups.

Under modern probability sampling with callbacks and household designation, perhaps only 15 per cent of the population is excluded: 5 per cent are totally inaccessible in private residences (e.g., those institutionalized, hospitalized, homeless, transient, in the military, mentally incompetent, and so forth), another 10 per cent refuse to answer, are unavailable after three callbacks, or have moved to no known address. A 20 per cent figure was found in the model Elmira study in its first wave (Williams, 1950), although other studies have reported much lower figures. Ross (1963) has written a general statement on the problem of inaccessibility, and Stephan and McCarthy (1958), in their literature survey, show from 3 to 14 per cent of sample populations of residences inaccessible.

Also to be considered in population restriction is the degree to which the accessible universe deviates in important parameters from the excluded population. This bias is probably minimal in probability sampling with adequate callbacks, but great with catch-as-catch-can and quota samples. Much survey research has centered on household behavior, and the great mass of probability approaches employ a prelisted household as the terminal sampling unit. This frequently requires the enlistment of a household member as a reporter on the behavior of others. Since those who answer doorbells overrepresent the old, the young, and women, this can be a confounding error.

When we come to more demanding verbal techniques, the universe rigidity is much greater. What proportion of the population is available for self-administered questionnaires? Payment for filling out the questionnaire reduces the limitations a bit, but a money reward is selectively attractive—at least at the rates most researchers pay. A considerable proportion of the populace is functionally illiterate for personality and attitude tests developed on college populations.

Not only does task-demandingness create population restrictions, differential volunteering provides similar effects, interacting in a particularly biasing way when knowledge of the nature of the task is involved (Capra & Dittes, 1962). Baumrind (1964) writes of the motivation of volunteers and notes, "The dependent attitude of most subjects toward the experimenter is an artifact of the experimental situation as well as an expression of some subjects' personal need systems at the time they volunteer" (p. 421).

The curious, the exhibitionistic, and the succorant are likely to overpopulate any sample of volunteers. How secure a base can volunteers be with such groups overrepresented and the shy, suspicious, and inhibited underrepresented? The only defensible position is a probability sample of the units to which the findings will be generalized. Even conscripting sophomores may be better than relying on volunteers.

Returning to the rigidity of sampling, what proportion of the total population is available for the studio test audiences used in advertising and television program evaluation? Perhaps 2 per cent. For mailed questionnaires, the population available for addressing might be 95 per cent of the total in the United States, but low-cost, convenient mailing lists probably cover no more than 70 per cent of the families through automobile registration and telephone directories. The exclusion is, again, highly selective. If, however, we consider the volunteering feature, where 10 per cent returns are typical, the effective population is a biased 7 per cent selection of the total. The nature of this selective-return bias, according to a recent study (Vincent, 1964), includes a skewing of the sample in favor of lower-middle-class individuals drawn from unusually stable, "happy" families.

There are more households with television in the United States than there are households with telephones (or baths). In any given city, one is likely to find more than 15 per cent of the households excluded in a telephone subscription list—and most of these are at the bottom of the socioeconomic scale. Among subscribers, as many as 15 per cent in some areas do not list their number, and an estimate of 5 per cent over all is conservative. Cooper (1964) found an over-all level of 6 per cent deliberately not listed and an additional 12 per cent not in the directory because of recent installations. The unlisted problem can be defeated by a system of random-digit dialing, but this increases the cost at least tenfold and requires a prior study of the distribution of exchanges. Among a sample of known numbers, some 50 per cent of dialings are met with busy signals and "not-at-homes." Thus, for a survey without callbacks, the accessible population of 80 per cent (listed-phone households) reduces to 40 per cent. If individuals are the unit of analysis, the effective sampling rate, without callbacks, may drop to 20 per cent. Random-digit dialing will help; so, too, will at least three callbacks, but precision can be achieved only at a high price. The telephone is not so cheap a research instrument as it first looks.

Sampling problems of this sort are even more acute for the research methods considered in the present monograph. Although a few have the full population access of public opinion surveys, most have much more restricted populations. Consider, for example, the sampling of natural conversations. What are the proportions of men and women whose conversations are accessible in public places and on public transport? What is the representativeness of social class or role?

8. Population stability over time.   Just as internal validity is more important than external validity, so, too, is the stability of a population restriction more important than the magnitude of the restriction. Examine conversation sampling on a bus or streetcar. The population represented differs on dry days and snowy days, in winter and spring, as well as by day of the week. These shifts would in many instances provide plausible rival explanations of shifts in topics of conversation. Sampling from a much narrower universe would be preferable if the population were more stable over time, as, say, conversation samples from an employees' restroom in an office building. Comparisons of interview survey results over time periods are more troubled by population instability than is generally realized, because of seasonal layoffs in many fields of employment, plus status-differentiated patterns of summer and winter vacations. An extended discussion of time sampling has been provided by Brookover and Back (1965).

9. Population stability over areas. Similarly, research populations available to a given method may vary from region to region, providing a more serious problem than a population restriction common to both. Thus, for a comparison of attitudes between New York and Los Angeles, conversation sampling in buses and commuter trains would tap such different segments of the communities as to be scarcely worth doing. Again, a comparison of employees' washrooms in comparable office buildings would provide a more interpretable comparison. Through the advantage of background data to check on some dimensions of representativeness, public opinion surveys again have an advantage in this regard.

Any enumeration of sources of invalidity is bound to be incomplete. Some threats are too highly specific to a given setting and method to be generalized, as are some opportunities for ingenious measurement and control. This list contains a long series of general threats that apply to a broad body of research method and content. It does not say that additional problems cannot be found.

An Interlude: The Measurement of Outcroppings

The population restrictions discussed here are apt to seem so severe as to traumatize the researcher and to lead to the abandonment of the method. This is particularly so for one approaching social science with the goal of complete description. Such trauma is, of course, far from our intention. While discussion of these restrictions is a necessary background to their intelligent use and correction, there is need here for a parenthesis forestalling excessive pessimism.

First, it can be noted that a theory predicting a change in civic opinion, due to an event and occurring between two time periods, might be such that this opinion shift could be predicted for many partially overlapping populations. One might predict changes on public opinion polls within that universe, changes in sampled conversation on commuter trains for a much smaller segment, changes in letters mailed to editors and the still more limited letters published by editors, changes in purchase rates of books on relevant subjects by that minute universe, and so on. In such an instance, the occurrence of the predicted shift on any one of these meters is confirmatory and its absence discouraging. If the effect is found on only one measure, it probably reflects more on the method than on the theory (e.g., Burwen & Campbell, 1957; Campbell & Fiske, 1959). A more complicated theory might well predict differential shifts for different meters, and, again, the evidence of each is relevant to the validity of the theory. The joint confirmation between pollings of high-income populations and commuter-train conversations is much more validating than either taken alone, just because of the difference between the methods in irrelevant components.

The "outcropping" model from geology may be used more generally. Any given theory has innumerable implications and makes innumerable predictions which are unaccessible to available measures at any given time. The testing of the theory can only be done at the available outcroppings, those points where theoretical predictions and available instrumentation meet. Any one such outcropping is equivocal, and all types available should be checked. The more remote or independent such checks, the more confirmatory their agreement.

Within this model, science opportunistically exploits the available points of observation. As long as nature abhorred a vacuum up to 33 feet of water, little research was feasible. When manufacturing skills made it possible to represent the same abhorrence by 76 centimeters of mercury in a glass tube, a whole new outcropping for the checking of theory was made available. The telescope in Galileo's hands, the microscope, the induction coil, the photographic emulsion of silver nitrate, and the cloud chamber all represent partial new outcroppings available for the verification of theory. Even where several of these are relevant to the same theory, their mode of relevance is quite different and short of a complete overlap. Analogously, social science methods with individually restricted and nonidentical universes can provide collectively valuable outcroppings for the testing of theory.

The goal of complete description in science is particularly

misleading when it is assumed that raw data provide complete description. Theory is necessarily abstract, for any given event is so complex that its complete description may demand many more theories than are actually brought to bear on it — or than are even known at any given stage of development. But theories are more complete descriptions than obtained data, since they describe processes and entities in their unobserved as well as in their observed states. The scintillation counter notes but a small and nonrepresentative segment of a meson's course. The visual data of an ordinary object are literally superficial. Perceiving an object as solid or vaporous, persistent or transient, involves theory going far beyond the data given. The raw data, observations, field notes, tape recordings, and sound movies of a social event are but transient superficial outcroppings of events and objects much more continuously and completely (even if abstractly) described in the social scientist's theory. Tycho Brahe and Kepler's observations provided Kepler with only small fragments of the orbit of Mars, for a biased and narrow sampling of times of day, days, and years. From these he constructed a complete description through theory. The fragments provided outcroppings sufficiently stubborn to force Kepler to reject his preferred theory. The data were even sufficient to cause the rejection of Newton's later theory had Einstein's better-fitting theory then been available.

So if the restraints on validity sometimes seem demoralizing, they remain so only as long as one set of data, one type of method, is considered separately. Viewed in consort with other methods, matched against the available outcroppings for theory testing, there can be strength in converging weakness.

THE ACCESS TO CONTENT

Often a choice among methods is delimited by the relative ability of different classes of measurement to penetrate into content areas of research interest. In the simplest instance, this is not so much a question of validity as it is a limitation on the utility of the measure. Each class of research method, be it the questionnaire or hidden observation, has rigidities on the content it can cover. These rigidities can be divided, as were population restrictions, into those linked to an interaction between method and materials, those associated with time, and those with physical area.

10. Restrictions on content. If we adopt the research strategy of combining different classes of measurement, it becomes important to understand what content is and is not feasible or practical for each overlapping approach.

Observational methods can be used to yield an index of Negro-white amicability by computing the degree of "aggregation" or nonrandom clustering among mixed groups of Negroes and whites. This method could also be used to study male-female relations, or army-navy relations in wartime when uniforms are worn on liberty. But these indices of aggregation would be largely unavailable for Catholic-Protestant relations or for Jewish-Christian relations. Door-to-door solicitation of funds for causes relevant to attitudes is obviously plausible, but available for only a limited range of topics. For public opinion surveys, there are perhaps tabooed topics (although research on birth control and venereal disease has shown these to be fewer than might have been expected). More importantly, there are topics on which people are unable to report but which a social scientist can reliably observe.

Examples of this can be seen in the literature on verbal reinforcers in speech and in interviews. (For a review of this literature, see Krasner, 1958, as well as Hildum & Brown, 1956; Matarazzo, 1962a). A graphic display of opportunistic exploitation of an "outcropping" was displayed recently by Matarazzo and his associates (1964). They took tapes of the speech of astronauts and ground-communicators for two space flights and studied the duration of the ground-communicator's unit of speech to the astronauts. The data supported their expectations and confirmed findings from the laboratory. We are not sure if an orbital flight should be considered a "natural setting" or not, but certainly the astronaut and his colleagues were not overly sensitive to the duration of individual speech units. The observational method has consistently produced findings on the effect of verbal reinforcers unattainable by direct questioning.

It is obvious that secondary records and physical evidence are high in their content rigidity. The researcher cannot go out and generate a new set of historical records. He may discover a new set, but he is always restrained by what is available. We cite examples later which demonstrate that this weakness is not so great as is frequently thought, but it would be naive to suggest that it is not present.

11. Stability of content over time.   The restrictions on content just mentioned are often questions of convenience. The instability of content, however, is a serious concern for validity. Consider conversation sampling again: if one is attending to the amount of comment on race relations, for example, the occurrence of extremely bad weather may so completely dominate all conversations as to cause a meaningless drop in racial comments. This is a typical problem for index-making. In such an instance, one would probably prefer some index such as the proportion of all race comments that were favorable. In specific studies of content variability over time, personnel-evaluation studies have employed time sampling with considerable success. Observation during a random sample of a worker's laboring minutes efficiently does much to describe both the job and the worker (R. L. Thorndike, 1949; Ghiselli & Brown, 1955; Whisler & Harper, 1962).

Public opinion surveys have obvious limitations in this regard which have led to the utilization of telephone interviews and built-in-dialing recorders for television and radio audience surveys (Lucas & Britt, 1950; Lucas & Britt, 1963). By what means other than a recorder could one get a reasonable estimate of the number of people who watch *The Late Show?*

12. Stability of content over area.   Where regional comparisons are being made, cross-sectional stability in the kinds of contents elicited by a given method is desirable.

Take the measurement of interservice rivalry as a research question. As suggested earlier, one could study the degree of mingling among men in uniform, or study the number of barroom fights among men dressed in different uniforms. To have a valid regional comparison, one must assume the same incidence of men wearing uniforms in public places when at liberty. Such an assumption is probably not justified, partly because of past experience in a given area, partly because of proximity to urban centers. If a cluster of military bases are close to a large city, only a selective group wear uniforms off duty, and they are more likely to be the belligerent ones. Another comparison region may have the same level of behavior, but be less visible.

The effect of peace is to reduce the influence of the total level of the observed response, since mufti is more common. But if all the comparisons are made in peacetime, it is not an issue. The problem occurs only if one elected to study the problem by a time-series design which cut across war and peace. To the foot-on-rail researcher, the number of outcroppings may vary because of war, but this is no necessary threat to internal validity.

Sampling of locations, such as bus routes, waiting rooms, shop windows, and so forth, needs to be developed to expand access to both content and populations. Obviously, different methods present different opportunities and problems in this regard. Among the few studies which have seriously attempted this type of sampling, the problem of enumerating the universe of such locations has proved extremely difficult (James, 1951). Location sampling has, of course, been practiced more systematically with pre-established enumerated units such as blocks, census tracts, and incorporated areas.

Operating Ease and Validity Checks

There are differences among methods which have nothing to do with the interpretation of a single piece of research. These are familiar issues to working researchers, and are important ones for the selection of procedures. Choosing between two different methods which promise to yield equally valid data, the researcher is likely to reject the more time-consuming or costly method. Also, there is an inclination toward those methods which have sufficient flexibility to allow repetition if something unforeseen goes wrong, and which further hold potential for producing internal checks on validity or sampling errors.

13. Dross rate.   In any given interview, a part of the conversation is irrelevant to the topic at hand. This proportion is the dross rate. It is greater in open-ended, general, free-response interviewing than it is in structured interviews with fixed-answer categories;

by the same token, the latter are potentially the more reactive. But
in all such procedures, the great advantage is the interviewer's
power to introduce and reintroduce certain topics. This ability
allows a greater density of relevant data. At the other extreme is
unobserved conversation sampling, which is low-grade ore. If one
elected to measure attitudes toward Russia by sampling conversations on public transportation, a major share of experimental effort
could be spent in listening to comparisons of hairdressers or
discussions of the Yankees' one-time dominance of the American
League. For a specific problem, conversation sampling provides
low-grade ore. The price one must pay for this ore, in order to get a
naturally occurring response, may be too high for the experimenter's resources.

14. Access to descriptive cues.   In evaluating methods, one
should consider their potential for generating associated validity
checks, as well as the differences in the universes they tap.
Looking at alternative measures, what other data can they produce
that give descriptive cues on the specific nature of the method's
population? Internal evidence from early opinion polls showed
their population biases when answers about prior voting and
education did not match known election results and census data.

On this criterion, survey research methods have great advantages, for they permit the researcher to build in controls with ease.
Observational procedures can check restrictions only for such
gross and visible variables as sex, approximate age, and conspicuous ethnicity. Trace methods such as the relative wear of floor tiles
offer no such intrinsic possibility. However, it is possible in many
instances to introduce interview methods in conjunction with other
methods for the purpose of ascertaining population characteristics. Thus, commuter-train passengers, window shoppers, and
waiting-room conversationalists can, on a sample of times of day,
days of the week, and so on, be interviewed on background data,
probably without creating any serious reactive effects for measures taken on other occasions.

15. Ability to replicate.   The questionnaire and the interview
are particularly good methods because they permit the investigator
to replicate his own or someone else's research. There is a toler-

ance for error when one is producing new data that does not exist
when working with old. If a confounding event occurs or materials
are spoiled, one can start another survey repeating the procedure.
Archives and physical evidence are more restricted, with only a
fixed amount of data available. This may be a large amount —
allowing split-sample replication — but it may also be a one-shot
occurrence that permits only a single analysis. In the latter case,
there is no second chance, and the materials may be completely
consumed methodologically.

The one-sample problem is not a issue if data are used in a
clearcut test of theory. If the physical evidence or secondary
records are an outcropping where the theory can be probed, the
inability to produce another equivalent body of information is
secondary. The greater latitude of the questionnaire and interview,
however, permit the same statement and provide in addition a
margin for error.

So long as we maintain, as social scientists, an approach to
comparisons that considers compensating error and converging
corroboration from individually contaminated outcroppings, there
is no cause for concern. It is only when we naively place faith in a
single measure that the massive problems of social research vitiate
the validity of our comparisons. We have argued strongly in this
chapter for a conceptualization of method that demands multiple
measurement of the same phenomenon or comparison. Overreli-
ance on questionnaires and interviews is dangerous because it
does not give us enough points in conceptual space to triangulate.
We are urging the employment of novel, sometimes "oddball"
methods to give those points in space. The chapters that follow
illustrate some of these methods, their strengths and weaknesses,
and their promise for imaginative research.

CHAPTER 2

Physical Traces: Erosion and Accretion

The fog had probably just cleared. The singular Sherlock Holmes had been reunited with his old friend, Dr. Watson (after one of Watson's marriages), and both walked to Watson's newly acquired office. The practice was located in a duplex of two physician's suites, both of which has been for sale. No doubt sucking on his calabash, Holmes summarily told Watson that he had made a wise choice in purchasing the practice that he did, rather than the one on the other side of the duplex. The data? The steps were more worn on Watson's side than on his competitor's.

In this chapter we look at research methods geared to the study of physical traces surviving from past behavior. Physical evidence is probably the social scientist's least-used source of data, yet because of its ubiquity, it holds flexible and broad-gauged potential.

It is reasonable to start a chapter on physical evidence by talking of Sherlock Holmes. He and his paperbacked colleagues could teach us much. Consider that the detective, like the social scientist, faces the task of inferring the nature of past behavior (Who did the Lord of the Manor in?) by the careful generation and evaluation of current evidence. Some evidence he engineers (by questioning), some he observes (Does the witness develop a tic?), some he develops from extant physical evidence (Did the murderer leave his eyeglasses behind?). From the weighing of several different types of hopefully converging evidence, he makes a decision on the plausibility of several rival hypotheses. For example:

H_1: The butler did it.
H_2: It was the blacksheep brother.
H_3: He really committed suicide.

This chapter discusses only the physical evidence, those pieces of data not specifically produced for the purpose of comparison and inference, but available to be exploited opportunistically by the alert investigator. It should be emphasized that physical evidence has greatest utility in consort with other methodological approaches. Because there are easily visible population and content restrictions associated with physical evidence, such data have largely been ignored. It is difficult even to consider a patently weak source of data when research strategy is based on single measures and definitional operationism. The visibly stronger questionnaire or interview looks to be more valid, and it may be if only one measure is taken. In a multimethod strategy, however, one does not have to exclude data of any class or degree solely because it is weak. If the weaknesses are known and considered, the data are usable.

It may be helpful to discriminate between two broad classes of physical evidence, a discrimination similar to that between the intaglio and the cameo. On one hand, there are the *erosion measures*, where the degree of selective wear on some material yields the measure. Holmes's solution of the stairs on the duplex is an example. On the other hand, there are *accretion measures*, where the research evidence is some deposit of materials. Immediately one thinks of anthropologists working with refuse piles and pottery shards. The trace measures could be further subdivided according to the number and pattern of units of evidence. We might have two subclasses: remnants, where there is only one or a few indicators of the past behavior available, and series, where there is an accumulative body of evidence with more units, possibly deposited over a longer period of time. For purposes of simplicity, it is easier to consider just the two main divisions of erosion and accretion.

Natural Erosion Measures

Let us look first at some erosion measures. A committee was formed to set up a psychological exhibit at Chicago's Museum of Science and Industry. The committee learned that the vinyl tiles around the exhibit containing live, hatching chicks had to be replaced every six weeks or so; tiles in other areas of the museum went for years without replacement (Duncan, 1963). A comparative study of the rate of tile replacement around the various museum exhibits could give a rough ordering of the popularity of the exhibits. Note that although erosion is the measure, the knowledge of the erosion rate comes from a check of the records of the museum's maintenance department.

In addition to this erosion measure, unobtrusive observation studies showed that people stand before the chick display longer than they stand before any of the other exhibits. With this additional piece of evidence, the question becomes whether or not the erosion is a simple result of people standing in one location and shuffling their feet, or whether it really does indicate a greater frequency of different people viewing the exhibit. Clearly an empirical question. The observation and the tile erosion are two partially overlapping measures, each of which can serve as a check on the other. The observation material is more textured for studies of current behavior, because it can provide information on both the number of viewers and how long each views the display. The erosion data cannot index the duration of individual viewing, but they permit an analysis of popularity over time, and do so with economy and efficiency.

Those readers who have attended American Psychological Association meetings have doubtless observed the popularity of conditioning exhibits displaying a live pigeon or monkey (a Skinner-boxed baby has also done well in recent years). This observation offers independent evidence for the general principle that dynamic exhibits draw more viewers than static ones. The hypothesis could be tested further by more careful comparison of tile wear about dynamic and static exhibits in the museum, making corrections for their positional distribution. At least part of the correction would be drawn from the previously mentioned research by Melton (1936) on response sets systematically present in museum traffic flow.

The wear on library books, particularly on the corners where the page is turned, offers an example of a possible approach that illustrates a useful overlap measure. One of the most direct and obvious ways to learn the popularity of books is to check how many times each of a series of titles has been removed from a library. This is an excellent measure and uses the records already maintained for other purposes. But it is only an indirect measure for the investigator who wants to know the relative amount of reading a series of books get. They may be removed from the library, but not read. It is easy to establish whether or not there is a close relationship between degree of wear and degree of checkouts from the library. If this relationship is positive and high, the hypothesis that books are taken out but selectively not read is accounted for. Note that the erosion measure also allows one to study the relative use of titles which are outside the span of the library-withdrawal measure. Titles placed on reserve, for example, are typically not noted for individual use by library bookkeeping. An alternative accretion measure is to note the amount of dust that has accumulated on the books studied.

Mosteller (1955) conducted a shrewd and creative study on the degree to which different sections of the *International Encyclopedia of the Social Sciences* were read. He measured the wear and tear on separate sections by noting dirty edges of pages as markers, and observed the frequency of dirt smudges, finger markings, and underlining on pages. In some cases of very heavy use, ". . . dirt had noticeably changed the color of the page so that [some articles] are immediately distinguishable from the rest of the volume" (p. 171). Mosteller studied volumes at both Harvard and the University of Chicago, and went to three libraries at each institution. He even used the *Encyclopaedia Britannica* as a control.

A variation of the erosion method has been suggested by Brown (1960) for studying the food intake of institutionalized patients — frequently a difficult task. If the question is one of overall food consumption of some administrative unit (say, a ward under special treatment conditions compared with a control ward), Brown makes the engagingly simple suggestion of weighing food trucks that enter and garbage trucks that leave. The unit could be varied to be an individual tray of food, the aggregate consignment to a floor or ward, or the total input and output of the hospital.

Natural Accretion Measures

There are large numbers of useful natural remnants of past behavior that can be exploited. We can examine now a few examples of behavior traces which were laid down "naturally," without the intervention of the social scientist.

The detective-story literature, again, is instructive. In a favorite example (Barzun, 1961), a case hinged on determining where a car came from. It was solved (naturally) by studying the frequencies to which the car's radio buttons were tuned. By triangulation of the frequencies, from a known population of commercial-station frequencies, the geographic source of the car was learned. Here was a remnant of past behavior (someone setting the buttons originally) that included several component elements collectively considered to reach a solution. Unimaginatively, most detective fiction considers much simpler and less elegant solutions — such as determining how fast a car was going by noting the degree to which insects are splattered on the windshield.

Modern police techniques include many trace methods, for example, making complex analyses of soil from shoes and clothing to establish a suspect's probable presence at the scene of a crime. One scientist (Forshufvud, 1961) uncovered the historic murder of Napoleon in 1821 on the basis of arsenic traces in remains of his hair.

Radio-dial settings are being used in a continuing audience-measurement study, with mechanics in an automotive service department the data-gatherers (Anonymous, 1962). A Chicago automobile dealer, Z. Frank, estimates the popularity of different radio stations by having mechanics record the position of the dial in all cars brought in for service. More than 50,000 dials a year are checked, with less than 20 per cent duplication of dials. These data are then used to select radio stations to carry the dealer's advertising. The generalization of these findings is sound if (1) the goal of the radio propaganda is to reach the same type of audience which now comes to the dealership, and (2) a significant number of cars have radios. If many of the cars are without radios, then a partial and possibly biased estimate of the universe is obtained. It is reported, "We find a high degree of correlation between what the rating people report and our own dial setting research" (p. 83).

The same approach could be used to study the selective appeal of different radio stations. Knowing that various shopping centers draw customers from quite discrete economic populations, one could observe dial settings in cars parked in the shopping

centers and compare them. As a validation check on the discrimination among the centers, one could (in metropolitan areas) note
local tax stickers affixed to the automobiles and compare these
with the economic data reported for tax areas by the United States
Census.

Dial checking is difficult in public areas, because one cannot
easily enter the car and make a close observation. And the locking
of cars is a selective phenomenon, even if one would risk entering
an unlocked car. Sechrest (1965b) has reported that a significantly
larger proportion of college women lock their cars than do college
men. He learned this by checking doors of automobiles parked
adjacent to men's and women's dormitories.

DuBois (1963) reports on a 1934 study which estimated an
advertisement's readership level by analyzing the number of different fingerprints on the page. The set of prints was a valid remnant,
and the analysis revealed a resourceful researcher. Compare this
with the anthropologist's device of estimating the prior population
of an archeological site by noting the size of floor areas (Naroll,
1962). Among the consistently detectable elements in a site are
good indicators of the floor areas of residences. When these can be
keyed to knowledge of the residential and familial patterns of the
group, these partial data, these remnants, serve as excellent
population predictors.

Other remnants can provide evidence on the physical characteristics of populations no longer available for study. Suits of
armor, for example, are indicators of the height of medieval
knights.

The estimable study of McClelland (1961), *The Achieving
Society,* displays a fertile use of historical evidence. Most of the
data come from documentary materials such as records of births
and deaths, coal imports, shipping levels, electric-power consumption, and remaining examples of literature, folk tales, and children's stories. We consider such materials in our discussion of
archival records, but they are, in one sense, a special case of trace
analysis. McClelland further reports on achievement-level estimates derived from ceramic designs on urns, and he indexes the
geographic boundaries of Greek trade by archeological finds of
vases. Sensitive to the potential error in such estimates, McClelland writes,

> So, rough though it is, the measure of the economic rise and fall of classical Greece was taken to be the area with which she traded, in millions of square miles, as determined by the location of vases unearthed in which her chief export commodities were transported [p. 117].

This measure was related to the need-for-achievement level of classical Greece, estimated from a content analysis of Greek writings.

Following the anthropological tradition of refuse study, two recent reports demonstrate that refuse may be used for contemporary as well as historical research.

Hughes (1958) observes:

> ... it is by the garbage that the janitor judges, and, as it were, gets power over the tenants who high-hat him. Janitors know about hidden love-affairs by bits of torn-up letter paper; of impending financial disaster or of financial four-flushing by the presence of many unopened letters in the waste. Or they may stall off demands for immediate service by an unreasonable woman of whom they know from the garbage that she, as the janitors put it, "has the rag on." The garbage gives the janitor the makings of a kind of magical power over that pretentious villain, the tenant. I say a kind of magical power, for there appears to be no thought of betraying any individual and thus turning this knowledge into overt power. He protects the tenant, but, at least among Chicago janitors, it is not a loving protection [p. 51].

Sawyer (1961) recounts the problem of estimating liquor sales in Wellesley, Massachusetts. In a city without package stores, the usual devices of observation of purchase or study of sales records are of no help. Sawyer solved the problem by studying the trash carted from Wellesley homes and counting the number of empty liquor bottles.

The duration of the sampling period is a consideration in studying traces of any product in which consumption of a visible unit takes a long time. The study must cover a large enough span to guarantee that a trace of the behavior will appear if, in fact, it did occur. With estimation of whisky consumption, there is the further demand that account be taken of such possibly confounding elements as holidays, birthdays, discount sales in nearby retail stores, and unusual weather. This is particularly true if estimates are being made of the relative consumption of specific types of liquor. A heat wave produces a substantial increase in the consumption of gin, vodka, and rum, while depressing consumption of scotch, brandy, and blended whiskies. Depending upon the area, an unusually high level of entertaining produces consumption of either more expensive or less expensive whisky than usual. The temporal stability of many common products that could be used to measure behavior is quite low.

Kinsey and his associates note the study of another trace measure—inscriptions in toilets. "With the collaboration of a number of other persons, we have accumulated some hundreds of wall inscriptions from public toilets" (Kinsey *et al.*, 1953, p. 673). Their findings show a significant difference between men's and women's toilets in the incidence of erotic inscriptions, either writings or drawings. Sechrest (1965a), studying inscriptions in Philippine and United States toilets, also found a difference between frequencies of male and female inscriptions—although female inscriptions seemed relatively more frequent in the Philippines. A widely circulated United States joke runs, "When a girl can see the handwriting on the wall, she's in the wrong restroom." Sechrest also found indications of greater sexual and homosexual preoccupation in the United States sample.

Some accretion data are built up quickly, and the problem of deciding on the appropriate period of study is negligible. Take the debris accumulation of a ticker-tape parade. The New York Sanitary Commission regularly notes how many tons of paper float down onto the streets during a parade. One might use this as material in estimating the enthusiasm of response for some popular hero. Because the Sanitary Commission has been reporting on how hard it works for years, it is possible to employ a control level of tonnages showered down upon other heroes. Did John Glenn get a more or less enthusiastic response from the New Yorkers of his day than did Charles Lindbergh from the New Yorkers of his? At best these data are suggestive, and the demise of the ticker-tape machine has meant a confounding of data for long-term historical analysis. While at one time ticker-tape parades had a dominance of ticker tape in the air, today it is confetti. One can make corrections, of course, but they must be tenuous.

Litter can also serve as a measure of conformity to restrictions. One can measure with a direct criterion the effectiveness of antilitter posters which vary in severity or style.

Experimenter Intervention

The methods discussed so far have all been ones in which the social scientist has taken the data as they come and not intervened in any way to influence the frequency or character of the indicator material. There are conditions under which the social scientist can intervene in the data-production process without destroying the nonreactive gains characteristic of trace and erosion data. He might want to do this, for example, to speed up the incidence of critical responses—a sometimes nagging annoyance with slowly eroding or accreting materials. Or he might want to guarantee that the materials under study were in fact equivalent or equal before they were modified by the critical responses. The essential point is that his intervention should not impair the nonreactivity of the erosion and trace measures by permitting the subjects to become aware of his testing.

Controlled Erosion Measures

John Wallace, our former colleague, once noted that it would be possible to estimate the activity level of children by measuring the rate at which they wear out shoes. It is theoretically possible to start at any point in time with the shoes that children are wearing, measure the degree of wear, and then later remeasure. The difference between the two scores might be a measure of the effect of some experimental variable. If the measurements were surreptitious, the experimenter would merely be noting a naturally occurring event and not involving himself with the materials.

Schulman and Reisman (1959) indexed the activity level of children by having them wear self-winding wristwatches which were adapted to record the child's amount of movement. Schulman, Kasper, and Throne (1965) have validated the "actometer" data against children's oxygen consumption.

Still another way to improve the data-gathering process is to manipulate the recording material. In some cases, one might treat the material to allow it to provide a more stable base. With floor tile, for example, surfaces are often coated to resist wear. Once the coating is worn through, erosion proceeds at a faster rate. For research purposes, it would be desirable to lay uncoated tiles and accelerate the speed with which information is produced.

In other cases, coating of materials may be desirable, either to provide a more permanent measure or to allow one where it otherwise would be impossible. The wear on public statues, reliefs, and so forth may provide an example. Throughout Europe, one may note with interest shiny bronze spots on religious figures and scenes. The rubbing which produced these traces is selective and becomes most visible in group scenes in which only one or two figures are shiny. The "Doors of Paradise" at the baptistry of San Giovanni in Florence demonstrate this particularly well.

A careful investigator might choose to work another improvement on the floor-erosion approach. An important bias is that each footfall is not necessarily an independent event. Once a groove on a stair becomes visible, for example, those who walk on that stair are more likely to conform to the position of the groove than are those who walked before it became visible. This is partly due to the physical condition of the stair, which tends to slide the person's foot into the groove, and also possibly due to a response tendency to follow in the footsteps of others. This may be partially controlled in newer settings by placing mats on the steps and noting their wear. The mats could also hide the already eroded grooves.

Controlled Accretion Measures

Just as with erosion measures, it is sometimes desirable for the researcher to tamper with materials pertinent to an accretion comparison. Noted earlier was a fingerprint study of advertising exposure (DuBois, 1963). Another procedure to test advertising exposure is the "glue-seal record" (Politz, 1958). Between each pair of pages in a magazine, a small glue spot was placed close to the binding and made inconspicuous enough so that it was difficult to detect visually or tactually. The glue was so composed that it would not readhere once the seal was broken. After the magazines had been read, exposure was determined by noting whether or not the seal was intact for each pair of pages, and a cumulative measure of advertising exposure was obtained by noting the total number of breaks in the sample issue. This method was developed because of a pervasive response-set tendency among questionnaire respondents to claim falsely the viewing or reading of advertisements. This particular measure was valuable in establishing the degree to which there was a spurious inflation of recall of advertisements. It was not used alone, but in consort with more standard interviewing practices to provide a validity check.

The content restrictions of this method are substantial. It does not provide data for a single page or advertisement, but instead only indicates whether or not a *pair* of pages were exposed to the person's eye. There is no direct evidence whether or not the person even looked at advertisements which appeared on this pair of pages. Nor is the method sensitive to how many people may have been exposed to a given pair of pages. One or more openings yields the same response.

The fingerprint method suffers from fewer restrictions, and it, too, could be improved by an unobtrusive move of the investigator. It is possible to select special paper which more faithfully receives fingerprints, thereby reducing the risk that the level of exposure will be underestimated. The greater fidelity of a selected paper would also improve the ability to discriminate among different fingerprints on the page. It is clearly impractical and unwise to base a complete study of advertising exposure on fingerprints; it is equally unwise not to consider coincidental methods which yield, as the glue seals do, independent validation data. Clearly, the greater the risk that awareness, response set, role evocation, and other variables present to valid comparisons, the greater the demand for independent, nonreactive, and coincidental measures.

From fingerprints to noseprints — and back to the museum for a final example. The relative popularity of exhibits with glass fronts could be compared by examining the number of noseprints deposited on the glass each day (or on some sample of time, day, month, and so forth). This requires that the glass be dusted for noseprints each night and then wiped clean for the next day's viewers to smudge. The noseprint measure has fewer content restrictions than most of the trace techniques, for the age of viewers can be estimated as well as the total number of prints on each exhibit. Age is determined by plotting a frequency distribution of the heights of the smudges from the floor, and relating these data to normative heights by age (minus, of course, the nose-to-top-of-head correction).[1]

TRANSFORMING THE DATA: CORRECTIONS AND INDEX NUMBERS

The examples provided suggest that physical-evidence data are best suited for measures of incidence, frequency, attendance, and the like. There are exceptions. In a closely worked-out theory, for example, the presence or absence of a trace could provide a critical test or comparison. But such critical tests are rare compared to the times when the physical evidence—be it deposit or erosion—is one part of a series of tests.

When dealing with frequency data, particularly when they are in time-series form, it is essential to ask whether or not there are any corrections which may be applied to remove extraneous sources of variance and improve the validity of comparisons.

More so than most classes of data, the type of frequency data yielded by physical materials is subject to influences which can be known (and corrected for) without substantial marginal research effort.

The museum measures of noseprint deposits or tile erosion can serve as examples. We can use these data to answer questions about the popularity of a given exhibit over time. Are the hatching chicks as popular now as they once were? Is there a boom in viewing of giant panda exhibits? The answers to these questions might be of interest in themselves, or we might want them to evaluate the effect of some other variable. We could conceive of a study estimating the effect of newspaper stories on public behavior. Did a story on the birth of a baby leopard in the zoo increase the number of zoo visitors *and* the number of viewers of a leopard exhibit in the natural history museum? The effect may be too transitory for the erosion measure to pick up, but the noseprint deposits could index it. Or do accounts of trouble in a far-off spot increase the number of persons showing interest in museum

---

[1]The authors were told of such a research project, but have been unable to locate the source. If the study is not apocryphal, we should like to learn the source and give proper credit to so imaginative an investigator.

collections from that area? The museum data might be one more outcropping of an effect that could be tested and used in consort with other measures to evaluate an effect.

In looking at the museum data, we could consider the news-paper-story question as a problem in the effect of an exogenous variable on a time series, and we are compelled to look for other sources of variation besides the story. We know something of the pool from which the critical responses come. Museum attendance varies seasonally (highest in summer, lowest in winter), varies cyclically (up on holidays, weekends, and school vacations), and has had a strong secular movement upward over time. All of these known influences on museum attendance are independent of the newspaper story. They may be partialled out of the total variance of the time series or, in descriptive statistics, be con-trolled in index numbers. Such corrections, however, are less critical for comparisons across areas. To the degree that these scores can be accounted for—in either inferential or descriptive terms—we achieve more sensitive research.

Auxiliary intelligence exists for most applications of physical-evidence data. It may be contained in records kept for other purposes, or come from prior knowledge. Consider the problem of estimating advertising exposure by the glue-seal method. In study-ing a single pair of pages, our only measure is the proportion of pages on which seals are broken. Of course, there are a number of variables known to influence the degree to which magazine pages are opened. The number of pages in the magazine, for example, or the magazine's policy of either clustering or dispersing advertise-ments throughout its pages will alter responses. Finally, readers of some magazines systematically and predictably read ads more than do readers of other magazines.

Each of these elements should be considered in evaluating the single medium under study. These factors might be combined into a baseline index which states the reasonable exposure expectation for an ad appearing in a very thin issue of Magazine A, with a dispersion strategy of ad placement. The observed score for the given pair of pages can thus be transformed into a number which is in some way related to the expected value.

This approach to "description" is the one argued in Chapter 1 —description and all research inferences are comparisons. When the control is not developed within the data-gathering of the study (as it is not in most of the possible physical-evidence measures), it can be generated by analysis of other available intelligence.

With more elaborate comparisons than evaluating a single museum exhibit, the problems of extraneous variables and the need for their control in both inference and description become magnified. Keeping with the museum, take the problem of comparing two exhibits located in different sections of the museum. The same information used earlier—the known variation by season, holidays, and so on—is again core intelligence for comparison of the observed physical evidence. The concern becomes one of interactions. At those predictably high and low attendance times, we can expect a significant interaction between the accessibility of the exhibit and the over-all level of attendance. The interaction could bias measures of both the number of viewers and the duration of time spent viewing.

We should expect the more accessible exhibit to have a significantly higher marginal lead on noseprints during high-attendance periods than during low-attendance periods. Some of the interactive difference may come from the greater individual fatigue with large crowds, which might restrict the length of time each visitor spends in the museum. Or the size of the crowds may slow movements so that a number of people with fixed time periods to spend in the museum do not get around as much. Or there may be a population characteristic such that a larger share of peak-time visitors are indifferent viewers who lack a compelling interest in the over-all content of the museum. They may view either more casually or more erratically.

Corrections must be made for both the main effects and the interactions in such cases, and the easiest way to make them is to prepare corrections based on known population levels and response tendencies. We should speak of statue rubbings per thousand bypassers, or the rate of floor-tile replacement in a specific display area per thousand summer visitors. These figures are first-line transformations that are valuable. They can become more valuable if enough is known to consider them as the numerator of an index fraction. With the study of past behavior giving the denominator, indices can be produced which account for irrelevant variance and make for better comparisons.

Up to this point, we have been talking only of corrections applied to a single measure. Following in the index-number tradition, we can also consider a piece of physical evidence either as one component of an over-all index composed of several different classes of data or as an element in a set of physical evidence combined to make an aggregate index.

One might want an over-all measure, extending over time, of the completeness with which an institution is being used. This could supplement information on the extent to which it is being attended. In a library, for example, the various types of physical evidence available (dust collection, page wear, card-catalogue wear) could be gathered together and each individual component weighted and then combined to produce the over-all index. Similarly for museums.

Assume that one wanted to note the effect of an anxiety-producing set of messages on the alleged link betweeen cigarettes and lung cancer. One could, in the traditional way, employ a before-after questionnaire study which measured attitudes toward cigarettes and obtained self-reports of smoking. Or, one could observe. If the anxiety-producing message were embedded in a lecture, at some point toward the middle, it would be possible to observe the frequency of cigarettes lit before, during, and after the mention of the deleterious effects of smoking. Or one could wire a sample of the chairs in the lecture hall and record the amount of squirming exhibited by the auditors at various points. Or, following Galton's (1885) suggestion, one could observe the amount of gross body movement in the audience. Or one could note the subsequent sale of books about smoking—ideally framing the setting so that equally attractive titles were available that argued the issue pro and con.

All of these alternatives are viable approaches to studying the effect of the message, with physical evidence an important element because of its ability to measure long-term effects and to extend the physical area of investigation beyond the immediate experimental setting. Depending on the degree of knowledge one had about the messages, the audience, and past effects, it would be possible to construct an index with differential weights for the various component measures of effect. Each of the single measures may be attacked for weakness, but taken cumulatively—as separate manifestations of an hypothesized effect—they offer greater hope for validity than any single measure, regardless of its popularity.

AN OVER-ALL EVALUATION OF PHYSICAL EVIDENCE DATA

The outstanding advantage of physical evidence data is its inconspicuousness. The stuff of analysis is material which is generated without the producer's knowledge of its use by the investigators. Just as with secondary records, one circumvents the problems of awareness of measurement, role selection, interviewer effects, and the bias that comes from the measurement itself taking on the role of a change agent. Thus, physical evidence is, for the most part, free of reactive measurement effects. It is still necessary to worry over possible response sets which influence the laying down of the data. With erosion measures, this might be so obvious a bias as the tendency for people to apply more pressure to stairs when going up than when going down, or the less obvious tendency to turn right.

With accretion measures, there is the question of whether the materials have selectively survived or been selectively deposited. Do some objects have a higher probability of being discarded in public places than others? Or, equally an issue, do some materials survive the intervening events of time better? Archeological research has always faced the problem of the selective survival of materials. Some of this selection comes from the physical characteristics of the material: clay survives; wood usually does not. Other selection comes from the potential value of the material which might be discarded. In writing of the small decorated stamps (seals) used by the ancient Mexican cultures, Enciso (1953) noted, "If any gold or silver was used, the stamps have yet to be found or have been melted long ago. Wood and bone have not survived the ravages of time. This may explain the abundant survival of clay stamps" (p. iv). In Naroll's (1956) phrase, the clay stamps are "durable artifacts." We also discuss this bias in our comments on archival and available records, but it is significant here for the restrictions it places on the content of physical-evidence data and thereby the ability to generalize findings.

Any single class of physical evidence is likely to have a strong population restriction, and all physical-evidence data are troubled by population problems in general. It is not, for example, easy to get descriptive access to the characteristics of a possible population restriction. One has the remnant of past behavior — a groove or a pile — and it says nothing by itself of those who produced the evidence.

We also must be cautious of physical data because they may vary selectively over time or across different geographical areas. It is possible to get some checks on the character of these restrictions by employing supplementary methods such as the interview or the questionnaire. Some inferences about the character of population bias may come also from a time-series analysis of the data, possibly linking the physical-evidence data to time series of other data hypothesized to be selectively contributing to the variance. In a systematic investigation, a careful sampling of both times and locations is possible, and internal comparison of the findings may offer some clues. But the assumption must be that any set of physical evidence is strongly subject to population restrictions, and supplementary information is always required.

Other methods also have population restrictions, and it may be possible to turn the fact of a restriction into an asset. There are, for example, certain subsets of the population virtually impossible to interview. In such situations, an enterprising investigator should ask whether the subject is leaving traces of behavior or material which offer some help in inferring the subject's critical behavior. In this type of problem, the physical evidence is the supplementary data, and is used to fill in the population restrictions of other methods used concurrently.

As for the content available to the reach of physical-evidence methods, there are substantial limitations. It is not often that an investigator tests a theory so precise in its predictions that the appearance or absence of a single trace is a critical test of the theory. Most of the time, physical evidence is more appropriate for indexing the extent to which an activity has taken place — the number of footfalls, the number of empties tossed aside. Because these activities are influenced by many other variables, we seldom have an absolutely clean expression of some state of being — thus the necessity for corrections and transformations. Yet if enough information does exist, or can be produced, the content restrictions are controllable because they are knowable.

There is the positive gain that the amount of dross in physical evidence is low or negligible. Typically, what is measured is relatively uncontaminated by a body of other material which must be discarded as not pertinent to the research investigation. One can pinpoint the investigation closely enough to eliminate the dross — something not possible in the more amorphous method of conversation sampling, or of observation of "natural" behavior.

Compared with other classes of research methods, we have noted few examples of prior research using physical evidence. This is not through preference, but because we have been unable to find more. Physical-evidence data are off the main track for most psychological and sociological research. This is understandable, but still regrettable. The more visible weaknesses of physical evidence should preclude its use no more than should the less visible, but equally real, weaknesses of other methods. If physical evidence is used in consort with more traditional approaches, the population and content restrictions can be controlled, providing a novel and fruitful avoidance of the errors that come from reactivity.

CHAPTER 3

Archives I: The Running Record

Possibly a wife was more likely to get an inscribed tablet if she
died before her husband than if she outlived him.

The tablet cited here is a tombstone, and the quotation is from
Durand's (1960) study of life expectancy in ancient Rome and its
provinces. Tombstones are but one of a plethora of archives
available for the adventurous researcher, and all social scientists
should now and then give thanks to those literate, record-keeping
societies which systematically provide so much material appropriate to novel analysis.

The purpose of this chapter is to examine and evaluate some
uses of data periodically produced for other than scholarly purposes, but which can be exploited by social scientists. These are
the ongoing, continuing records of a society, and the potential
source of varied scientific data, particularly useful for longitudinal
studies. The next chapter looks at more discontinuous archives,
but here the data are the actuarial records, the votes, the city
budgets, and the communications media which are periodically
produced, and paid for, by someone other than the researcher.

Besides the low cost of acquiring a massive amount of pertinent data, one common advantage of archival material is its
nonreactivity. Although there may be substantial errors in the
material, it is not usual to find masking or sensitivity because the
producer of the data knows he is being studied by some social
scientist. This gain by itself makes the use of archives attractive if
one wants to compensate for the reactivity which riddles the
interview and the questionnaire. The risks of error implicit in
archival sources are not trivial, but, to repeat our litany, if they are
recognized and accounted for by multiple measurement techniques, the errors need not preclude use of the data.

More than other scholars, archeologists, anthropologists, and historians have wrestled with the problems of archival data. Obviously, they frequently have little choice but to use what is available and then to apply corrections. Unlike the social scientist working with a contemporaneous problem, there is little chance to generate new data which will be pertinent to the problem and which will circumvent the singular weakness of the records being employed.

Naroll (1962) recently reviewed the methodological issues of archives in his book *Data Quality Control*. His central argument focuses on representative sampling. Does the archeologist with his thousand-year-old pottery shards, or the historian with a set of two-hundred-year-old memoirs, really have a representative body of data from which to draw conclusions? This is one part of "Croce's Problem." Either one is uncertain of the data when only a limited body exists, or uncertain of the sample when so much exists that selection is necessary.

Modern sampling methods obviate the second part of the problem. We can know, with a specified degree of error, the confidence we can place in a set of findings. But the first part of Croce's problem is not always solvable. Sometimes the running record is spotty, and we do not know if the missing parts can be adequately estimated by a study of the rest of the series. That is one issue. But even if the record is serially complete, the collection of the secondary sources impeccable, and the analysis inspired, the validity of the conclusions must rest on assumptions of the adequacy of the original material.

There are at least two major sources of bias in archival records — selective deposit and selective survival. They are the same two concerns one meets in dealing with physical-evidence data. Durand's study of the ancient Roman tombstones illustrates the selective-deposit concern. Does a study of a properly selected sample of tombstones tell us about the longevity of the ancient Romans, or only of a subset of that civilization? Durand, as noted, suggests that the timing of a wife's death may determine the chance of her datum (CCCI-CCCL) being included in his sample. It is not only the wives who die after their husbands who may be underrepresented. There is, too, a possible economic or social-class contaminant. Middle- and upper-class Romans were more likely to have tombstones (and particularly those that survived until now) than those in the lower reaches of Roman society. This bias is a risk to validity to the degree that mortality rates varied across economic or social classes—which they probably did. The more affluent were more likely to have access to physicians and drugs, which, given the state of medicine, may have either shortened or lengthened their lives. It is to Durand's credit that he carefully suggests potential biases in his data and properly interprets his findings within the framework of possible sampling error.

This same type of sampling error is possible when studying documents, whether letters to the editor or suicide notes. We know that systematic biases exist among editors. Some try to present a "balanced" picture on controversial topics regardless of how unbalanced the mail. With the study of suicide notes, the question must be asked whether suicides who do not write notes would have expressed the same type of thoughts had they taken pen in hand. Any inferences from suicide notes must be hedged by the realization that less than a quarter of all suicides write notes. Are both the writers and nonwriters drawn from the same population?

The demographer cannot get new Romans to live and die; the psychologist cannot precipitate suicides. And therein is the central problem of historical data. New and overlapping data are difficult to obtain from the same or equivalent samples. The reduction of error must come from a close internal analysis which usually means fragmenting the data into subclasses and making cross-checks.

An alternative approach is feasible when reports on the same phenomenon by different observers are available. By a comparative evaluation of the sources, based on their different qualifications, inferences may be drawn on the data's accuracy (Naroll, 1960; Naroll, 1961). In examining an extinct culture, for example, one can compare reports made by those who lived among the people for a long period of time with reports from casual visitors. Or there can be a comparison of the reports from those who learned the indigenous language and those who did not. For those items on which there is consensus, there is a higher probability that the item reported is indeed valid. This consensus test is one solution to discovery of selective deposit or editing of material. It does not eliminate the risk that all surviving records are biased in the same selective way; what it does do is reduce the plausibility of such an objection. The greater the number of observers with different qualifications, the less plausible the hypothesis that the same systematic error exists.

Sometimes selective editing creeps in through an administrative practice. Columbus kept two logs — one for himself and one for the crew. Record-keepers may not keep two logs, but they may choose among alternative methods of recording or presenting the data. Sometimes this is innocent, sometimes it is to mask elements they consider deleterious. In economic records, bookkeeping practices may vary so much that close attention must be paid to which alternative record system was selected. The depreciation of physical equipment is an example. Often deliberate errors or record-keeping policy can be detected by the sophisticate. At other times, the data are lost forever (Morgenstern, 1963).

One more example may serve. A rich source of continuing data is the *Congressional Record*, that weighty but sometimes humorous document which records the speeches and activities of the Congress. A congressman may deliver a vituperative speech which looks, upon reflection, to be unflattering. Since proofs are submitted to the congressman, he can easily alter the speech to eliminate his peccadillos. A naive reader of the *Record* might be misled in an analysis of material which he thinks is spontaneous, but which is in fact studied.

A demurrer is entered. Even if the data were originally produced without any systematic bias that could threaten validity, the risk of their selective survival remains. It is no accident that archeologists are pottery experts. Baked clay is a "durable artifact" that cannot be digested and decays negligibly. Naroll (1956) comments that artifacts survive because they are not consumed in use, are indifferent to decay, and are not incorporated into some other artifact so as to become unidentifiable. Discrete and durable, they remain as clues, but partial clues; other evidence was eaten, rotted, or re-employed. Short of complete destruction, decay by itself is no problem. It only becomes one when the rate and distribution of decay is unknown. If known, it may become a profitable piece of evidence — as Libby's (1963) work with radiocarbon dating shows.

For the student of the present, as well as of the past, the selective destruction of records is a question. Particularly in the political area, the holes that exist in data series are suspect. Are records missing because knowledge of their contents would reflect in an untoward way on the administration? Have the files been rifled? If records are destroyed casually, as they often are during an office move, was there some biasing principle for the research comparison which determined what would be retained and what destroyed?

When estimating missing values in a statistical series, one is usually delighted if all but one or two values are present. This gives confidence when filling in the missing cells. If the one or two holes existing in the series have potential political significance, the student is less sanguine and more suspicious of his ability to estimate the missing data.

ACTUARIAL RECORDS

Birth, marriage, death. For each of these, societies maintain continuing records as normal procedure. Governments at various levels provide massive amounts of statistical data, ranging from the federal census to the simple entry of a wedding in a town-hall ledger. Such formal records have frequently been used in descriptive studies, but they offer promise for hypothesis-testing research as well.

Take Winston's (1932) research. He wanted to examine the preference for male offspring in upper-class families. He could have interviewed prospective mothers in affluent homes, or fathers in waiting rooms. Indeed, one could pay obstetricians to ask, "What would you like me to order?" Other measures, nonreactive ones, might be studies of adoption records, the sales of different layette colors (cutting the data by the class level of the store), or the incidence of "other sex" names — such as Marion, Shirley, Jean, Jerry, Jo.

But Winston went to the enormous data bank of birth records and manipulated them adroitly. He simply noted the sex of each child in each birth order. A preference for males was indicated, he hypothesized, if the male-female ratio of the last child born in families estimated to be complete was greater than that ratio for all children in the same families. With the detail present in birth records, he was able to segregate his upper-class sample of parents by the peripheral data of occupation, and so forth. The same auxiliary data can be employed in any study to serve as a check on evident population restrictions — a decided plus for detailed archives.

This study also illustrates the time-sampling problem. For the period studied, and because of the limitation to upper-class families, Winston's measure is probably not contaminated by economic limitations on the absolute number of children, a variable that may operate independently of any family sex preference. Had his study covered only the 1930's, or were he making a time-series comparison of economically marginal families, the time factor could offer a substantial obstacle to valid comparison. The argument for the existence of such an economic variable would be supported if a study of the 1930's showed no sex difference among terminal children, but did show significant differences for children born in the 1940's.

Economic conditions are only one of the factors important to errors due to timing. Wars, depressions, and acts of God are all events which can pervasively influence the comparisons of social science data. The subjective probability of their influence may be awkward to assign, yet the ability to control that influence through index numbers and other data transformations is a reasonable and proper practice.

There are many demographic studies of fertility levels in different societies, but Middleton (1960) showed a shrewd understanding of archival sources in his work. He developed two sets of data: fertility values expressed in magazine fiction, and actuarial fertility levels at three different time periods. For 1916, 1936, and 1956, he estimated fertility values by noting the size of fictional families in eight American magazines. A comparison with the population data showed that shifts in the size of fictional families closely paralleled shifts in the true United States fertility level.

Middleton had a troublesome sampling problem. Since only a small number of magazines continued publication over the period from 1916 to 1956, was the group of eight long-term survivors a proper sample? This durable group may not have been representative, but it was quite proper. The very fact that these eight survived the social changes of the 40 years argues that they probably reflected the society's values (or those of a sufficiently large segment of the society to keep the magazine economically alive) more adequately than those which failed. The issue was not one of getting a representative sample of all magazines, but, instead, of magazines which printed material that would have recorded more faithfully the pertinent research information.

Christensen (1960) made a cross-cultural study of marriage and birth records to estimate the incidence of premarital sex relations in different societies. He simply checked off the time interval between marriage and birth of the first child — a procedure which showed marked differences in premarital conception, if not in activity among cultures. His study illustrates some of the problems in cross-cultural study. The rate of premature births may vary across societies, and it is necessary to test whether this hypothesis can explain differences. Data on the incidence of premature births of later-born children in each society permit this correction. A population problem to be guarded against in these cross-cultural studies, however, is the differential recording of births, marriages, and the like. There are many societies in which a substantial share of marriages are not formally entered in a record-keeping system, although the parties initially regard the alliance to be as binding as do those in other societies where records are more complete. The incidence in Mexico of "free-union" marriages is both extensive and selective — more prevalent among working classes than other groups (Lewis, 1961).

Simple marriage records alone were used by Burchinal and Kenkel (1962) and Burchinal and Chancellor (1962). The records were used as a handy source by Burchinal and Kenkel to study the association between religious identification and occupational status. The records provided a great body of data from which to work, but also posed a sampling question. Are men about to be grooms a good base for estimating the link between religion and occupation? The small cadre of confirmed bachelors is excluded from the sample universe, and depending upon the dates of the records studied, there can be an interaction between history and groom-dom.

A later study by Burchinal and Chancellor (1963) took the complete marriage and divorce records of the Iowa Division of Vital Statistics for the years 1953 and 1959. From these records, the authors compared marriages of same-religion and mixed-religion pairs for longevity. As might be expected, they found mixed marriages to be significantly shorter-lived than same-religion ones. Of the mixed marriages, those partners who described themselves as Protestants without naming a specific affiliation showed the highest divorce rate.

It might be well to note that such data may be contaminated by self-selection error. Persons entering mixed marriages may be more unstable or more quick to see divorce as a solution. Such people might not increase the chances of a durable marriage by choosing a mate of the same religion.

These same marriage records could be employed as tests of functional literacy. Taking a time series of marriage records, what is the proportion of people signing "X" at varying points in history?

Of all the marriage-record studies, probably none is more engaging than Galton's (1870) classic on hereditary genius. Galton used archival records to determine the eminence of subjects defined as "geniuses" and additional archives to note how their relatives fared on eminence. Few scientists have been so sensitive as Galton to possible error in drawing conclusions, and, in a section on occupations, he notes that many of the judges he studied postponed marriage until they were elevated to the bench. Even so, their issue of legitimate children was considerable. In Stein and Heinze's (1960) summary: "Galton points out that among English peers in general there is a preference for marrying hieresses, and these women have been peculiarly unprolific" (p. 87). And on the possible contaminant of the relative capacities of the male and female line to transmit ability:

> ... the decidedly smaller number of transmissions along the female line suggests either an "inherent incapacity in the female line for transmitting the peculiar forms of ability we are now discussing," or possibly "the aunts, sisters and daughters of eminent men do not marry, on the average, so frequently as other women." He believes there is some evidence for this latter explanation [p. 89].

Galton (1872) even used longevity data to measure the efficacy of prayer. He argued that if prayer were efficacious, and if members of royal houses are the persons whose longevity is most widely and continuously prayed for, then they should live longer than others.

Data showed the mean age at death of royalty to be 64.04 years, men of literature and science 67.55 years, and gentry 70.22 years.

Another pioneering study, Durkheim's *Suicide* (1951), shows an active exploration of archival source possibilities. He concluded that "the social suicide rate can be explained only sociologically" (p. 299) by relating suicide levels to religion, season of the year, time of day, race, sex, education, and marital status, doing all of this for different countries. All of these variables were obtained from available archives, and their systematic manipulation presaged the morass of cross-tabulations that were later to appear in sociological research.

Wechsler (1961) integrated three different classes of archival data in his correlational study of the relationships among suicide, depressive disorders, and community growth. He went to the census for data on population change, to mental-illness diagnoses in hospital records, and to the vital statistics of the state to get the suicide incidence.

Another study employing death records is Warner's (1959) work, *The Living and the Dead*. Death and its accoutrements in Yankee City were the subject of this multimethod research. Warner consulted official cemetery documents to establish a history of the dead and added interviewing, observation, and trace analysis as aids to his description of graveyards. "Their ground and burial lots were plotted and inventory was taken of the ownership of the various burial lots, and listings were made of the individuals and families buried in them" (p. 287).

His findings are of interest for what they say of response tendencies in the laying down of physical evidence. Here the response tendencies, and the way in which they vary across social-class groups, become the major clues to the analysis. Warner found the social structure of Yankee City mirrored (if this be the proper verb) in the cemetery; he found evidence on family organization, sex and age differentiation, and social mobility. For example, the father was most often buried in the center of the family plot, and headstones of males were larger than those of females. In some cases, Warner found that a family which had raised its social status moved the graves of their relatives from less prestigious cemeteries to more prestigious ones.

Tombstones would be an interesting source of data for comparative analysis of different cultures. In matriarchal societies, for example, is the matriarch's stone substantially larger than the husband's? Does the husband get a marker at all? What are the differences in societies with extended versus nuclear family structures?

Warner's findings tie in with Durand's (1960) study of ancient Rome. In both studies, the relative dominance of the male was demonstrated by the characteristics of the tombstones.

A more recent commentary on tombstones comes from Crowald (1964), who wandered through Moscow's Novo-Devich cemetery, noting the comparative treatment of old czarists and modern communists. After noting that over Chekhov's grave a cherry tree is appropriately blooming, he states:

> ... the cemetery also tells a quieter, more dramatic tale. Climbing out of some weedy grass is the washboard-sized marker of Maxim Litvinov, once a Stalin foreign minister and the wartime Soviet envoy to America. His mite of a marker reminds what happened to those who fell from Stalin's favor [p. 12].

Just as in ancient Rome, the timing of a wife's death makes a difference in the nature of the tombstone. Here, this potential contaminant is used as a piece of evidence.

> Novo-Devich does show, too, that things have changed in Russia since Stalin. For example, there is the great marble monument to Rosa Kaganovich. She was the wife of Lazar Kaganovich, the Stalin lieutenant booted from power in 1957 by Premier Nikita S. Khrushchev. Kaganovich is in full disgrace, but he fell after Stalin died. So his wife, who died in 1961, still got her big place in the cemetery. Fresh flowers decorate her marble [p. 12].

These objects are just big and small pieces of stone to the uninformed, but to the investigator who possesses intelligence on those buried and relates it to the stones, the humble and grandiose memorials are significant evidence.

In Rogow and Lasswell's (1963) discussion of "game politicians," they note,

> ... his relations with his immediate family were not close; indeed his wife and children saw less of him during his active life than certain key individuals in his political organization. As a result he is remembered less by his family than by the state

which he dominated for so many years. His grave in the family
plot is unattended, but his statue stands in front of the state
capitol building [p. 48].[1]

And for a novelistic treatment of what remains behind, there
is Richard Stern's (1960) commentary on Poppa Hondorp.

> The obituaries were Poppa Hondorp's measure of human worth.
> "There's little they can add or subtract from you then," was his
> view. Poppa's eye had sharpened over the years so that he could
> weigh a two-and-a-half-inch column of ex-alderman against
> three-and-a-quarter inches of inorganic chemist and know at a
> glance their comparative worth. When his son had one day
> suggested that the exigencies of the printer and make-up man
> might in part account for the amount of space accorded a
> deceased, Poppa Hondorp had shivered with a rage his son
> knew he should never excite again. "Don't mess with credos,"
> knew young Hondorp, so the obituaries were sacrosanct; the
> *Times* issued mysteriously from an immaculate source [p. 24].

Frequently, one has a choice among different archival
sources, and a useful alternative are directories, whether of resi-
dents, association members, or locations. Ianni (1957-1958) elected
to use city directories as the primary source of data in his study of
residential mobility. An analysis of these directories over time
allowed him to establish the rates of mobility, and then relate these
mobility indices to the acculturation of ethnic groups.

It is obviously a tedious task to perform such an analysis, and
the work includes a high amount of dross. If possible, such
mobility levels might be more efficiently indexed by access to
change-of-address forms in the post office. But the question here
becomes one of population restriction. Is the gain in efficiency that
comes from use of change-of-address forms worth the possible loss
in completeness of sampling? The answer comes, of course, from a
preliminary study evaluating the two sources of data for their
selective characteristics.

For some studies, more selective directories are indicated,
and the inclusion of a person in a directory serves as one element
in the researcher's discriminations. *Who's Who in America* doesn't
print everybody's name, nor does *American Men of Science*. W. H.

---

[1]Arnold A. Rogow and Harold D. Lasswell, *Power, Corruption, and Rectitude*,
© 1963. Reprinted by permission of Prentice-Hall, Inc., Englewood Cliffs, New
Jersey.

Clark (1955) used both of these sources in his "A Study of Some of the Factors Leading to Achievement and Creativity with Special Reference to Religious Skepticism and Belief." Boring and Boring (1948) used *American Men of Science* to choose the psychologists studied in their useful article on the intellectual genealogy of American psychologists. Fry (1933) had earlier used *Who's Who in America* in a study entitled "The Religious Affiliations of American Leaders." (See also Lehman & Witty, 1931.)

Fry's work showed that if one depends on the editors of such directories for selective inclusion, one must also rely on the individuals listed for complete reporting. All of the problems associated with self-report are present, for the individual has a choice of whether or not he will include all data, and whether he will report accurately. The archive serves as an inexpensive substitute for interviewing a large sample of subjects stratified along some known or unknown set of variables. Fry found that a 1926 religious census showed 3.6 per cent of the general population to be Jews, while only .75 per cent of the entries in *Who's Who in America* were listed as Jews. Does this mean that Jews are less distinguished, are discriminated against in being invited to appear in the directory, or is there selective reporting by the Jews of their religion? Fry gave a partial answer to the question by a check of another directory—*Who's Who in American Jewry*. He found 432 persons in this directory who had reported no Jewish affiliation in *Who's Who in America*, thereby raising the Jewish percentage to 2.2. By raising the question of another plausible hypothesis for a comparison (3.6 per cent of the population compared with .75 per cent in the directory), he structured a question which was testable by recourse to a second archival source highly pertinent to the hypothesis.

Babchuk and Bates (1962) employed the membership list of the American Sociological Association in their work, "Professor or Producer: The Two Faces of Academic Man." After first procuring a list of all sociology Ph.D.'s for a given period from the *American Journal of Sociology*, they referred to four different membership directories of the ASA for a measurement of the degree of identification with the profession. "A number of persons in the sample never became affiliated with the Association; this fact was interpreted as meaning that such persons lacked an 'orientation to [the] discipline.'" [p. 342].

Kenneth Clark (1957) used the American Psychological Association's directory in his study of the psychological profession. For any study extending over a long time period, the APA directory can be frustrating. As the number of psychologists grew, the detail in the individual listings shrank. Thus, the number of items on which a complete time series could be produced were reduced as tighter and tighter editing took place. The measuring instrument was constant in its content for only a few pieces of information. The change in the number of available categories of information is a detectable shift in the quality of the measure. Other changes, such as increasingly difficult requirements for membership or individuals responding to the greater bulk of the directory by writing more truncated listings, may change the character of the instrument in a less visible way and produce significant differences which are, in fact, only recording artifacts.

Digging into the past, Marsh (1961) obtained the names of 1,047 Chinese government officials from the government directories of 1778 and 1831-1879. He then correlated the ranks of the officials with the time required to reach a particular rank and with other factors such as age and family background. If there was no differential recording, one may conclude with Marsh that the rich get there faster.

POLITICAL AND JUDICIAL RECORDS

An archival record — votes — is the dependent variable for office holders, the absolute criterion measure; but for the social scientist, it is only an indicator. Votes cast by the people determine the politician's most important piece of behavior (staying in office), and votes cast by the legislator are the definitive test of his position and alliances.

Dozens of studies are available that have evaluated voting statistics by party or by individual. The *ad hoc* rhetorical condemnations of an opponent's record are at one end of a scale that is anchored by sophisticated factor analysis on the other. In the interest of space, we have limited our examples to studies which have reported either unique or more convoluted manipulations of the essentially simple data.

The political slant of legislators has been a popular research topic. "Progressivism" in the United States Senate was assessed by Gage and Shimberg (1949). They wanted a sample of votes which would measure progressivism and picked ten bills for one congress and eight for another, getting coefficients of reproducibility of .88 and .91, respectively. With these data they studied a series of questions: Are younger senators more progressive than older ones? (No); Do senators from the same state tend to vote the same? (No); Are regional differences significant? (Yes).

MacRae (1954b) also studied the same type of legislative tendency in his paper on the influence on voting of constituent pressure and congressional social grouping. He selected his sample of critical votes by consulting the roll calls published by the *New Republic* and the *CIO News*. His assumption was that these sources would only publish reports of votes on issues germane to their presumably liberal readers. From these, he obtained a "liberal index" depending upon the direction of the vote.

A finer breakdown was made by Dempsey (1962), who estimated conservative votes, but divided them along party and nonparty issues. His subject was party loyalty in the Senate, and he used the reports of roll-call votes on individual senators to provide a "Loyalty Shift Index."

Moving over to the House, and the employment of all roll-call votes, Riker and Niemi (1962) looked at the question of congressional coalitions. They took votes on 87 roll calls, noting whether a congressman (1) voted on the winning side, (2) voted on the losing side, (3) did not vote when eligible, (4) did not vote when ineligible. The rolls were classified into subsets, and finally an index of coalitions was produced.

Farris (1958) also used roll-call votes to study coalitions within the Congress. His article is of strong interest, because it details the methodological issues the political scientist faces in isolating ideological groups. Farris elected to use Guttman scaling techniques on a sample of roll-call votes from the House in the seventy-ninth Congress. His sampling of votes was studied, and he excluded 94 of the 231 possible roll calls because either there was no quorum, the vote was nearly unanimous, or sharp partisanship was shown. His scales included bills on "foreign policy" and "labor." "...it is possible to construct three-, four-, and five-position ideological groupings by cross-tabulating members' positions on the several analytic issues" (p. 328).

An elaborate set of analyses conducted by MacRae (1954a) illustrates a more complex analysis of multiple archival sources. MacRae asked how politicians with different seniority reduced the inherent insecurity of their elective jobs. The results are too extensive to report, but these are among the variables used:

Seniority (number of consecutive terms of office)

Number of representatives from each party elected in different years

Rates of vote-getting performance (an index of the legislator's vote compared with a control of the gubernatorial vote by the candidate of the same party)

Primary-election performance (ratio to nearest competitor)

Guttman liberal-conservative scale of voting issues

Voting behavior on key bills.

Only two classes of data are used — general election statistics and legislative voting — but MacRae's analysis indicates the richness of these archives for the venturesome student.

The political scientist must work with roll-call votes; the desultory ayes and nays on voice votes are never traceable to their sources. An empirical question (one on which we can find no substantial research study) is the difference between bills voted on by roll call or by voice. It is reasonable to expect that a difference exists and that some systematic criterion is at work. It may be that only the more significant votes get a roll call, but it is also possible that some significant bills go through on a voice vote because leaders of both parties choose to avoid the record on some sensitive issues.

Taking the roll calls with proper hedging, though, there is the choice of which bills yield the best evidence for a particular research question, as well as directional decisions determining the liberal or conservative stand on particular bills. The population of congressmen voting sometimes varies substantially also, for some decide to evade a vote and a public stand on the bill. The "pairing" system, in which an absent congressman may announce what his vote would have been had he been present, eliminates some of this absentee error, but so long as congressmen avoid a vote, some population restriction is present.

The content analysis of political speeches is another workaday practice of politicians and diplomats. In a study of group tension, for example, Grace and Tandy (1957) studied 13 speeches made by Soviet delegates before the League of Nations. Political tension may be indexed in many ways (see Bugental, 1948), but one method is to search for archival evidence of activities designed to reduce tension and uncertainty.

For congressmen, one device is to study the degree to which they make use of their franking (free mail) privilege. The rate of mail sent from congressional offices varies systematically, in a pattern closely linked to the proximity of the election year. We are not aware of any such study, but it should be possible to get an indirect measure of a congressman's perception of his job security by evaluating the use of this privilege. There are many speculations, for example, on what defines a "safe" seat for re-election to the Congress. A journalistic benchmark is a classification based on the extent of the congressman's victory. If he was elected by more than 55 per cent of the vote, his seat is described as safe; if by less than 55 per cent, it is described as dangerous. It would be of interest to study the extent of mail sent out (correcting for different-size constituencies) by the margin of victory in the last election. Such an analysis, combined with other intelligence, may provide a more empirical definition of how congressmen themselves designate "safe" and "dangerous" seats.

The behavior of the congressman can also be used to study those outside the Congress. It is a common practice for a congressman to insert into the *Congressional Record* newspaper columns which reflect his point of view. In a study of political columnists, Webb (1962a; 1963) employed these data for an estimate of liberalism-conservatism among 12 Washington columnists. Individual members of Congress were assigned a liberal-conservative score by evaluations of their voting record published by two opposing groups—the conservative Americans for Constitutional Action and the liberal Committee on Political Action of the AFL-CIO. The two evaluations correlated −.75 for Senators and −.86 for House members. Columnists were then ordered on the mean score of the Congressmen who placed their articles into the *Record*.

It would be valuable to supplement such an analysis with a comparative study of how various writers treat the same event. Cogley (1963) suggested this in his verse on the interpretation of the Papal encyclical, *Pacem in Terra:*

> David Lawrence read it right
> Lippmann saw a Liberal light,
> William Buckley sounded coolish,
> Pearson's line was mostly foolish ...
> To play the game you choose your snippet
> Of Peace on Earth and boldly clip it [p. 12].

In off-year and primary elections, only a small share of eligible voters cast ballots. But this selective behavior is not damaging to validity, since the critical variables — election or no election, margin of victories — are posited directly on this selectivity. Lustig (1962) studied pro-integrationist voting by matching aggregate data on demographic characteristics and pro-integrationist votes. Precinct votes in a southern campaign between a segregationist and an integrationist were compared with census information. This is an admittedly gross approach, but the sanctity of the voting booth precludes, usually, a direct study of individual voting behavior. One can go back to survey questioning and relate these findings to the actual voting records, but the error in self-report of voting behavior is so great that such a potentially reactive approach is highly questionable. Digman and Tuttle (1961) have provided one of the few pieces of research in which investigators were able to sample individual ballots randomly. For most archival studies, however, this degree of precision is unobtainable.

The voting records of the people can also be used to measure the effect of experimenter intervention in pre-election settings. Among the memorable studies in social science is Gosnell's (1927) field experiment on getting out the votes. Selecting 12 electoral precincts, Gosnell divided them into experimental and control conditions. The experimental precincts were sent a series of nonpartisan messages encouraging registration and voting in a forthcoming election, while the control precincts received only the normal pre-election stimulation — generally of a politically partisan nature. The effect of the mail effort was determined by an analysis of registration lists, pollbooks, and census material. Here Gosnell intervened in a "natural" way, established controls, and employed inexpensive archival records as his tellingly appropriate dependent variable. Hartmann's (1936) study of "emotional" and "rational" political campaign pieces also used votes.

Bain and Hecock (1957) further demonstrated the ability to test persuasion principles in a natural laboratory free from the reactive biases of the university research suites. They were interested in the effect of physical position on alternative choices, and found data in the aggregate voting statistics from Michigan elections. Michigan was chosen because of (1) the absence of a law requiring ballots to be burned after the election (an obvious impediment to archival studies of voting behavior) and (2) the systematic rotation of candidates names on the Michigan ballot. This rotation is practiced in several states, and represents an assumption that position on the ballot does indeed have an effect. "Under [California] state law, the incumbent's name goes first on the ballot, and political handicappers give as much as a 20 per cent edge — greater than the margin of most senatorial victories — to this psychological primacy" (Anonymous, 1964d, p. 28).

Because of the Michigan system of rotation, Bain and Hecock could work an orthogonal analysis, establishing the vote of each candidate and each position on the ballot. The findings supported the assumptions of veteran political hands and the ballot constructors: there was a significant position effect. It would be a provocative study to take this and other naturally occurring possibilities for a position effect (e.g., the sale of goods in a supermarket when placed in different shelf positions), and compare the results with those derived from the traditional experimental laboratory.

Schwartz and Skolnick (1962a) proposed a study of positive and negative incentives in tax compliance using changes in taxpaying in experimental and control groups as the dependent variable measure. This study would depend on the cooperation of the Internal Revenue Service, which cannot legally disclose information concerning the returns of any individual taxpayer (Schwartz, 1961). The problem can be avoided by group comparisons in which the individual's identity is not revealed to the researcher. Another device is to study tax compliance in a state such as Wisconsin where individual returns are legally available for research purposes.

The votes of a judicial body provide data for other than obvious research. Kort (1957; 1958), Schubert (1959; 1963), Nagel (1962), and Ulmer (1963) have employed mathematical analyses of past voting behavior by United States Supreme Court justices to predict future votes — a more systematic attempt at the common game played by working lawyers and constitutional law experts.

The same body of information, Supreme Court decisions, was

used by Snyder (1959) in a study of the degree of uncertainty in the whole United States judicial system. In one measure, uncertainty was defined by the number of reversals of lower-court decisions by the high court. With the precedent principle of *stare decisis* at work in our court system, there should be few reversals if certainty is high. Moreover, to the degree that there is certainty (predictability) of outcome upon appeal, there will be cases fought up through the inferior courts.

Green (1961) demonstrated the large store of judicial data available to the social scientist. He gathered a sample of 1,437 cases from 1956-1957 police and court records of Philadelphia, in order to study uniformity in sentencing and the criteria by which sentences were decided. Three sets of variables were isolated as sentencing criteria: legal factors, legally irrelevant factors, and factors in the criminal prosecution. The relative severity of different types of sentences was measured by the extent of deprivation of civil liberty. A series of nonparametric tests "provide assurance that the deliberations of the sentencing judge are not at the mercy of his passions or prejudices but comply with the mandate of the law" (p. 102).

There is a very real population restriction in using such data — one that has been differential over time. It is a highly plausible hypothesis that appellate cases brought before the United States Supreme Court are not representative of the body of cases appearing before the inferior courts. Historically, a substantial share of high-court cases have involved affluent litigants, for the cost of steering a case through the courts is demanding of both money and time. Some of the change in representativeness over time has come from the increasing affluence of our society, but more has come from the growth of well-financed vested-interest groups who will assume the costs of litigation for a party. The spurting growth within civil-rights groups of both legal talent and money, documented by Vose (1959) and Krislov (1963), has meant an increasing number of cases before the appellate courts that might have never been appealed fifty years ago. Thus, any comparison over time of the behavior of the court system relative to some legal issue must take account of this variation.

There may be some bias from the selection of cases (a content restriction), for only a portion of the cases submitted to the

Supreme Court are granted certiorari, i.e., accepted for ruling. In research on some issues, it may be that the Court has systematically excluded from consideration pertinent cases, or has excluded a critical subclass. As in all cases of archival analysis, it is necessary to determine whether or not confounding population restrictions exist. The advantage of legislative and judicial records is that one can learn something of the nature of these restrictions. It is a matter of record which legislators did not vote on roll calls, and which cases were rejected for consideration by the court.

OTHER GOVERNMENT RECORDS

Some government records are orthodox sources for the social scientist. The birth, death, and marriage archives, as we have already seen, can be used for straightforward descriptive work or for less direct applications. Other records have less visible, but equally fruitful, applications. In this section are examples of research which has used power failures, municipal water pressure, parking-meter collections, and the like as research data.

The weather is a reasonable start. Durkheim (1951), as noted above, used weather as one of the variables in his study of suicide. An early investigation by Lombroso (1891) also used archival analysis to note the effect of weather and time of year on scientific creativity. He drew a sample of 52 physical, chemical, and mathematical discoveries and noted the time of their occurrence. His evidence, shaky as it is, showed that 22 of the major discoveries occurred in the spring, 15 in the autumn, 10 in the summer, and 5 in winter.

There are studies, too, on the relationship between phases of the moon and mental disorders. One made during World War II showed psychosomatic illnesses to increase in the South Pacific with the fullness of the moon. It was subsequently discovered that Japanese bombing attacks followed the same pattern.

Of all the studies using available records, few can measure up to E. L. Thorndike's (1939) work on the goodness of cities. Aware that "only the impartial study of many significant facts about cities enables us to know them" (p. 147), Thorndike gathered 37 core pieces of information about each of 310 United States communities. To develop his "goodness scale," he combined these to produce 297 characteristics for each city. And this in the era before computers! Examples of Thorndike's measures are infant death rate, percentage of sixteen- and seventeen-year-olds attending school, average salary of high-school teachers, and per capita acreage of public parks.

Thorndike went further and gathered ratings of cities from various occupational groups. He noted that "thoughtful people realize that popular opinions about cities derived from brief visits and from what is heard and read about cities, are likely to err" (p. 142). How far they are likely to err (using his statistical data as criteria) is demonstrated by these findings: infrequency of extreme poverty correlates .69 with Thorndike's over-all goodness of cities, but −.18 for the judgments of clergymen and social workers; the infant death rate (reversed) correlates .82 with the aggregate statistical index, but .03 with businessmen's ratings of the cities. Few could read this report and not reap methodological profit.

Mindak, Neibergs, and Anderson (1963) took the ongoing records of parking-meter collections as one index of the effect of a Minneapolis newspaper strike. They hypothesized that one of the major effects of the strike would be a decrease in retail shopping. Since most of the parking meters were located in the downtown shopping area, revenue collection from them was a good piece of evidence on the strike's effect. The data showed marked decreases during the months of the strike, using a control of previous years.

City budgets were the stuff of Angell's (1951) study on the moral integration of American cities. He prepared a "welfare effort index" by computing local per capita expenditures for welfare and combined this with a "crime index" based on FBI data to get an "integration index."

Ross and Campbell (1965) showed that a close analysis of traffic fatalities discounted the claim that a crackdown on speeding in Connecticut had resulted in any significant decrease in the number of traffic fatalities.

A particularly interesting and novel use of data comes from the study of city water pressure as it relates to television viewing. For some time after the advent of television, there were anecdotal remarks about a new periodicity in water-pressure levels — a periodicity linked to the beginning and end of programs. As the televi-

sion show ended, so the reports ran, a city's water pressure
dropped, as drinks were obtained and toilets flushed. A graphic
display of this hypothesis was provided by Mabley (1963), who
published a chart showing the water pressure for the city of
Chicago on January 1, 1963. This was the day of a particularly
tense Rose Bowl football game, and the chart shows a vacillating
plateau until the time the game ended, when the pressure level
plummets downward.

Using this approach, one could study the relative popularity of
different retirement times. Since a large amount of water is used
by many people at bedtime, a comparison of the troughs at 9:00,
9:30, 10:00, and so on could be made. Similarly, a comparison
could be made in the morning hours to estimate time of arising.
Two problems arise. Do those who retire early use the same
amount of water as those who retire late? It is, after all, possible
that a smaller number of showers and baths would be taken by
those who retire late — particularly in areas with a high number of
apartment dwellers. Another difficulty of such a study is comparison across different time areas. Many people end the day by
viewing television news. In the metropolitan Chicago area, for
example, some three million people watch the 10:00 P.M. news-
casts. But the last major television newscast in the Eastern areas
is at 11:00 P.M. This one-hour variation might influence the times
of people going to bed. The water-pressure index could help
establish whether it did or not. Similarly, it could be used to study
the relative amount of attendance paid to entertainment and
commercial content of television. The critical point of study in this
research would be the water-pressure levels at the times of mid-
show commercials. The prior decision of viewers to turn the set off
at a specified hour would influence the water-pressure index for
commercials at the beginning and end of shows, but should be a
minor rival hypothesis for those embedded within the entertainment content of the program.

A similar measure, a more catastrophic one, has been manifest in the United Kingdom. This measure, electric-power failures,
gives plausibility to the hypothesis that it is commercials (and not
earlier decisions to turn the set off) which influence the drops in
water pressure. At the time of the introduction of the United
Kingdom's commercial television channel, a series of power fail-

ures hit the island. Whole areas were blacked out, and it was noticed that the timing of the power failures coincided with the time of commercials on the new television channel. The explanation provided was that viewers left their sets to turn on electric water heaters to make tea. The resulting power surge, from so many heaters plugged in simultaneously, overloaded the capacity of a national power system unequipped to handle such peaks. The commercials remain; new power stations have been built. This measure is a more discontinuous one than water pressure, but it would be of value to compare the water-pressure levels with power demands. If the hypothesis is correct that the English were plugging in water heaters, one should find a higher correlation between the two measures in the United Kingdom (with a small time lag as water precedes power) than in the United States.

Another imaginative link between two time series of archival data was provided by DeCharms and Moeller (1962). They gathered the number of patents issued by the United States Patent Office from 1800 to 1950. Relating these to population figures, they prepared a patent production index for 20-year periods over the 150-year span. These data were then matched to findings from a content analysis of children's readers for the same period, with a prime focus on achievement imagery. The matching showed a strong relationship between the amount of achievement imagery in their sample of books and the number of patents per million population.

THE MASS MEDIA

Among the most easily available and massive sources of continuing secondary data are the mass media. The variety, texture, and scope of this enormous data pool have been neglected for too long. In this section, we present a selected series of studies which show intelligent manipulation of the mass media. We have necessarily excluded most content analyses and focused on a few which illustrate particular points.[2]

It is proper to start this section by citing Zipf, who sought order in diverse social phenomena by his inventive use of data that

[2]For general treatment of content analysis, see Berelson (1952); Pool (1959); North et al. (1963).

few others would perceive as germane to scientific inquiry. In a model study, Zipf (1946) looked at the determinants of the circulation of information. His hypothesis was that the probability of message transfer between one person and another is inversely proportional to the distance between them. (See also Miller, 1947; Stewart, 1947; Zipf, 1949.) Without prejudice for content, he made use of the content of the mass media, as well as sales performance. How many and how long were out-of-town obituaries in the *New York Times*? How many out-of-town items appeared in the *Chicago Tribune*? Where did they originate? What was the sales level in cities besides New York and Chicago of the *Times* and *Tribune*? To this information from and about the mass media, Zipf added other archival sources. He asked the number of tons of goods moved by Railway Express between various points, and checked on the number of bus, railroad, and air passengers between pairs of cities. All of these were appropriate outcroppings for the test of his hypothesis on inverse proportionality, and in all cases the data conform, more or less closely, to his prediction.

Other investigators have used the continuing record of the newspaper for their data. Grusky (1963b) wanted to investigate the relationship between administrative succession and subsequent change in group performance. One could manipulate leaders in a small-group laboratory, but, in addition, one can go, as Grusky did, to the newspapers for more "natural" and less reactive intelligence. From the sports pages and associated records, Grusky learned the performance of various professional football and baseball teams, as well as the timing of changes in coaches and managers. Does changing a manager make a difference, or is it the meaningless machination of a front office looking for a scapegoat? It does make a difference, and this old sports-writer's question is a group-dynamics problem, phrased through the stating of two plausible rival hypotheses. In another study, Grusky (1963a) used baseball record books to study "The Effects of Formal Structures on Managerial Recruitment." He learned that former infielders and catchers (high-interaction personnel) were overrepresented among managers, while former pitchers and outfielders (low-interaction personnel) were underrepresented.

This public-record characteristic of the newspaper also allows linguistic analysis. If verbal behavior really is expressive, then one should be able to study a President's position on issues by studying the transcripts of his press conferences. Those answers on which a President stumbles in syntax, or which are prefaced by a string of evasive dependent clauses, may be symptomatic of trouble areas. Similarly, those questions which receive unusually long or short replies may reflect significant content areas.

Analysis of transcripts such as these can be very difficult, and often not enough substantive knowledge is available to rule out alternative hypotheses. A President is briefed on what are likely to be the topics of reporters' questions, and he has an opportunity to rehearse replies. The setting is not a nonreactive one, and the awareness of his visibility and the import of his answers may influence their content and form. One must also make each President his own control. The verbal styles of Eisenhower, Kennedy, and Johnson varied so greatly that any verbal index of syntax, glibness, or folksiness must be adjusted for the response tendencies of the individual President.

Less august reporting, that of the society news, served James (1958) as evidence of community structure. The reporting of social events is highly selective, of course, and most useful for studies of the upper class (cf. Coleman & Neugarten, in preparation). The court-tennis victory of a truckdriver is not reported, nor the visit of his wife to Dubuque for the weekend.

Comparison across different cities might be differentially affected by shifts in the selectivity of society editors. It is a good assumption that the size of the city in which the paper is printed is related to the selectivity of its social news: the larger the city, the greater the probability that a smaller segment of the city's population appears in the society pages.

Middleton (1960), mentioned earlier, conducted a longitudinal study of the fertility values in magazine fiction, linking them to the actuarial fertility figures. This research suggested that the media, if carefully selected, can serve as a mirror of the society's values — or at least of some selective elements within the society.

How are psychologists, psychiatrists, and other psychologically oriented personnel differentiated by the society? One can ask people of course, and one should. But of value, too, is a study of what the mass media contain on the question. Ehrle and Johnson (1961) plucked 4,760 cartoons, all of which pictured psychological personnel, from six different consumer magazines. Their evidence suggests no substantial differentiation among the groups. This finding could be further tested by observing psychologists at cocktail parties and noting how often they are asked, "Now how is a psychologist different from a psychiatrist?" Or one could ask the psychologists to relate their cocktail-party experience.

Ray (1965) has written of multiple confirmation through different sources of published material, noting as an example, "values of Hitler's Germany were compared with those of other countries by content analyses of plays (McGranahan and Wayne, 1948), songbooks (Sebald, 1962), handbooks for youth organizations (Lewin, 1947), speeches (White, 1949) and the press (Lasswell, 1941)."

Most of these have been examples of partial evidence contained in the mass media of attitudes or social structure. Even the most vitriolic critics of television commercials will admit that the media themselves are a force within the society for socialization of the young and attitude change of the old. Thus, they justify study. G. A. Steiner (1963), for example, demonstrated the salience of television for a national United States sample by showing the extreme alacrity with which sets are repaired. Before television, it had been said that a cigarette was the only object so compelling that deprivation would cause one to walk out in a snowstorm. This energy allocation is also inferred in the advertising slogan, "I'd walk a mile for a Camel."

Much work exists on the political bias of the media. A content analysis of press bias during presidential campaigns is as predictable as the campaigns themselves, but a fine, relatively unused, source is photographs. The element of editorial selectivity which is a contaminant in some other studies becomes the center of analysis. Editors have a large pool of photographs of a candidate from which to pick, and the one they eventually choose is a revealing piece of intelligence. One of the writers has noted this in American political campaigns, and Matthews (1957) has suggested that it is a phenomenon that might be studied across societies. Writing of the British press, he states:

> They [photographs] can be made to lie . . . as Lord Northcliffe was one of the first to discover. When he was using the *Daily Mail* to try to get Asquith out as Prime Minister and Lloyd George in, he once issued this order: "Get a smiling picture of

Lloyd George, and underneath put the caption 'Do It Now,' and
get the worst possible picture of Asquith and label it: 'Wait and
See' " [p. 165].

As in all these studies of the running record, there is the
opportunity for time-series analysis. One could learn if a medium
is changing in its posture to a candidate (or potential candidate),
and observe when. This last information, on the time of modifica-
tion, can help to validate other sources of data on the medium's
attitude.

The selective practice has been so prevalent over time that it
is likely to have little "instrument decay" to invalidate time-series
analysis. It continues now, and offers some possibilities for interesting new research. A television interviewer told Malcolm X, the
late Black Nationalist leader, that he was surprised at how much
Malcolm smiled. The Negro leader said that newspapers refused to
print smiling pictures of him. For less extreme, but still marginal,
leaders, what is the pattern across time and regions? Of equal
interest would be the photographic strategy toward Richard Nixon
after his 1962 defeat for the California governorship. In a caustic
and venomous statement immediately after the campaign, Nixon
castigated the press for what he perceived as its anti-Nixon
stance. To casual observers, there was an immediate decrease in
the favorability of the Nixon photographs printed.

Tannenbaum and Noah (1959) studied press bias another way,
analyzing the verbs that appeared in sports headlines. They asked
how many runs in baseball equal a "romp" or how many points in
football equal "X rolls over Y." In addition to providing descriptive
information on the empirical limits of such verb usage, they demonstrated a home-town bias. The one-run margin might yield either
"Sox Edged 8-7" or "Sox Bludgeon Yankees 8-7."

Winship and Allport (1943) were unconcerned with selling
newspapers, but they did want to know something of the effect of
positive and negative stimuli. Their study was conducted during
the early years of World War II, and they were opportunistic
enough to exploit the "victories" and "withdrawals" blazoned on
headlines. Do potential readers buy more or fewer papers when
positive headlines are used? For the measure of effect, they took
the street-stand sales of newspapers from four major cities, ignoring the relatively invariant element of home-delivered news-

papers. No significant sales difference could be traced to optimistic and pessimistic headlines.

Optimism is a central element in another study — Griffith's (1949) original and adroit research on horse-race betters. The newspapers supplied the odds, results, and payoffs for 1,386 horse races run in the spring and summer of 1947. His hypothesis is worth quoting:

> If the psychological odds equaled the a posteriori [odds] given by the reciprocal of the percentage [of] winners, the product of the number of winners and their odds would equal the number of entries at each odd group after correction of the odds had been made for loss due to breakage and take. If the product exceeds the number of entries, the psychological odds were too large; if the product is less than the number of entries, the odds were too small [p. 292].

The results, which should receive some distribution beyond the archives of the *American Journal of Psychology*, suggest that long shots and favorites are overbet, while not enough money is put on horses with middle-range odds.

The DeCharms and Moeller (1962) study of patents and achievement imagery in children's readers was mentioned above. Others have worked with the content of books, attempting to puzzle out the popular mystery of why some books sell and others don't. Berreman (1940) gathered data on the sales of books as reported by the *New York Herald Tribune* book-review section and publicity outlays for individual titles, and performed a content analysis: 60 titles were grouped into 12 classes by setting, theme, and treatment of theme. He concluded, to oversimplify his complex Ph.D. dissertation, that content was more important than publicity. His findings suggest that content probably depressed the sale of the well-promoted poor sellers and "made" best sellers which had only feeble marketing efforts. (Cf. Kappel, 1948; Harvey, 1953).

Sales data permit the testing of hypotheses on the way in which items of popular culture rise and fall in favor. One hypothesis now being tested by Eugene Webb and Robert Armstrong is that sales of a book decline logarithmically once the sales peak has been reached. Data collected so far show only weak support for this hypothesis. Webb (1962b) demonstrated in a similar study that ratings of television westerns declined logarithmically once they started to slide in popularity.

Parker (1963) worked on the effect of the introduction of television by studying library records. His topic was the differential effect of television on the reading of books. A time series was prepared of withdrawals, by type of book, from libraries in a series of Illinois cities — both before and after television came to town. In one of the findings that looks like common sense (after the research is read), he learned that the withdrawals of nonfiction titles were unaffected, but that there was a significant drop in the withdrawal of fiction titles.

R. W. Jones (1960) used the extent of library facilities and personnel as the "index of progressivism" of a group of 154 Illinois towns. He corrected the raw figures by applying census data on community size, social class, race, occupation and income, population age, and rate of community growth.

Library withdrawals were also used by Parker (1964), who showed how a radio book-review program influenced the circulation of the books discussed.

Interest in library withdrawals was used by Vernon and Brown (1963), who measured the "dynamic information seeking process" among tuberculosis patients. They predicted (and found) that the patients of uninformative doctors would be significantly higher than patients of informative doctors in the degree to which they sought out information relevant to their disease. They indexed this by the proportion of patients in the two groups who took "tuberculosis" and "non-tuberculosis" books from a hospital library. In this study, the authors depended upon the reports of patients to define informative and uninformative doctors.

Rashkis and Wallace (1959) demonstrated that the researcher does not have to depend upon self-reports of the degree of attention paid by medical personnel. They observed the notes made by attending nurses on a patient's bedside record, notations that were both informal and required. The attention paid to the patient was measured by the frequency of these notes per patient. This helps to circumvent the possibility that perception of how much attention is being paid to one by medical personnel is heavily contaminated by the patient's degree of illness. The same amount of attention would probably be differentially perceived under preop-

erative, postoperative, and about-to-be-released states. The bedside chart may be more trustworthy.

Soviet writings on psychology could hardly be classed as mass
media, but the findings of O'Connor's (1961) research are of
substantive interest to any social scientist. O'Connor studied the
amount of partisan philosophical (as opposed to empirical) content
in Russian journal articles and notes "a tendency to move away
from philosophical prolegomena in journal articles and towards a
direct discussion of experimental material" (p. 14, cited in Brozek,
1964).

DATA TRANSFORMATIONS AND
INDICES OF THE RUNNING RECORD

Of all the different classes of data treated in this monograph,
none has so great a need for transformation as those cited in this
chapter. Because the data are drawn from continuous records
which typically extend over long periods of time, all the extraneous
events of history are at work to threaten valid research comparisons.

Perhaps the most obvious of these is the change in the size of
the population. The population increase has meant that the
absolute values of actuarial and allied data are relatively useless
for comparative purposes. In studies employing election records,
for instance, the absolute number of votes cast provides an
inadequate base for most research purposes. It gives Mr. Nixon
little comfort, we are sure, to know that he garnered more votes in
1960, as a loser, than did any preceding winning candidate except
Eisenhower. Similarly, the absolute number of entries associated
with population level has changed over time. This secular trend in
the data is often best removed. Thus, Ianni (1957-1958) had to
construct a relative index of residential mobility over time, and
DeCharms and Moeller (1962) transformed patent production to an
index tied to population.

Time also works its effect by a change in the composition of a
critical group. The number of congressmen in the House of Representatives may stay relatively stable over a long time period, but
the characteristics of these congressmen change — and, in changing, produce a set of rival hypotheses for some investigator's

explanation of a research comparison. A recent Supreme Court ruling on reapportionment of the House (to reflect population distribution more adequately) will mean substantial changes in the aggregate voting behavior of the House, influencing the decisional setting for all congressmen, both those there before the change and the new members.

With known changes in composition, it may be necessary to segregate research findings by time periods in which relatively homogeneous external conditions held. This is a grosser correction than the more continuous correction possible for data linked to population. Even with population, though, the only thoroughly reliable data — the census totals — are produced only once every ten years. The accuracy of intervening estimates, whether from the Census Bureau itself or the highly reliable *Sales Management* magazine, are high but still imperfect.

The frailty of individual sets of records, which is discussed below, has caused many investigators to employ indices which combine several different types or units of information. The adequacy of such combinations rests, of course, on the degree to which the component elements are adequate outcroppings of the research hypothesis, as well as the degree to which appropriate weights can be assigned to the elements. Setting these questions aside, however, it is apparent that combined indices must be employed when an investigator lacks a theory so precise and subtle as to predict a single critical test, or, when the theory's precision is adequate, no data exist for the critical test. For E. L. Thorndike's (1939) purpose in studying cities, there was no acceptable alternative to transforming such data as park area and property values into indices. And for MacRae (1954b) and Riker and Niemi (1962), the unstable nature of a single vote by a congressman forced the construction of indices of samples of votes, which were hopefully a less ephemeral source for comparisons. MacRae needed a "liberal index," Riker and Niemi, an "index of coalitions." Because the individual unit was highly suspect as a sampling of the critical behavior under study, the sampling had to be expanded. There occurs, too, the attendant questions of how the units are to be stated, weighted, and combined.

One of the major gains of the running record, then, is the capability to study a hypothesis as external conditions vary over time. Such analysis demands that the investigator consider all possible transformations before making comparisons, and also decide whether indices will provide a more stable and valid base for hypothesis testing. This requirement is not as pronounced in the discontinuous archival records cited in the chapter that follows nor among the observational and physical-evidence methods.

OVER-ALL EVALUATION OF RUNNING RECORDS

It should be obvious that we prize the potential for historical analysis contained in running records.

> The best fact is one that is set in a context, that is known in relation to other facts, that is perceived in part in the context of its past, that comes into understanding as an event which acquires significance because it belongs in a continuous dynamic sequence . . . [Boring, 1963, p. 5].

If a research hypothesis, particularly for social behavior, can survive the assaults of changing times and conditions, its plausibility is far greater than if it were tested by a method which strips away alien threats and evaluates the hypothesis in an assumptive, one-time test. Validity can be inferred from a hypothesis' robustness. If the events of time are vacillating, as they usually are, then only the valid hypothesis has the intellectual robustness to be sustained, while rival hypotheses expire.

One pays a price in such time-series analysis, the necessary price of uncertainty. We again agree with that gentle stylist Boring (1963): "The seats on the train of progress all face backwards; you can see the past but only guess about the future" (p. 5). A hypothesis might not hold for anything but the past, but if the present is tested, and a new, possibly better, hypothesis produced, those same running records are available, as economical as ever, for restudy and new testing.

For all the gains, however, the gnawing reality remains that archives have been produced for someone else and by someone else. There must be a careful evaluation of the way in which the records were produced, for the risk is high that one is getting a cutrate version of another's errors. Udy (1964) wrote of ethnographic data:

> Researchers who use secondary sources are always open to the
> charge that they are cavalier and uncritical in their use of
> source materials, and cross cultural analysis — particularly
> when large numbers of societies are used with information
> taken out of context — is particularly vulnerable to such criti-
> cism [p. 179].

At the beginning of this chapter, we detailed the operating
questions of selective deposit and selective survival of archives.
Both these contaminants can add significant restrictions to the
content and contributing populations of the archival materials. In
the discussion of individual research studies, we have noted how
roll-call votes, marriage records, reports of congressional speeches,
letters to the editor, crime reports, and other records are all
subject to substantial population or content restrictions in their
initial recording. To a lesser degree, the selective survival of
records can be a serious contaminant, and in certain areas, such as
politics, it is always a prime question.

Those contaminants which threaten the temporal and cross-
sectional stability of the data are controllable through data transformation and indexing methods — if they can be known. Happily,
one of the more engaging attributes of many of these records is
that they contain a body of auxiliary data which allows the investigator good access to knowledge of the population restrictions.
We have noted this for the absentee contaminant in congressional
voting and the selective choice of cases in judicial proceedings.
With the actuarial material on birth, marriage, and death, it is
often possible to find within the records, or in associated data
series such as the census, information which will provide checks
on the extent to which the research population is representative of
the universe to which the findings are to be generalized.

If the restrictions can be known, it is possible to consider the
alternative of randomly sampling from the body of records, with a
stratification control based on the knowledge of the population
restriction. This is feasible for many of the records we have
mentioned because of their massiveness. Indeed, even if no substantial population contaminants exist, it is often advisable to
sample the data because of their unwieldy bulk. Since usually they
can be divided into convenient sampling units, and also frequently
classified in a form appropriate for stratification, the ability to

sample archival materials, particularly those in a continuous series, is a decided advantage for this class of data. The sampling of
observations, or of traces of physical evidence, is markedly more
difficult.

The population restrictions are potentially controllable
through auxiliary intelligence; the content restrictions are more
awkward. For all the varied records available, there may still be no
single set, or combination of sets, that provides an appropriate test
of an hypothesis.

Something of this content rigidity is reflected in Walter Lippmann's (1955) discussion of the "decline of the west." Lippmann
writes of the turn of the century when

> The public interest could be equated with that which was
> revealed in election returns, in sales reports, balance sheets,
> circulation figures, and statistics of expansion. As long as peace
> should be taken for granted, the public good could be thought of
> as being immanent in the aggregate of private transactions [p.
> 16].

Yet many of the studies reported in this chapter have revealed
the power of insightful minds to see appropriate data where
associates only see "someone else's" records. There is little
explicit in patent records, city water-pressure archives, parking-
meter collection records or children's readers to suggest their
research utility. It required imagination to perceive the application, and a willingness to follow an unconventional line of data
collection. Imagination cannot, of course, provide data if none are
there. Our thesis is solely that the content limitations of archival
records are not as great as the social scientist bound by orthodoxy
thinks.

There is no easy way of knowing the degree to which reactive
measurement errors exist among running archival records. These
are secondhand measures, and many of them are contaminated by
reactive biases, while others are not. The politician voting on a bill
is well aware that his action will noted by others; he may not be
aware that an observer in the gallery made a note of the tic in his
left eye when his name was called to vote. The records contributed
by the person or group studied—the votes, the speeches, the
entries written for directories—are produced with an awareness
that they may be interpreted as expressive behavior. Thus, those

errors that come from awareness of being tested, from role elicitation, from response sets, and from the act of measurement as a change agent are all potentially working to confound comparisons. With other data, such as the reports of presidential press conferences and census figures, the investigator has the additional bias of possible interviewer error passed along.

For data collected by a second party, by someone other than the producer (birth and death records, weather reports, power failures, patents, and the like), the risk of awareness, role, or interviewer contaminants is present but low. The main problem becomes one of instrument decay. Has the record-keeping process been constant or knowably variant over the period of study? As cited earlier, suicides in Prussia jumped 20 per cent between 1882 and 1883. It may be that response sets on the part of the record-keepers, or a change in administrative practice, threatens valid comparisons across time periods or geographic areas. To know of this variation is extremely difficult, and it represents one of the major drawbacks to archival records.

In summary, the running archival records offer a large mass of pertinent data for many substantive areas of research. They are cheap to obtain, easy to sample, and the population restrictions associated with them are often knowable and controllable through data transformations and the construction of indices. But all content is not amenable to study by archival records, and there is an ever present risk that reactive or other elements in the data-producing process will cause selective deposit or survival of the material. Against this must be balanced the opportunity for longitudinal studies over time, studies in which one may test a hypothesis by subjecting it to the rigor of evaluation in multiple settings and at multiple times.

CHAPTER 4

Archives II: The Episodic and Private Record

In the preceding chapter, we outlined the joys and sorrows of those archives on which there is typically a running time record. Here we continue our discussion of archives, but center on those which are more discontinuous and usually not a part of the public record. Such data are more difficult to come upon than the public records, unless the investigator is affiliated with some organization producing the material. The insurance sales of a casualty company, the nurse's record on a bedside clipboard, and last year's suicide notes from Los Angeles are more available to the "inside" investigator than they are to the curious outsider. But if these records are more difficult and costly to acquire than public records, they can often provide a gain in specificity of content. The amount of irrelevant dross commonly declines as an investigation is limited to a particular set of privately produced data.

We have already mentioned the risks to validity inherently present in archival records. The main analytic difference between the records mentioned in this and in the earlier chapter is the common inability to make longitudinal analyses of the private data. Sometimes security is the reason, sometimes the data are stored for shorter periods, sometimes financial and labor costs preclude an analysis over time. Whatever the cause, this is a major loss. The best defense against it is to find a related set and combine both — one continuous and the other discontinuous — for a more textured series of comparisons.

Some of the data in this chapter are episodic in character, but complete in reporting; many sources do maintain long and accurate record-keeping systems. The military is one such source, and Lodge (1963) has conducted a provocative correlational study with

United States Navy records. All those who have learned his results on air crashes tend now, as passengers, to squint studiously at their pilots' height. Dipping back into the Navy records, Lodge collected reports of 680 jet plane accidents, and then searched other records for the height of the pilots. He learned that men exceeding the average height of 72 inches had significantly more accidents than their shorter contemporaries. This may be traced to the design of aircraft cockpits and the visual angle on instrument panels.

We have divided the sources into three gross classes: sales records, institutional records, and personal documents. All three are potential substitutes for direct observation of behavior. This is most obvious with personal documents, where the unavailability of a source may force the investigator to use whatever alternatives are available. But sales and institutional records may work in the same way, and can broaden the scope of an investigation which is primarily based on observation. They may fill in holes present in an observational series, or be used to produce a broader sampling of the behavior under study.

Chadwick Alger once suggested to us that it would be profitable for a political scientist to sit in the Delegates' Lounge of the United Nations and observe how much whisky was downed. By keying the consumption rate to action before the UN, Alger felt that an index of tension might be developed. In such a setting, the sales records of the bar might be an even better measure, for they are less amenable to instrument-decay errors and permit a closer noting of type of drink ordered (Scotch, Canadian, Cuba libres, and so forth).

Brown (1960) suggested that records of soap consumption be substituted for ratings of the cleanliness of institutionalized patients — ratings which are, after all, observation one step removed. Brown points out two ways of measuring soap usage: a liquid soap could be measured by reading the level of liquid in the dispenser each day, or bar soap by a measure of the water displacement at the beginning and end of the period studied.

Two other examples, both employing records of whisky consumption, illustrate the substitution of sales records for observation. Hotel and restaurant records could be employed in a comparative study of occupations. One can observe members of an occupation and attribute traits to them, but valuable auxiliary information might come from the records on drink consumption and petty thievery in convention hotels. Do anthropologists take more soap and towels away with them than do mechanical engineers? Such an analysis is posited on the assumption that those who attend conventions (and who stay, steal, and drink in convention hotels) are a representative sample of the profession.

Hillebrandt (1962) sought data on the sale of alcoholic drinks at Chicago airports in his study of passenger anxiety produced by air crashes. He failed to use the proposed data because of the insensitivity of the instrument. At that time, the major Chicago airport had recently been completed, and the construction of bars had not caught up with demand. Thus, there was negligible variance from day to day in sales, and the small amount that existed seemed to be based upon the bartenders' speed, not on exterior factors.

Sales Records

In a society as oriented to marketing and record keeping as ours, sales data abound for study of a varied body of content. As noted above, Hillebrandt (1962) did not get to use bar sales as a measure. He continued with his study, however, and used the volume of air passengers. With a complete set of data over time, he was able to transform the data, correcting for systematic sources of variance irrelevant to his hypothesis. He partialled out the seasonal variation in air traffic, for example, and accounted for the secular changes in traffic level at Chicago's two major airports. The residual material demonstrated that crashes were only a very short-term depressant on travel. Just as with the bar sales, there is some rigidity in his data which tends to blunt comparisons. A certain number of people have no alternative to flying, regardless of how dissettling was a major crash the day before. Webb and Campbell plan to continue this analysis with a complementary measure. With the same exogenous variable, they hope to plot the number and dollar value of trip insurance policies taken out by travelers at Chicago airports. Buying trip insurance is a low-cost and simple behavior which should index anxiety of air travelers. With the bar facilities now expanded to exceed demand, it will be possible to perform an analysis containing three sales components: bar sales, trip insurance sales, and ticket sales. Each of these must be corrected for the systematic biases present, but they should provide a more sensitive and nonreactive set of possible outcroppings of anxiety than any single variable study, particularly one based on the interviewing of travelers.

Insurance, a paid-for hedge against risk, is an admirable measure of the effect of disaster. Just as one can examine trip insurance sales and link them to crashes, one can examine the timing of casualty insurance sales and link them to the occurrence of hurricanes or tornadoes. Add to this sales of life insurance (compared to the time of death of close friends or relatives), and one has a three-way index of the general effect of disaster.

These same data could be used to test Zipf's (1946) hypothesis further. Is the amount of casualty insurance taken out inversely proportional to the distance from the disaster? How the mapping of insurance underwriting compares to a meteorological map of tornado probability would be a necessary control. It might be that the hypothesis holds only in areas which have had tornado experience. This would give support to Zipf's hypothesis, but even greater support would come if a significant amount of insurance were written in proximate areas with little or no tornado experience. What, in brief, is the nature of the generalization of effect?

How unlikely a source of research material is the sale of peanuts! Yet, continuing in the vein of study of anxiety or tension, peanut sales are a possibility that should be systematically explored. An anecdotal report appeared in the *Chicago Sun-Times* from the concessionaire in that city's baseball parks. He casually observed that peanut sales after the seventh inning of a game are significantly higher than earlier—but only during a tight game. If the game is one-sided, there is no late-inning increase in peanut purchasing. Is this a sound, nonreactive measure of involvement or tension? It may be, but it illustrates the problems associated with such archival measures—one must pay special heed to rival hypotheses. One hypothesis is that fans, during the increasingly tense moments of the late innings, absentmindedly lean over and compulsively crunch their way through more peanuts than earlier.

But one should look at population restrictions. It may be that the finding (if it may be legitimatized as such) on the increase coming only in tight games is an artifact of selective attendance and not tension. There is a hyperbolic curve of attendance in a one-sided game. A substantial number of fans usually arrive late, and another substantial group leave early if the game appears to be already decided. The population potential for peanut purchasing is thereby variable across innings, and the effect of a tight game should be to reduce the early departures and provide a larger base for sales in later innings. For a finer test, a simple correction would be to transform the peanut sales into unit sales per X thousand fans per inning—a transformation possible by clocking turnstile movement in and out.

Another test of the hypothesis, using the same data, is possible, although we can report no findings. The tension hypothesis would get strong support if, in a population of one-sided games, fans left in substantial numbers early and sales stayed stable from the middle through the later innings. This would be reflected in an ascending consumption curve if correction were made for those in attendance.

But one other element of population restrictions remains to be considered. We have examined only the issue of the absolute number of fans available in the park to buy the peanuts. Is there any plausibility to the notion that those who leave early are more or less devoted to peanuts? One might determine this by interview at the exit gate, or by looking for traces of peanut shells in vacated seats.

Sales data can also be used to infer popularity and preference. The impact of Glenn's orbital flight was evidenced by record-breaking sales of the commemorative stamp issued to mark it. Similarly, the sale of commemorative Kennedy stamps and the great demand for Kennedy half-dollars after their issuance, as well as all the special books and the reappearance of *Profiles in Courage* on the best-seller list, provide persuasive evidence, if any were needed, of the man's influence on public thinking.

Another measure of the popularity of a man is the value of his autograph in the commercial market. The supply level must be controlled, of course, but it is of some interest that the following prices held at the end of 1964:

John Hancock	$250.00
Winston Churchill	225.00
Napoleon I	185.00
Charles Dickens	125.00
Ralph Waldo Emerson	110.00
César Franck	75.00
Daniel Webster	65.00
Calvin Coolidge	55.00
John Quincy Adams	37.50
Aldous Huxley	22.50

The sales and pictorial content of stamps are a useful but unused bit of expressive intelligence. An analysis of the illustrations on stamps may give indications of the state of political opinion in the nation. What does an analysis of illustrations printed during the early years of the Fascist regimes in Germany and Italy show? It has been suggested that stamp illustrations presage aggressive political action. Perhaps somewhere a philatelistic psychologist has prepared this study, using illustrated sets of stamp catalogues by year of issue.

A possible flaw in such analysis is a potential datum for another topic of study. Each nation does not print its own stamps. Many former colonial territories continue, as a cost-saving device, to use secondhand engravings and the printing facilities of the former governing power. The stamp illustration may thereby reflect an economic and not a political decision. But whether or not a former colonial territory still relies on the old power is itself a clue to relations between the two. One could, for example, compare former British and French colonies in Africa. Or compare new nations within what was a single colonial area. Guinea prints her own stamps; Mali buys hers from France.

The diffusion of information among physicians was the topic of Coleman, Katz, and Menzel's (1957) research. Instead of the more standard, and reactive, tactic of interviewing doctors, they elected to go to pharmacy records for information about which doctors prescribed what drugs when. Sampling at intervals over a 15-month period, they related the physician's adoption of new drugs to his social network. Such hardnosed data can be a useful check on interviewing data, provided the effect of collecting such records does not alter the behavior of the record-keepers. This is a very implausible risk with drug prescriptions, but a reasonable one when dealing with less legally controlled records. The danger is not so much in masking information as it is in improving it. The record-keeper may perform a more conscientious job because he knows that his work is being put to some use. If the investigator using such records stresses the greater glory to man that will come from the record-keeper offering his cooperation, he may actually be increasing the risk that the instrumentation process will change — thereby threatening the validity of comparisons over time.

The social-network variable employed by Coleman, Katz, and Menzel can be measured by other methods than the standard interview or sociogram. To study the extent to which interaction among different departments of a university took place, one could use orthodox procedures. In addition, so humble a document as a desk calendar might be checked. This record can provide information on who lunched with whom, with what degree of frequency, and across what departments. Not everyone notes such engagements (a population restriction), and the desk calendar is not a likely source for learning of other engagements, such as social dinners or meetings so regular that they don't have to be noted (content restrictions). Staying just with the lunch dates, one route to learn the character of the restrictions would be to enlist the aid of waiters in faculty clubs. The reader can conjure up objections to this assistance.

Drug-sale records are in common use by pharmaceutical houses to evaluate the sales effort of their detail men. Both the houses and the detail men have learned that the verbal statement or the observed enthusiasm of a doctor for a new drug is a highly unstable predictor of what he will prescribe. If records are available for checks on self-reports, they should by all means be used. Such checks are particularly useful when the data are produced continuously by the same subjects, for then a correction can be applied to the self-reports. If the assumption can be made that the character of the error is constant over time, it may not be necessary to run both sets of data concurrently.

Something of an analogous correction can be seen with economic forecasters. Firms which employ more than one forecaster are said to compute the response-set characteristic of the forecaster (optimism or pessimism) and apply a secret correction to his periodic predictions. This is a rather interesting data transformation, since its existence shows the set rigidity of the forecasters. They, too, know whether they have been over- or underestimating, yet that knowledge does not produce potent enough feedback to overcome the response set. Morgenstern (1963) notes reports of the same type of corrections applied by Soviet planners in the 1930's.

Boring (1961) has detailed how a similar type of response error was an early *cause célèbre* in astronomy. Differences in reaction times among astronomical observers became known, and the phrase "personal equation" was coined to describe the bias. In an evolving history, the contaminant existed but was unknown, became known and the cause of study for the purpose of eliminating its biasing effect, and then became the substantive material of a large body of psychological research.

The sale of stocks was used by Ashley (1962) in a study interesting for what it says of positive and negative reward. Isolating firms which announced an unexpected dividend or earnings statement, either up or down, Ashley traced the stock prices following the announcement. An unexpectedly high dividend influenced the price of the stock for about 15 days, while an unexpectedly low dividend or earnings statement had an effect for only about four days. There are other places to measure extinction than in a Skinner box. See, for instance, Winship and Allport's (1943) study on newspaper headlines, mentioned earlier, and Griffith's (1949) research on horse-race odds—both studies of optimism-pessimism. Hamilton (1942) has also conducted an interesting content analysis on the rise of pessimism in widely circulated Protestant sermons.

A more common use of sales records (but still surprisingly uncommon) is as a measure of propaganda effectiveness. Within advertising, particularly, there has been extensive writing on the inadequacy of survey methodology to predict the advertiser's major criterion, sales. An excellent annotated bibliography reviewing advertising's effect on sales has been prepared by Krueger and Ramond (1965).

Henry (1958) gives numerous examples of the discrepancies between respondents' reports and sales figures, indicating that the reasons a consumer gives for buying a product cannot be relied upon. Reactive measures thus suspect, other methods of consumer preference measurement must be found.

Henry mentions an example of a controlled sales experiment on "shelf appeal." One brand of candy is sold in three types of wrappers, with variables such as shelf position and number of units displayed controlled. The dependent variable is the sales level of the different packages.

There is an ideal experimental medium for advertising research in direct-mail sales efforts. Lucas and Britt (1963) comment upon a number of studies which have varied such elements as the color of paper, inclusion of various incentives, and stamping a return envelope by hand or by meter. They also cite the example of a department store which might send out a monthly statement to customers containing one of ten variants of an advertisement selling a specific product. The average return per layout would then be determined by subsequent sales.

The large mail-order houses (Sears, Ward, Spiegel and others) regularly conduct controlled experiments on different thematic appeals. This is easily performed by varying the content of the appeal and simply counting the returns attributable to the different sources. In a revealing finding, one of these houses discovered that an advertisement describing a self-riding lawnmower as something of an adult's toy dramatically outsold an appeal which argued its superior functional merits.

Using sales results of a promotional campaign, Blomgren and Scheuneman (1961) found a "scare" approach was less effective for selling seat belts than one that featured a professional racing driver and appealed to masculine control and relaxation.

Over thirty years ago, Jahoda-Lazarsfeld and Zeisel (1932) studied the impact of the depression by noting the level of grocery sales. The same measure is used now to evaluate the efficacy of different sales themes. A before-after design was used by the National Advertising Company (1963) to learn the effect of large outdoor signs placed in the parking lots of three shopping centers. They used store audits to determine the sales of products advertised on the signs and then compared these data to sales from a control sample of equivalent stores. Another method of "pretesting" advertising themes is to place treatments of the theme in prominent places within a supermarket and then observe sales.

This has been done by comparing sales attributable to a single theme against a control of past sales, and also by employing multiple themes and comparing one against, the other. In this latter approach, close attention has been paid to time-sampling problems, so as to protect the equivalence of the populations exposed to each version.

One could similarly experiment with vending machines, although we do not know of any such research. By random assignment of the display of experimental cigarette packages to machines, or by systematically varying exhortatory messages over machines, one could employ lever-pulling as the effectiveness measure.

Aside from the commercial applications of such research, direct-mail advertising, vending machines, and the like offer a fine natural laboratory for the study of persuasion. Mindak, Neibergs, and Anderson (1963) used the sales of tickets to parades and to a civic aquatennial as one of their several measures of the effect of a newspaper strike. Roens (1961) reported on the use of different combinations of media to carry the same propaganda theme (for Scott paper), and Berreman's (1940) study of factors affecting the sale of novels found that publicity elements had little effect.

DeFleur and Petranoff (1959) investigated subliminal persuasion by sales measures. Since the alleged subliminal effect was first reported (with no data) as the result of a filmed message, they flashed "Buy Product X" on a screen subliminally for several experimental weeks. The effect of this was measured by the deviation from normal of a food wholesaler's orders. No significant effect was observed.

The stuff of commercial persuasion, advertisements proper, has been employed in a number of ways for other purposes. The want-ad columns of newspapers have served as economic predictors (Fowler, 1962). Contrariwise, they may provide the data for historical analysis. The Security First National Bank of Los Angeles compiles a regional index of want-ad frequency and reports variance over time in this index coincidental with basic economic data. A management consulting firm prepares an index based only on advertisements for engineers and scientists. Although incomplete data are reported by Fowler, she writes that the firm "likes to consider its index as a leading indicator of how the economy fares, rather than a coincident indicator" (p. 12). That optimistic assessment illustrates the necessity for considering the time-linked nature of a measure. The statement was true for a long period of time — from the late forties possibly up to 1964. But since the employment of engineers and scientists is intimately tied to defense contracts, a major change in Defense Department policy will throw off employment levels, thus the ads, thus the indicator. Just such a change occurred during Secretary Robert McNamara's administration, and the 1964 advertisement levels should be negatively correlated with the state of the economy.

Advertisements have also been used to test theories of social change. Assuming that ads reflect values, Dornbusch and Hickman (1959) sampled 816 issues of the *Ladies Home Journal* and analyzed the content of advertising to estimate the degree of "other-directedness" displayed. These data tested Riesman's hypotheses on the history of "other-directedness." Two classes of indices were employed: (1) endorsements by persons or groups and (2) claims that a product is related to satisfactions in interpersonal relations.

Singh and Huang (1962) made a cross-cultural study of advertising, comparing American and Indian advertising for similarity and relating the findings to socioeconomic and cultural factors. Since they used print advertising, it is important to take account of differential literacy rates in such comparisons. If the advertisers are addressing their messages to literate "prospects" and reflecting the values of those "prospects," the differential literacy rate may interact with magazine readership and prospect status to yield differences between societies that are spurious. This is less a concern with broadcast advertising, although there may be a population restriction in that those who either own or are more available to radio or television receivers vary systematically across countries.

INDUSTRIAL AND INSTITUTIONAL RECORDS

Among the finest work to be found on discussion of multiple methods and the criterion problem is that of the industrial psychologists. One rarely finds such attention to the relative merits of ratings versus observation versus performance versus interviewing versus questionnaires versus tests. Guion (1961) has offered an excellent short treatment of this subject, as have Ghiselli and Brown (1955) and Whisler and Harper (1962). But these have not supplanted the singular statements on "criteria of criteria" by R. L. Thorndike (1949).[1]

The number of private records marshalled by the industrial psychologists has been impressive. Amount and quality of output are probably the most frequently used behavioral measures, and are usually expressed in some transformed score — the number of units produced by a worker or department per unit of time, the amount of sales per unit of time, or the profitability of activity by dollars invested by the firm. The known subjectivity of ratings by supervisors or foremen increasingly moved many of the specialists in this area to pure behavioral measures, but ratings remain because of the difficulty in making behavioral measures comparable.

Private records have their difficulties, and Whisler and Harper (1962) are helpful in illustrating problems in making comparisons across departments or workers. The factors involved in any such comparison of records are numerous and vary from one situation to another — the type of work, physical working conditions, work group cohesion, and the like. Ghiselli and Brown (1955) struggle with the problem of appropriate controls for work behavior and offer a series of possible work standards: group average production, rates of selected individuals known to be "good" workers (with some discounting then applied), experimentally determined times for tasks, and "rational analysis" by people familiar with the problem.

We review a body of studies with data drawn from the institutional records of companies, schools, hospitals, and the military. A good share of these come from industry, but the overlap with other institutions is marked.

Most of the current writers argue for multidimensional criteria. Ghiselli and Brown (1955) give the humble example of a streetcar motorman, indicating a series of proficiency measures:

1. Number of collisions with pedestrians
2. Number of traffic violations

[1]For other articles of methodological interest on criteria see Brogden and Taylor (1950), Gordon (1950), Fiske (1951), Bass (1952), Severin (1952), Rush (1953), MacKinney (1960), and Turner (1960).

3. Number of commendations from public
4. Number of complaints from public
5. Number of times company rules broken
6. Number of sleepovers (tardiness)
7. Number of times schedules broken
8. Number of reprimands from inspectors
9. Ratings by inspectors
10. Errors reported by dispatchers.

As always with multiple measures such as these, the question comes up of the advisability of combining the various measures into a single composite score. Consider in the list above the problem of weighting each of the ten variables. Ghiselli and Brown suggest multiple cutoffs — establishing a minimum performance level for *each* component element of the index. The way in which the variables are combined, and the final score reached, can be disastrously misleading if some minimum standard is not met on each of the tasks of the job. They offer the highly reasonable example that an airline pilot should be able to land a plane as well as take one off — perhaps not so gracefully, but still with an irreducible degree of proficiency (cf. Coombs, 1963).

Another multimeasure study, this one of ship effectiveness in the Navy, was conducted by Campbell (1956). Rather than rely solely on ratings by the captain or crew members, Campbell examined the ship records for reports of ship inspections, torpedo firings, re-enlistment rates of those aboard, requests for transfer, and disciplinary actions. Snyder and Sechrest (1959) combined behavioral violations and ratings in their work showing the positive effect of directive therapy in defective delinquents.

Re-enlistment rates are a measure of job turnover, and Evan (1963) explored this topic in research on student workers. Personnel records were examined to find a possible relationship between job turnover and departmental placement. He reasoned that a high level of interaction on the job with other student workers would have a stress-reducing effect and result in a lower rate of job turnover. He supported this hypothesis by showing that the larger the number of students with whom a worker could interact, the lower the rate of quitting.

Knox (1961) added absenteeism to job turnover and correlated both with age, seniority, and the distance of the worker's home from the factory. Melbin (1961) also used absenteeism and job turnover in research on psychiatric aids. He compared these data to archival reports on work assignments. The correlational methods limited his ability to establish cause-and-effect relationships, but he was able to trace a double-directioned effect between changes in work assignments and absences.

Job turnover is an ambiguous measure — sometimes it is an administrative action, sometimes an action dictated by the individual employee. R. L. Thorndike (1949) holds that administrative actions should be considered as a discrete class of criteria. Along with many others, Guilford (1956) used the record of pay increases as his measure of the firm's appraisal of the individual. Weitz (1958) suggests the imperfectly correlated measure of promotion within the company, while Jay and Copes (1957) speak of job survival as a criterion. Merely to stay on a job, without being fired, is indicative of an administrative decision that the employee is not too bad.

Whisler and Harper (1962) also speak of seniority as a criterion and discuss the implications of this in the union-management struggle over definition of criteria. They state that seniority has appeal because of its qualities of objectivity and precision, and that it is not a simple case of the union wanting seniority and the management fighting it. Promotion from within the management group and the high value placed on experience is evidence of the use of seniority within the management tier.

One could also observe other management actions which reflect the esteem with which an employee is held. The rug on the floor, the drapes on the window, the white telephone, the second secretary, and the corner office are all salient cues to an employee's success with the firm.

Other industrial research with absentee records has included Amthauer's (1963) work on social psychological settings and Bernberg's (1952) study of departmental morale. Amthauer took absenteeism as his dependent variable and considered a string of independent variables: motivation, intelligence, persistence, and stability, as well as the individual's relationship with apprentices and with instructors. Note that although absenteeism is not implicitly reactive, the other measures of individual psychological characteristics were. So, too, for Bernberg, who measured departmental morale by measures with high reactive risk, but matched these against an elaborated set of absentee measures. He took four variants of absenteeism as his variables: unexcused absence of one day or longer, tardiness, absence of less than one day, and trips to the medical unit not resulting from accident or disease. For a review of studies focused on absenteeism in the industrial setting, see Brayfield and Crockett (1955).

The unions keep books, too, and Stuart (1963) was canny enough to use grievance records in a study of racial conflict. He collected 364 verbatim records of the grievance board of a large union in the textile industry—data extending over a seven-year period. The complaints were analyzed to determine feelings, attitudes, and actions against Negro and Spanish-speaking workers who comprised a majority of the union. Their complaints are important evidence, but there is the risk of the bias one notes in studies of political speeches. Although the events occurred in the past, and the investigator did not intrude in the production of the data, the subjects were very much aware that their remarks were "on the record." This perforce limits the degree of generalization possible.

McGrath (1962) also used indirect data in his study of friendship and group behavior. The dependent variable was the competitive performance of rifle teams, plotted against whether the team had given favorable or unfavorable ratings to former teammates and how the team had been rated. I. D. Steiner (1964) comments on a possible restriction on generalization: "Additional research is needed to determine whether the individualistic orientation which was a boon to rifle teams would also promote productivity in situations calling for cooperative group action" (p. 434).

Hall and Willerman (1963) studied the effect of college roommates on grade performance. They set up experimental combinations of dormitory roommates with varying academic ability. Students rooming with high-ability students obtained better grades than those rooming with low-ability students; this condition held, however, only when the roommate was later born in his family. Hall and Willerman conclude that these results support Schachter's (1959) thesis that first-born students are more susceptible to influence and later-born ones are more influential.

Stouffer (Stouffer *et al.*, 1949) was among those reporting on sick-call data, drawing statistics from the Office of the Air Surgeon on members of heavy bomber crews in the European theater during June, 1944. Sick-call rate was correlated with self-evaluations of physical condition. Stouffer suggests that the contrast between attitudes toward one's physical condition and behavior with respect to physical symptoms reflected the men's tendency to save up complaints until their tour of 30 missions was completed. He speculates that they might have been motivated by a fear of not completing a tour of combat duty and thus running the risk of postponing a return to the United States.

More military records were used by Fiedler and his associates (Fiedler et al., 1958; Fiedler, 1962). These studies examined "adjustment" in nonclinical populations — Army units and student populations. For the Army personnel, they obtained sick-call data, disciplinary-offense ratings, and court-martial records; for the students, course grades, number of visits to the student health center, and student counseling bureau visits. Little relationship was found among these measures of "adjustment," underlining the problem of combining pieces of evidence which *look* to be similar in reflecting some characteristics.

In a more circumscribed investigation, Mechanic and Volkart (1961) probed sick-call visits further, with a population of college students. They showed the frequency of visits to be positively related to the subject's degree of stress and his tendency to play the sick role. Medical visits are not a pure measure of a single trait, and few single archival measures are ever pure. The employment of multiple measures of the same hypothesized "trait" is always indicated (Campbell & Fiske, 1959). We stress this because many of the researchers who have been venturesome enough to employ nonreactive data have done so to define or classify subjects — often then administering questionnaires and interviews to the subjects. This is a highly appropriate device to combine research methods, but its validity is posited on the accuracy of the trait definition contributed by the initial record. A multiple-method approach is the best hedge against error (cf. R. L. Thorndike, 1949).

Schwartz and Stanton (1950) suggest a study of the social situation of the hospital combining observational and archival materials. The observation is of negative incidents in a ward, and the archive is a measure of incontinent behavior: the amount and type of laundry done for that ward. In their exploratory observational study, they kept complete records of the patients' daily activities, and were able to determine connections between certain types of negative incidents and incontinent behavior. They further suggest that the laundry record could be useful in establishing the effects of changes in therapeutic methods within a ward.

WRITTEN DOCUMENTS

The last major class of more or less private archives is personal documents. These have been more the bailiwick of the historiographer than the behavioral scientist, but a number of notable studies have been performed using personal documents. Cox (1926), in Volume 2 of Terman's *Genetic Studies of Genius*, used documentary evidence of all kinds, and, on the history of science side, we have Terman's early (1917) study estimating Galton's IQ. Centering on records of Galton's prowess between the ages of three and eight (he could read any English-language book by five and knew the *Iliad* and *Odyssey* by six), Terman compared them with the ages at which other children are able to accomplish the same or similar achievements and estimated Galton's IQ to be not far from 200.

There have been important methodological works, such as G. W. Allport's (1942) monograph, *The Use of Personal Documents in Psychological Science*, and facilitating method papers, such as Dollard and Mowrer's (1947) system to determine the amount of tension in written documents by a "Discomfort Relief Quotient."

But for all this, written documents have been another of the underdeveloped data resources of social science. In the examples that follow, we cite some of the major studies using written documents and illustrate some of the rival hypotheses coincident with them.

One could not think of letters as a research source without bringing to mind Thomas and Znaniecki's (1918) classic study of the Polish peasant. Letters sent between Poland and the United States were one of the major elements in a data pool that included autobiographies, newspaper accounts, court proceedings, and the records of social agencies. Rather by happenstance, Thomas learned that there was an extensive correspondence between the two countries and that many of the letters were being thrown away. From this lead, advertisements were placed which offered to pay for each letter produced.

There are, to be sure, substantial questions about the population and content restrictions in the letters Thomas and Znaniecki gathered; there are in any body of voluntarily produced (even for pay) research materials. Typically, they only had one side of the exchange, a common and frustrating condition often bemoaned by biographers and historians. In a commentary on this study, Riley (1963) states:

> In all such instances, then, their data refer only to selected members of each group (family) and cover only part of the interaction. These gaps illustrate an important potential limitation in the use of available data generally: not having been assembled for the purpose of the investigation, the data may be fragmentary or incomplete, thus depriving the researcher of valuable information.
>
> Another limitation is that such privately owned and spontaneously produced materials may be rare or difficult to obtain. Owners of letters, diaries, or other personal documents may sometimes object to their use for research purposes. . . . Moreover, situations producing appropriate materials may be rare. The continuing exchange of letters, for example, seems to depend upon long-term or frequent separation of the members, as well as upon a custom of detailed letter writing. Nevertheless, there are no doubt many instances in which similar data are available for further research, as, for instance, when servicemen are separated from their families [pp. 242-243].

Riley thus points out that the dross rate may be high ("situations producing appropriate materials may be rare"), and that population restrictions may be present (". . . exchange. . . seems to depend upon long-term or frequent separation . . . owners may sometimes object to their use"). Specifically for cross-cultural comparison purposes, there is the question of differential literacy rates. How many of the Polish peasants could write? If they could not, and had letters written for them by others, say, village scribes, did the presence of these intervening persons serve to alter the content of the letters? On the voluntary supplying of the letters, did the correspondent give up only a biased sample? A money incentive might have to be prohibitively high to pry loose some love letters, for example, or letters which detailed complaints about the correspondent's frugality in sending money back home.

In Sunday feature articles, one sometimes reads another group of one-way letters: those sent from children in summer camp to their parents. By themselves, they are instructive of a child's perception of the surrounding world. Salzinger (1958) got the other end of this candid correspondence as well, and analyzed the content of mail from children and parents, comparing the letters for similarity on "wants," "demands," and "requests."

Janowitz (1958) dealt with letters and diaries captured from German soldiers. His concern was the impact of propaganda on these troops, and "when these letters dealt with the German writer himself, or his small circle of friends, they contained testimony of considerable value. Many made valuable propaganda documents, especially captured undelivered mail" (p. 734). This last point is of interest, for the undelivered mail is a subset of mail which is most recent and most pertinent for evaluation of propaganda effect. Letters captured on the person of troops may also be particularly valuable, for they contain not only the most recent expressions of feeling, but may also include letters the writer may have been postponing mailing. Such uncertain writings may be prime indicators of attitudes and morale, for the easy stereotypes of "I'm fine Ma and the food's not bad" are more likely to be quickly dispatched.

Letters to political figures are another source of data. For some magnificent examples of these, as well as a general treatment of the topic, one can examine *Dear F. D. R.* (Sussman, 1963, an earlier report of which is in Sussman, 1959. See also Dexter, 1963).

A particularly fine discussion of possible sources of error in letters is presented in Dexter's (1964) chapter on letters to congressmen. He notes that congressmen do not necessarily see any cause for alarm in a barrage of negative mail.

> One "pro-labor" Senator, out of curiosity, had his staff check up the writers of 100 letters he received advocating support of a higher minimum wage. It was found that 75 writers were eligible to register, but of these only 33 actually were registered. Furthermore, the letters were advocating his support of a measure on which he had been particularly active, and the content of the

mail showed no realization of the stand he had so publicly taken. The Senator could scarcely get excited about these letter writers as either a source of opposition or of support on the basis of that issue [p. 399].[2]

If the only goal of the senator is to stay in office, the mail from an ineligible voter is only so much dross. His greater concern is the lack of any intelligence from the great mass of eligible voters who don't write.

Dexter goes on to discuss why mail is important, but speaks of the congressman's description of "genuine," "junk," and "stimulated" mail. Of interest is the way in which they are discriminated.

> It [mail] is not believed if "junk," i.e., press releases or other broadcast mailings, nor if it be stimulated. Stimulated mail is not entirely easy to define. In its pure form it consists of virtually identical postcard messages written under the instigation of a single company, union or interest group. (One company even mailed the postcards for its workers, fearing that they would not know who their congressman was.) Congressmen look for signs of stimulation — similarity of phrasing ("They all used the same argument.") or even stationery ("They handed out the paper.") and time of mailing ("You could tell the hour or minute someone pushed the button.") . . . it is hard to fool a congressman as to when mail is stimulated. Some organizations urge their members to write in their own words, on their own stationery, and as personally as possible. Congressional assistants tell us that perhaps one in fifty persons who write such a letter will enclose the original printed notice from the organization urging an individualized apparently spontaneous letter [p. 403].

As for the extent of this false element in spontaneous mail,

> Most of the mail sent on the Reciprocal Trade Act was in some sense stimulated . . . [for] Eastern and Southern congressmen . . . Westinghouse, Dow, Monsanto, and Pittsburgh Plate Glass may have stimulated 40 per cent or more of all the mail received on the issue in 1954. . . . Mail in favor of reciprocal trade was equally stimulated and perhaps by even fewer prime

[2]Reprinted with permission of The Free Press of Glencoe from *People, Society and Mass Communications*, edited by L. A. Dexter and D. M. White. Copyright © 1964 by The Free Press of Glencoe, a division of The Macmillan Company. Based upon "Congressmen and the People They Listen To," Massachusetts Institute of Technology, 1955, and *American Business and Public Policy*, Atherton, New York, 1963.

movers. Our impression is that three-fourths of all antiprotectionist mail was stimulated directly or indirectly by the League of Women Voters [pp. 403-404].

A check on the true level of protest mail was made by the Xerox Corporation. Flooded with negative letters after sponsorship of a television series on the United Nations, they hired a group of handwriting experts to examine the mail. "A total of 51,279 protests had been received. The handwriting experts determined that the letters were written by 12,785 persons. The latter figures practically equalled the number of favorable letters" (Kupcinet, 1965). No mention is made of an equivalent analysis of the "pro" letters.

This selective bias in the population mailing letters to congressmen or others results in an invalid generalization on the state of public opinion, but it can serve as evidence of how the major pressure groups are responding. The bias itself is not fatal; only not knowing of it is.

Earlier, we mentioned the problem of population-restriction bias in suicide notes, observing that less than 25 per cent of all suicides leave final notes. Osgood and Walker (1959) took this into account in their study of motivation and language behavior. Reasoning from behavioral principles, they predicted that the content of suicide notes should differ significantly from control notes and simulated suicide notes. Persons about to take their life should be highly motivated (something of an understatement), and this motivation should increase the dominant responses in their hierarchies; a higher than normal level of stereotypy should be present. Content analysis by six different stereotypy indices supported their prediction. This study is a good example of relating "natural phenomena" that exist in the outside world to principles derived from laboratory experimentation. There are many tests for theoretical postulates available in settings other than the laboratory, and joint testing in the laboratory and outside may yield powerful validity checks.

Spiegel and Neuringer (1963) also tested a specific hypothesis by the employment of suicide notes. They examined the proposition that inhibition of the experience of dread ordinarily evoked by suicidal intention is a necessary condition for suicidal action. They drew on the Los Angeles County Coroner's office for their material, noting a control of "false" suicide notes. Other suicide-note studies have been conducted by Gottschalk and Gleser (1960) and by Schneidman and Farberow (1957).

Art work is another expressive personal document that may provide data—as is shown by all the clinical psychologists who look at Van Gogh's paintings and say, "That man was in trouble!" An equally *post hoc* analysis, but with more analytic elegance, has been contributed by Barry (1957). He studied the complexity of art form as related to severity of socialization. From Whiting and Child's 76 nonliterate societies on which socialization data are available, he found 30 with at least ten extant examples of graphic art—either displays in museums or illustrations in ethnographic reports. There was a low-level association between complexity of art form and degree of severity of socialization. The unknown question is whether a higher or lower level of association would have been detected had the data been available for more than 30 societies. Were those who were more gentle in socialization less likely to produce art work which has survived to the present? Note, too, that there is the selective screen of museum curators and ethnographers. Materials might have survived physically from the other 46 societies, but have been defined as of insufficient artistic or scientific worth to display behind glass or on paper.

What might be considered an equally primitive art form was studied by Solley and Haigh (1957) and by Craddick (1961). Both investigations showed that the size of children's drawings of Santa Claus was larger before Christmas than after. Sechrest and Wallace (1964) asked whether the size of the Santa Claus drawing might be traced to a generalized expansive euphoria associated with the excitement of the season, and whether children might be expected to draw almost any object larger during the Christmas season. Their experimentation showed this was not the case, and the Santa Claus was the only one of three objects drawn larger. Craddick (1962) also found that the mean size of drawings of witches decreased at Halloween time. Berger (1954), working from doodles in the notebooks of college students, found a correlation of .75 between graphic constriction in the doodles and neurotic tendency.

A CONCLUDING NOTE

In this review of archival studies, we have seen the versatility of the written record. Not only has the content of study varied, but also the functions these data have served.

For some research purposes, there were few alternatives to archives — not a particularly luminary recommendation, but certainly a compelling one. With suicides, for example, there is no choice but to wait until a population defines itself operationally. Once this happens, one can go to farewell notes, biographical material, and interviews with relatives; but one cannot go to the subject. So, too, for the general student of the past. For one like Terman (1917), who chose to study Galton, there was no easy alternative to consulting the written record.

In a limited content area, the archival record provides *the* dependent variable. Just as votes are the ultimate criterion for the politician, sales and work performance are the ultimate criteria for some applied social scientists. It has been of interest in the history of research in both advertising and personnel that relatively direct criterion variables have been ignored, while less pertinent ones were labored over. (Measuring "willingness to buy" by questionnaire methods is an example, although it does have some utility in prediction studies.)

There are also a few studies in which records were used as a medium through which theoretical principles could be tested. Such studies are too few, but these records offer superb opportunities to validate hypotheses generated in less natural and more reactivity-prone settings. There are restrictions, but it should be recognized that there are restrictions in any single class of information. Berlyne (1964), in commenting on some highly controlled experimental work, wrote:

> Skinner and his associates have concentrated on situations in which an animal can perform a particular kind of response repeatedly at a high rate. The findings yielded by this kind of experiment have been extrapolated without much hesitation, and not always with specific empirical warrant, to a diversity of human activities, including those on which the most important social problems hinge [pp. 115-116].

Osgood and Walker (1959) used suicide notes to study the effect of heightened motivation on response hierarchies. Also using records as a testing medium, Mosteller and Wallace (1963) went to records of 1787-1788 for their comparative study of a Bayesian procedure with a classical statistical approach. They demonstrated that both procedures reached the same conclusion on the disputed authorship of some of *The Federalist Papers*.[3]

The great majority of these studies, however, have used the archives for indirect evidence. Stuart's (1963) study of union grievances and the state of race relations, Parker's (1963) study of library withdrawals to show the effect of television, and the measurement of the size of Santa Clauses (Solley & Haigh, 1957; Craddick, 1961; Sechrest & Wallace, 1964) all reveal the inventive unveiling of valuable evidence. But only partial evidence—for the reasons traced in the preceding chapter show the need for care in generalizing from such analyses. Here, as with the running public records, there is a heavy demand for consideration of possible data transformations and for the construction of multiple indices. If it is agreed that the archives typically provide only partial evidence, and if the desirable research strategy is to generate multiple displays of overlapping evidence, then the way in which these partial clues are pieced together is critical.

We should recognize that using the archival records frequently means substituting someone else's selective filter for your own. Although the investigator may not himself contaminate the material, he may learn that the producer or repository already has. A thoughtful consideration of the sources of invalidity may provide intelligence on these, either by suggesting astute hedges or new analyses to answer rival hypotheses. In any event, the Chinese proverb still holds:

The palest ink is clearer than the best memory.

[3]For an excellent general treatment of "identifying the unknown communicator," see Paisley (1964), where studies in painting, literature, and music are reviewed.

CHAPTER 5

Simple Observation

Who could he be? He was evidently reserved, and melancholy. Was he a clergyman? — He danced too well. A barrister? — He was not called. He used very fine words, and said a great deal. Could he be a distinguished foreigner come to England for the purpose of describing the country, its manners and customs; and frequenting city balls and public dinners with the view of becoming acquainted with high life, polished etiquette, and English refinement? — No, he had not a foreign accent. Was he a surgeon, a contributer to the magazines, a writer of fashionable novels or an artist? — No: to each and all of these surmises there existed some valid objection. — "Then," said everybody, "he must be somebody." — "I should think he must be," reasoned Mr. Malderton, with himself, "because he perceives our superiority, and pays us much attention."

(Sketches from Boz)

Charles Dickens displayed a ready touch for observationally scouring the behavior of this mysterious gentleman for evidence with which to classify him — even going so far as to put out the hypothesis that the man was a participant observer. In this chapter, the first of two on observational methods, our interest is focused on situations in which the observer has no control over the behavior or sign in question, and plays an unobserved, passive, and nonintrusive role in the research situation. The next chapter details studies in which the observer has played an active role in structuring the situation, but in which he is still unobserved by the actors. Since we have limited our discussion to measures with low risks of reactivity, the visible "research-observer" approach and the participant-observation method have been minimized here.[1]

---

[1]More standard treatments of research methods may be consulted for extensive discussion of observational techniques with the observer visible. See Goode & Hatt (1952), Festinger & Katz (1953), Good & Scates (1954), Selltiz et al. (1959), Riley (1963), Kerlinger (1964), and Madge (1965). These same works also contain material on analysis of documentary and secondary source materials.

VISIBLE OBSERVERS

The patently visible observer can produce changes in behavior that diminish the validity of comparisons. Arsenian (1943) noted that the simple presence of an adult sitting near a door seemed to lend assurance to a group of nursery-school children. The opposite change was noted by Polansky and associates (1949) in studying the effect of the presence of observers among young boys at a summer camp. There the observers were a threat and became objects of active aggression. Not only is change produced which reduces the generalizability of findings, but if one were comparing children in two settings varying in the visibility of observers or the reaction to observers, internal validity would take a blow.

The effect of the observer may erode over time, as Deutsch (1949) has shown, and thereby produce a selective contaminant in observational data series. The defense against this is to permit the effect of the observer contaminant to wear off, and start analysis with data subsequent to the time when the effect is negligible. This is similar to experimental controls for practice effects in learning experiments, and presumes that the effect will wear off quickly enough not to waste too much data. And that in turn is based on the researcher's ability to measure the independent effect of observation in the series.

Bales (1950) tested whether different arrangements of observers would selectively bias group behavior. Observers sat with the group, or behind a one-way screen with the group aware they were there, or behind the screen with the group unsure if they were there. He found no difference in group behavior under these conditions. All conditions were applied in a laboratory, however, and all the groups knew they were being tested. These factors might overpower the possibly weaker effects of the physical position of the observer.

No matter how well integrated an observer becomes, we feel he is still an element with potential to bias the production of the critical data substantially. The bias may be a selective one to jeopardize internal validity, or, perhaps more plausibly, it may cripple the ability of the social scientist to generalize his findings very far beyond his sample. A number of writers (cf. Bain,

1960; Gullahorn & Strauss, 1960; Gusfield, 1960; Wax, 1960) have argued for the participant-observation method as a device to circumvent some of the contaminations of studies employing an "outside" observer. It may do that, but there is still a high risk of contaminants surviving to invalidate comparisons.

PARTICIPANT OBSERVATION

Riley (1963) has suggested that the participant-observation studies are subject to two classes of error—"control effect" and "biased-viewpoint effect." The control effect is present when the measurement process itself becomes an agent working for change: "the difficulty with control effect in participant observation, and in many other research designs, is that it is unsystematic . . . " (p. 71). The biased-viewpoint effect includes what we have discussed under the label of intra-instrument processes. The instrument (the human observer) may selectively expose himself to the data, or selectively perceive them, and, worse yet, shift over time the calibration of his observation measures.

This has been suggested by Naroll and Naroll (1963), who speak of the anthropologist's tendency to be disposed to "exotic data." The observer is more likely to report on phenomena which are different from those of his own society or subculture than he is to report on phenomena common to both. When the participant observer spends an extended period of time in a foreign culture (a year among the Fulani or six months with a city gang), those elements of the culture which first seemed notable because they were alien may later acquire a more homey quality. His increased familiarity with the culture alters him as an instrument.

Riley suggests that the control effect may be reduced by the observer assuming an incognito role, even though ethical questions are raised, but,

> on the other hand, the covert observer may find complete immersion in the system, and subsequent likelihood of a biased viewpoint, more difficult to avoid. Limited to his specified role, he may be cut off from valuable channels of information, unable to solicit information not normally accessible to his role without arousing suspicions [p. 72].

Associated with this class of observation is the use of the informant, who is a participant observer one selective screen away from the investigator. Back (1960) writes of the traits of the good informant (knowledgeability, physical exposure, effective exposure, perceptual abilities, availability of information, motivation) and points out some of the difficulties of receiving valid and appropriate data from informants.

Dalton (1964) gives an excellent pro-and-con analysis of participant observation in his commentary on the methods used in *Men Who Manage*. Dalton's pro list is longer than the con one, and he employs the intriguing terminology of "established circulator" and "peripheral formalist."

As a final note on participant observation, we cite Lang and Lang's (1960) report, in which participant observers became participants. Two scientific observers of audience behavior at a Billy Graham Crusade in New York made *their* "Decision for Christ" and left the fold of observers to walk down the aisle. This is in itself an interesting measure. What a testimony to the Reverend Mr. Graham's persuasive skills, when sociological observers are so swayed that they leave their posts!

Stephen Leacock said, "Let me hear the jokes of a nation and I will tell you what the people are like, how they are getting along, and what is going to happen to them" (Manago, 1962). This may be too haughty a claim for conclusions possible from one set of observational data, but we note below studies which produce impressive findings from the opportunistic use of observation of events over which the investigator has no control.

These simple observation studies have been organized into the following categories: exterior physical signs, expressive movement, physical location, language behavior (conversation sampling) and time duration. The breadth of these measures is notable, and they are "simple" only in that the investigator does not intervene in the production of the material.

Exterior Physical Signs

Most of the exterior physical signs discussed are durable ones that have been inferred to be expressive of current or past behavior. A smaller number are portable and shorter-lived. The bullfighter's beard is a case in point. Conrad (1958) reports that the bullfighter's beard is longer on the day of the fight than on any other day. There are supporting comments among matadors about this phenomenon, yet can one measure the torero's anxiety by noting the length of his beard? The physical task is rather difficult, but not impossible in this day of sophisticated instrumentation. As in all these uncontrolled measures, one must draw inferences about the criterion behavior. Maybe it wasn't the anxiety at all. Perhaps the bullfighter stands farther away from the razor on the morning of the fight, or he may not have shaved that morning at all (like baseball pitchers and boxers). And then there is the possible intersubject contaminant that the more affluent matadors are likely to be shaved, while the less prosperous shave themselves.

A less questionable measure is tattoos. Burma (1959) reports on the observation of tattoos among some nine hundred inmates of three different institutions. The research measure was the proportion of inmates with tattoos: "significantly more delinquents than nondelinquents tattoo themselves." Of course, one could hardly reverse the findings and hold that tattooing can be employed as a single measure of delinquency. Returning to the bull ring for a moment, "There are many ordinary bullfighters, but ordinary people do not fight bulls" (Lea, 1949, p. 40).

More formal classification cues are tribal markings and scars. Doob (1961) reports on a walk he and an African companion took through a Nigerian market.

> I casually pointed to a dozen men, one after the other, who had facial scars. My African friend in all instances named a society; then he and I politely verified the claim by speaking to the person and asking him to tell us the name of his tribe. In eleven instances out of twelve, he was correct. Certainly, however, he may have been responding simultaneously to other cues in the person's appearance, such as his clothing or his skin color [p. 83].

In a report whose authors choose to remain anonymous (Anonymoi, 1953-1960), it was discovered that there is a strong association between the methodological disposition of psychologists and the length of their hair. The authors observed the hair length of psychologists attending professional meetings and coded the meetings by the probable appeal to those of different methodological inclinations. Thus, in one example, the length of hair was compared between those who attended an experimental set of papers and those who attended a series on ego-identity formation. The results are clear cut. The "tough-minded" psychologists have shorter-cut hair than the long-haired psychologists. Symptomatic interpretations, psychoanalytic inquiries as to what is cut about the clean-cut young man, are not the only possibilities. The causal ambiguity of the correlation was clarified when the "dehydration hypothesis" (i.e., that lack of insulation caused the hard-headedness) was rejected by the "bald-head control," i.e., examining the distribution of baldheaded persons (who by the dehydration hypothesis should be most hardheaded of all).

Clothes are an obvious indicator, and A. M. Rosenthal (1962), wrote of "the wide variance between private manners and public behavior" of the Japanese:

> Professor Enright [British lecturer in Japan] and just about every other foreigner who ever visited Japan have noted with varying degrees of astonishment that there is a direct relationship between the politeness of a Japanese and whether or not he is wearing shoes [p. 20].

It is quite likely that this relationship reflects the selective distribution of shoes in the Japanese society more than any causal element, an example of a population restriction. The economically marginal members of the Japanese population should, one would think, be more overt in expressing hostility to foreign visitors than those who are economically stable — and possession of shoes is more probably linked to affluence than it is to xenophobia.

Shoe styles, not their presence, have been used as the unit of discrimination in the United States society where almost everybody does wear shoes. Gearing (1952), in a study of subculture awareness in south Chicago, observed shoe styles, finding features of the shoe to correspond with certain patterns of living. In general, the flashier shoe more often belonged to the more culturebound individual. Similar concern with feet was shown by the OSS Assessment Staff (1948) when, because standard uniforms reduced the number of indicators, they paid special attention to shoes and socks as a prime indication "of taste and status."

Despite the general consensus on clothing as an indicator of status, little controlled work has been done on the subject. Flugel (1930) wrote a discursive book on clothing in general, and Webb

(1957) reported on class differences in attitudes toward clothes and clothing stores. Another investigation shows many differences between clothing worn by independent and fraternity-affiliated college males. Within the fraternity groups, better grades are made by the more neatly dressed (Sechrest, 1965b).

Kane (1958; 1959; 1962) observed the clothing worn by outpatients to their interviews. He has considered pattern, color, texture, and amount of clothing, relating these characteristics to various moods, traits, and personality changes. In a more reactive study, Green and Knapp (1959) associated preferences for different types of tartans with need achievement; it would be of interest to see if this preference pattern were supported in clothing purchased or worn.

A southern chief of detectives has discussed using clothing clues as predictor variables. In a series of suggestions to police officers, he noted the importance of dress details. When Negroes are planning a mass jail-in, "The women will wear dungarees as they enter the meeting places" (Anonymous, 1965).

Jewelry and other ornamental objects can also be clues. Freud gave his inner circle of six, after World War I, rings matching his own. On another intellectual plane, observers have noted that in some societies one can find illiterates who buy only the top of a pen and then clip it to clothing as a suggestion of their writing prowess. One could observe the frequency of such purchases in local stores, or less arduously, examine sales records over time from the manufacturer, considering the ratio of tops to bottoms for different countries or regions. The observation method would have an advantage in that one could make coincidental observations on the appearance of those purchasing the tops alone, or isolate a sample for interviewing. The archival record of top and bottom shipments is infinitely more efficient, but more circumscribed in the content available for study.

As part of their study of the social status of legislators and their voting, MacRae and MacRae (1961) observed the houses lived in by legislators and rated them along the lines suggested by Warner (Warner, Meeker, & Eells, 1949). This house rating was part of the over-all social-class index produced for each legislator.

Observation of any type of possession can be employed as an index if the investigator knows that there is a clear relationship between possession (ownership) of the object and a second variable. Calluses, for example, can serve as an observable indicator of certain classes of activity. Different sports make selective demands on tissue, for example, and the calluses that result are reliable indicators of whether one is a squash player or a golfer. Some occupations may also be determined by similar physical clues.

With these measures used alone, validity is often tenuous. Phillips (1962) is unusual in giving multiple indicators of the changes in Miami resulting from the influx of a hundred thousand Cubans. Two years following the Castro revolution, he observed:

> Bilingual street signs (No Jaywalking; Cruce por la Zona para Peatones)
> "A visitor hears almost as much Spanish as English."
> Signs in windows saying "Se Habla Espanol"
> Stores with names like "Mi Botanica" and "Carniceria Latina"
> Latin-American foods on restaurant menus
> Supermarkets selling yucca, malanga, and platanos
> The manufacture of a Cuban type of cigarette
> Radio broadcasts in Spanish
> Spanish-language editorials in the English-language newspapers
> Services held in Spanish by 40 Miami churches.

Perhaps Phillips was overstating his case, but the marshalling of so much, and so diverse, observational evidence is persuasive. For a prime source in such studies of the unique character of cities, and their changes, there is that eminent guide, the classified telephone directory. It can yield a wide range of broad content information on the economy, interests, and characteristics of a city and its people. Isolating the major United States cities, which ones have the highest numbers of palmists per thousand population?

Expressive Movement

The more plastic variables of body movement historically have interested many observers. Charles Darwin's (1872) work on the expression of emotions continues to be the landmark commentary. His exposition of the measurement of frowning, the uncovering of teeth, erection of the hair, and the like remains provocative reading. The more recent studies on expressive movement and personality measurement are reviewed by Wolff and Precker (1951). Of particular interest in their chapter is the emphasis on consistency among different types of expressive movement. They review the relation between personality and the following measures: facial expression, literary style, artistic style, style of speech, gait, painting and drawing, and handwriting. Not all of these studies are nonreactive, since the central criterion for this is that the subject is not aware of being measured.

Examples of using expressive movement as a response to a particular stimulus — i.e., stimulus-linked rather than subject-linked — are provided in the work of Maurice Krout (1933; 1937; 1951; 1954a; 1954b). Although this work was done in a laboratory setting, it was under facade conditions. That is, subjects were unaware of the true purpose of the research, considering the experiment a purely verbal task. There is a good possibility for application of Krout's (1954a) approach in less reactive settings. He elicited autistic gestures through verbal-conflict situations, and his analysis deals primarily with digital-manual responses. An example of his findings is the correlation between an attitude of fear and the gesture of placing hand to nose. Darwin (1872) mentioned pupil dilation as a possible fear indicator.

Kinesics as a subject of study is relevant here, although as yet large amounts of data are not available. Birdwhistell (1960; 1963) has defined kinesics as being concerned with the communicational aspects of learned, patterned, body-motion behavior. This system of nonverbal communication is felt to be inextricably linked with the verbal, and the aim of such study is to achieve a quantification of the former which can be related to the latter. Some "motion qualifiers" have been identified, such as intensity, range, and velocity. Ruesch and Kees (1956) have presented a combination text-picture treatment in their book, *Non-Verbal Communication*. An example of the impressionistic style of observation is provided by Murphy and Murphy (1962), who reported on the differences in facial expressions between young and old Russians: "While faces of old people often seemed resigned, tired and sad, generally the children seemed lively, friendly, confident and full of vitality" (p. 12).

Something of the detail possible in such studies is shown in Wolff's (1948; 1951) work on hands. In the first study, Wolff observed the gestures of mental patients at meals and at work, concluding, "I found sufficient evidence that correlations exist (1) between emotional make-up and gesture, (2) between the degree of integration and gesture" (1948, p. 166). The second study was anthropometric, and Wolff compared features of the handprints of schizophrenics, mental defectives, and normals. The hands were divided into three major types: (1) elementary, simple and regressive; (2) motor, fleshy and bony; and (3) small and large. On the basis of an individual's hand type, measurements, nails, crease lines, and type of skin, she delineates the main characteristics of their personality, intelligence, vitality, and temperament.

Without necessarily endorsing her conclusions, we report the finding of a confused crease-line pattern peculiar to the extreme of mental deficiency. Other structural characteristics such as concave primary nails, "appeared to a greater or lesser degree in the hands of mental defectives . . . but were completely absent in the hands of the control cases" (Wolff, 1951, p. 105).

A journalistic account of the expressive behavior of hands has been given by Gould (1951). Here is his description of Frank Costello's appearance before the Kefauver crime hearings:

> As he [Costello] sparred with Rudolph Halley, the committee's counsel, the movement of his fingers told their own emotional story. When the questions got rough, Costello crumpled a handkerchief in his hands. Or he rubbed his palms together. Or he interlaced his fingers. Or he grasped a half-filled glass of water. Or he beat a silent tattoo on the table top. Or he rolled a little ball of paper between his thumb and index finger. Or he stroked the side piece of his glasses lying on the table. His was video's first ballet of the hands [p. 1].[2]

It is of interest that conversations of male students with females have been found to be more frequently punctuated by quick, jerky, "nervous" gestures than are conversations between two males (Sechrest, 1965b).

Schubert (1959) has suggested that overt personal behavior could be used in the study of judicial behavior. In presenting a psychometric model of the Supreme Court, he suggests that the

[2] © 1951 by the New York Times Company. Reprinted by permission.

speech, grimaces, and gestures of the judges when hearing oral arguments and when opinions are being delivered are rich sources of data for students of the Court.

On the other side of the legal fence, witnesses in Hindu courts are reported to give indications of the truth of their statements by the movement of their toes (Krout, 1951). The eminent American legal scholar J. H. Wigmore, in works on judicial proof and evidence (1935; 1937), speaks of the importance of peripheral expressive movements as clues to the validity of testimony.

That these cues can vary across societies is demonstrated by Sechrest and Flores (in press). They showed that "leg jiggling" is more frequent among Filipino than American males, and held that jiggling is a "nervous" behavior. As evidence of this, they found jiggling more frequent in coffee lounges than in cocktail lounges.

The superstitious behavior of baseball players is a possible area of study. Knocking dust off cleats, amount of preliminary bat swinging, tossing dust into the air, going to the resin bag, and wiping hands on shirts may be interpreted as expressive actions. One hypothesis is that the extent of such superstitious behavior is related to whether or not the player is in a slump or in the middle of a good streak. This study could be extended to other sports in which the central characters are relatively isolated and visible. It should be easier for golfers and basketball players, but more difficult for football players.

From a practical point of view, of course, coaches and scouts have long studied the overt behavior of opponents for clues to forthcoming actions. (It is known, for example, that most football teams are "right sided" and run a disproportionate number of plays to the right [Griffin, 1964].) Does the fullback indicate the direction of the play by which hand he puts on the ground? Does the linebacker rest on his heels if he is going to fall back on pass defense? Does the quarterback always look in the direction in which he is going to pass, or does he sometimes look the other way, knowing that the defense is focusing on his eyes?

A police officer reported eye movement as a "pickup" clue. A driver who repeatedly glances from side to side, then into the rearview mirror, then again from side to side may be abnormally cautious and perfectly blameless. But he may also be abnormally furtive and guilty of a crime. Another officer, in commenting on auto thefts, said, "We ... look for clean cars with dirty license plates and dirty cars with clean plates," explaining that thieves frequently switch plates (Reddy, 1965).

In a validation study of self-reported levels of newspaper readership, eye movement was observed when people were reading newspapers in trains, buses, library reading rooms, and the street (Advertising Service Guild, 1949). A number of interesting eye movement and direction studies have been conducted in controlled laboratory settings. Discussion of them is contained in the following chapter on observational hardware.

PHYSICAL LOCATION

The physical position of animals has been a favored measure of laboratory scientists, as well as of those in the field. Imanishi (1960), for example, described the social structure of Japanese macaques by reporting on their physical grouping patterns. The dominant macaques sit in the center of a series of concentric rings.

For people, there are the familiar newspaper accounts of who stood next to whom in Red Square reviewing the May Day parade. The proximity of a politician to the leader is a direct clue of his status in the power hierarchy. His physical position is interpreted as symptomatic of other behavior which gave him the status position befitting someone four men away from the Premier, and descriptive of that current status position. In this more casual journalistic report of observations, one often finds time-series analysis: Mr. B. has been demoted to the end of the dais, and Mr. L. has moved up close to the middle.

The clustering of Negroes and whites was used by Campbell, Kruskal, and Wallace (1965) in their study of seating aggregation as an index of attitude. Where seating in a classroom is voluntary, the degree to which the Negroes and whites present sit by themselves versus mixing randomly may be taken as a presumptive index of the degree to which acquaintance, friendship, and preference are strongly colored by race, as opposed to being distributed without regard to racial considerations. Classes in four schools were studied, and significant aggregation by race was found, varying in degree between schools. Aggregation by age, sex, and race has also been reported for elevated trains and lunch counters (Sechrest, 1965b).

Feshbach and Feshbach (1963) report on another type of

clustering. At a Halloween party, they induced fear in a group of boys, aged nine to twelve, by telling them ghost stories. The boys were then called out of the room and were administered questionnaires. The induction of the fear state was natural, but their dependent-variable measures were potentially reactive. What is of interest to us is a parenthetical statement made by the authors. After describing the ghost-story-telling situation, the Feshbachs offer evidence for the successful induction of fear: "Although the diameter of the circle was about eleven feet at the beginning of the story telling, by the time the last ghost story was completed, it had been spontaneously reduced to approximately three feet" (p. 499).

Gratiot-Alphandery (1951a; 1951b) and Herbinière-Lebert (1951) have both made observations of children's seating during informal film showings. How children from different age groups clustered was a measure used in work on developmental changes.

Sommer (1961) employed the position of chairs in a descriptive way, looking at "the distance for comfortable conversation." Normal subjects were used, but observations were made after the subjects had been on a tour of a large mental hospital. Distances among chairs in a lounge were systematically varied, and the people were brought into the lounge after the tour. They entered by pairs, and each pair was asked to go to a designated area and sit down. A simple record was made of the chairs selected.

The issue here is what one generalizes to. Just as the Feshbachs' subjects drew together during the narration of ghost stories, it would not be unrealistic to expect that normal adults coming from a tour of a mental hospital might also draw closer together than would be the case if they had not been on the tour. Their seating distance before the tour would be an interesting control. Do they huddle more, anticipating worse than will be seen, or less?

Sommer (1959; 1960; 1962) has conducted other studies of social distance and positioning, and in the 1959 study mentions a "waltz technique" to measure psychological distance. He learned that as he approached people, they would back away; when he moved backward during a conversation, the other person moved forward. The physical distance between two conversationalists also varies systematically by the nationality of the talkers, and there are substantial differences in distance between two Englishmen talking together and two Frenchmen in conversation. In a cross-cultural study, this would be a response-set characteristic to be accounted for.

Sommer's work inspired a study in Germany (Kaminski & Osterkamp, 1962), but unfortunately it is not a replication of Sommer's design. A paper-and-pencil test was substituted for the actual physical behavior, and 48 students were tested in three mock situations: classroom, U-shaped table, and park benches. Sechrest, Flores, and Arellano (1965) studied social distance in a Filipino sample and found considerably greater distance in opposite-sex pairs as compared with same-sex pairs. Other tests include measuring the distance subjects placed photographs away from themselves (Smith, 1958; Beloff & Beloff, 1961) and Werner and Wapner's (1953) research on measuring the amount of distance walked under conditions of danger.

Sommer (1960) noted how the physical location of group members influenced interactions. Most communication took place among neighbors, but the corner was the locus of most interaction. Whyte (1956) observed that air conditioners were dispersed in a nonrandom way in a Chicago suburban community, and Howells and Becker (1962) demonstrated that those who sat facing several others during a discussion received more leadership nominations than did those who sat side by side.

Leipold's (1963) dissertation carried the work further, paying special attention to the individual response-set variable of "personal space," the physical distance an organism customarily places between itself and other organisms. Leipold gathered personality-classification data on a group of 90 psychology students, divided them into two groups on the basis of introversion-extraversion, and administered stress, praise, or neutral conditions to a third of each group. He evaluated the effect of the conditions, and the tie to introversion-extraversion, by noting which of several available seats were taken by the subjects when they came in for a subsequent interview. The seats varied in the distance from the investigator. In one of his findings, he reports that introverted and high-anxious students, defined by questionnaire responses, kept a greater physical distance from the investigator (choosing a farther chair) than did extraverted and low-anxious students. Stress conditions also resulted in greater distance.

That random assignment doesn't always work is shown in Grusky's (1959) work on organizational goals and informal leaders — research conducted in an experimental prison camp. He learned that informal leaders, despite a policy of random bed assignments, were more likely to attain the bottom bunk. Grusky also considered such archival measures as number of escapes, general transfers, and transfers for poor adjustment. On all of these measures, leaders differed significantly from nonleaders. It must be remembered that this was an experimental prison camp, and the artificiality of the research situation presents the risk that a "Hawthorne effect" may be present. What would be valuable would be another study of regular prison behavior to see if these findings hold in a nonexperimental setting.

On still another plane, the august chambers of the United Nations in New York, Alger (1965) observed representatives at the General Assembly. Sitting with a press card in the gallery, he recorded 3,322 interactions among representatives at sessions of the Administrative and Budgetary Committee. Each interaction was coded for location, initiator, presence or exchange of documents, apparent humor, duration, and so on. His interest was in defining the clusters of nations who typically interacted in the committee.

Using the same approach, it might be possible to get partial evidence on which nations are perceived as critical and uncertain during debate on a proposed piece of UN action. Could one define the marginal, "swing" countries by noting which ones were visited by both Western and Bloc countries during the course of the debate? Weak evidence, to be sure, for there is the heavy problem of spatial restriction. One can only observe in public places, and even expanding the investigation to lobbies, lounges, and other public meeting areas may exclude the locus of the truly critical interactions. This bias might be selective, for if an issue suddenly appeared without warning, the public areas might be a more solid sampling base than they would be for issues which had long been anticipated and which could be lobbied in private. That the outside observer must have a broad understanding of the phenomenon and parties he is observing is indicated in Alger's study. He comments on the high level of interaction with the Irish delegate, which was not a reflection of the political power of Ireland, but instead the result of the easy affability of the man. This affability might truly influence the power position of his country, and hence be an important datum in that sense, but it is more likely to confound comparisons if it is used as evidence on a nation.

Barch, Trumbo, and Nangle (1957) used the behavior of automobiles in their observational study of conformity to legal requirements. We are not sure if this is more properly coded under "expressive movement," but the "physical position" category seems more appropriate. They were interested in the degree to which turn-signalling was related to the turn-signalling behavior of a preceding car. For four weeks, they recorded this information:

1. Presence or absence of a turn signal
2. Direction of turn
3. Presence of another motor vehicle 100 feet or less behind the turning motor vehicle when it begins to turn
4. Sex of drivers.

Observers stood near the side of the road and were not easily visible to the motorists. There was the interesting finding that conforming behavior, as defined by signalling or not, varied with the direction of the turn. Moreover, a sex difference was noted. There was a strong positive correlation if model and follower were females, and also a high correlation if left turns were signalled. But on right turns, the correlation was low and positive. Why there is a high correlation for left turns and a low one for right turns is equivocal. The data, like so many simple observational data, don't offer the "why," but simply establish a relationship.

Several of the above findings have been verified and perturbingly elaborated by a finding that signalling is more erratic in bad weather and by drivers of expensive autos (Sechrest, 1965b). Blomgren, Scheuneman, and Wilkins (1963) also used turn signals as a dependent variable in a before-after study of the effect of a signalling safety poster. Exposure to the sign increased signalling about 6 per cent.

OBSERVATION OF LANGUAGE BEHAVIOR: CONVERSATION SAMPLING

Language is a hoary subject for observation, with everything from phonemes to profanity legitimate game. Our interest here is more circumscribed and centers on language samples collected unobtrusively. This means excluding much useful research, Mahl's (1956) study of patients' speech in psychotherapy sessions, for example. The incidence of stuttering, slips of the tongue, and the like is important data, but because the data were collected in a therapist-patient setting, they do not apply here.

We would be curious to read the findings of a nonreactive study which investigated slips of the typewriter as a measure. The employment of these regularly appearing slips somehow evaded Freud (1920) in his major work on the topic. Sechrest (1965b) has demonstrated a higher number of gross errors (skipping lines, poor spacing, and repositioning of hands) when subjects are copying erotic passages than when copying passages from a mineralogy text. Winick (1962) studied some sixty thousand messages written by passers-by on a typewriter outside a New York store, but his analysis centered on coding of content. The data are also amenable to study of spelling errors, spacing, and the like.

We have taken one area of language research, conversational sampling, and traced it historically to illustrate the methodological issues.

Dittmann and Wynne (1961) demonstrate a modern approach. They coded verbal behavior, with the source of language a radio program—the NBC show "Conversation." To study emotional expression, the authors examined "linguistic" phenomena (junctures, stress, pitch) and "paralinguistic" phenomena (voice set, voice quality, and vocalizations of three types). A problem comes from the possibility that a man's awareness of participation in a radio show—particularly the effects of nervousness on speech—could lead to conditions that bias the production of the critical responses.

Kramer (1963) has reviewed the literature on the nonverbal characteristics of speech, concentrating on personal characteristics and emotional correlates. In a later article (1964), he reports a methodological study of techniques to eliminate verbal cues. The three major methods are: a constant ambiguous set of words for various emotional expressions; filtering out the frequencies which permit word recognition; speech in a language unknown to the listener.

More satisfactory is language analysis which draws its samples from speech of subjects unaware of observation. One of the earliest mentions of conversation as a source of psychological data subject to quantification was made by Tarde (1901). Although he performed no studies on conversation himself, Tarde made several suggestions for potential areas of study, such as variation in speed of talking among cultures and categorization of topics by social-class differences.

For the first reported study of conversations, we can look at H. T. Moore's (1922) work on sex differences in conversation—a canny and delightful research that triggered a whole series of hidden-observer language studies.

Moore sought to prove that there was a definite mental differentiation between the sexes, regardless of what previous studies (to 1922) had shown. To test this, he argued for a content analysis of "easy conversation." Especially at the day's end, he held, conversation should provide significant clues to personal interest.

So Moore slowly walked up Broadway from 33rd Street to 55th Street about 7:30 every night for several weeks. He jotted down every bit of audible conversation and eventually collected 174 fragments. Each was coded by the sex of the speaker and by whether the company was mixed or of the same sex. It is not necessary to cite his findings at length, but one should not pass attention: in male to male conversations Moore found 8 per cent in the category "persons of opposite sex"; for female to female conversations, this topic occupied 44 per cent of the language specimens.

Some of the limitations of conversation sampling are obvious. Moore could record only intelligible audible conversation. Speech that is muttered, mumbled, or whispered may contain significantly different content than loud and clear speech. The representative character of the speech samples is further questioned by the representativeness of the speakers. Walkers on Broadway are probably not even a good sample of Manhattan. In short, there is a strong risk of sampling rigidity in both the talkers and the talk.

We can look, chronologically, at the conversation-sampling studies that followed Moore's and note the efforts of other investigators to reduce error due to data-collecting procedure.

Landis and Burtt (1924) published the first study stimulated by Moore's classic. They were sensitive to positional sampling biases and improved upon Moore's procedure by sampling a wider variety of places and situations. With an experimenter who "wore rubber heels and cultivated an unobtrusive manner," they gathered samples of conversation, adding an estimate of the social status of the speaker. The broadened locations included streetcars, campuses, railroad stations, athletic events, parties, department stores, theater and hotel lobbies, restaurants, barber shops, churches, and streets in both commercial and residential areas. After their analysis, Landis and Burtt concluded that the source of the collection was only a minor factor. Landis (1927) broadened the sampling base even further, reporting in an article entitled "National Differences in Conversation." He sampled conversations in Oxford and Regent streets in London and compared these results to the earlier Landis and Burtt (1924) findings from Columbus, Ohio.

The monitoring of telephone conversations was the device by which French, Carter, and Koenig (1930) measured the degree to which the most common words contributed to the total word usage of conversations. This study of the repetitiousness of language was later used as a control for the repetitiousness of speech of schizophrenics and college students (Fairbanks, 1944).

Stoke and West (1931) tried to limit the number of variables in their conversation-sampling study and restricted the sample to undergraduate college students, sampling from random bull sessions held at night in residence halls. The participant observers were 36 college students who worked with a checklist of probable topics and the data and number of people in the conversation. A limitation of this "observe — withdraw — record" approach is that the observer cannot hope to record adequately the duration of responses. The approach is also vulnerable to the criticism that the observers' reports are subject to bias, beyond the initial selective perception one, because of the gap between event and notation.

Moving away from the campus, and more to the Moore approach, Sleeper (1931) sampled conversations in the upper level of Grand Central Terminal in New York, during the rush hour from 5:00 P.M. to 6:30 P.M. Sleeper's procedure reflected the dross-rate problems of such data, as he added a recording variant by excluding all "environmentally stimulated" conversation.

Mabie (1931) and McCarthy (1929) employed free-play periods to sample the conversation of children. The visibility of the recorder is a great problem here, and the studies represent reactive methodology. It may be that, as Mabie claims, the children's awareness of her presence had no effect on their conversation. This is uncertain, and our inclination would be to consider that her presence, notebook in hand, would introduce a strong risk of biasing the character of the overheard statements. When asked by the children what she was doing, Mabie told them that she was writing down what the children liked to do during play periods. That response itself could predispose the children to verbalize evaluative comments more frequently.

Surreptitious observation is the only class which fits into what we would call nonreactive testing. Take the studied surreptitiousness of Henle and Hubble (1938). Students were again the subjects, and

> The investigators took special precautions to keep subjects ignorant of the fact that their remarks were being recorded. To this end, they concealed themselves under beds in students' rooms where tea parties were being held, eavesdropped in dormitory smoking rooms and washrooms, and listened to telephone conversations [p. 230].

Without extending their explanation, Henle and Hubble report that "unwitting subjects were pursued in the streets, in department stores, and in the home."

Escaping from under the bed, Carlson, Cook, and Stromberg (1936) studied sex differences in conversation by monitoring lobby conversations at the intermissions of 13 regular concerts of the Minneapolis Symphony and at six University of Minnesota concerts. The self-selection of subjects may be a serious risk to external validity (Who goes to Minneapolis Symphony concerts and who doesn't?), but the whispering problem is not so great in a research setting like a crowded theater, where a premium is placed on loudness.

The size of the group is a clear influence on the degree to which the experimenter must mask himself. For observing two-person communication, it may well be necessary to hide under a bed. In a large public gathering, the problem of visibility is solved; the individual providing the conversation sample expects to find unfamiliar people close to him, and the experimenter need not hide. Only the recording of the language need be hidden. But it is not as simple as that. Even though the presence of the observer may cause no surprise, the same situation which permits accept-ance of the stranger may also have worked to inhibit a class or classes of verbal behavior. For some experiments this may be unimportant—those in which the difference between public and private utterances is negligible. For other experiments, it may be substantial. This is an empirical question for each experimenter to solve. It must be accepted as one of the possible content limita-tions of conversational sampling.

Watson, Breed, and Posman (1948) displayed their concern about the representativeness of college students by deliberately excluding them from their sample of New York talkers. No campus locations were used, and an attempt was made to eliminate "any-one distinguishable as a college student." Working at all times of day and night, they sampled uptown, midtown, and downtown Manhattan, including the following locales: business, amusement, and residential streets and parks; subways, buses, ferries, taxis, and railroad stations; lobbies of movie houses and hotels; stores, restaurants, bars, night clubs. Each observer recorded verbatim what he had heard as soon as possible after hearing it. The sampling of respondents was resolved as well by Watson, Breed, and Posman as it has been by anyone.

Contrast this with the participant-observation type of ap-proach suggested by Perrine and Wessman (1954). The investiga-tor posed as a stranger to the state, initiated casual conversation with subjects, and then directed conversation to political issues by commenting on recent newspaper headlines and the like. The conversation was recorded as soon as possible after leaving the subject, along with sex, race, location, and estimated age and socioeconomic class. The enormous methodological issue in this type of conversation recording is the 60 to 70 per cent rate of refusal. If nothing else, the eavesdropping approach reduces the problem of self-selection of the sample—at least that bias attrib-utable to willingness to participate in a survey. Not everyone will chip into a conversation with some stranger who wants to talk about state politics. To use such data as the basis of inferring the state of public opinion is dubious.

Doob (1961) writes of a girl in an African market who "was carefully shadowed in the interest of scholarly research." In an approach described by Doob as "unsystematic eavesdropping," he notes:

> She began talking, and listening, before she entered the market's gate. Within a period of ten minutes — the duration of the research — she spoke with more than twenty people: some she greeted perfunctorily, others she talked to for a few moments concerning relatives and friends. No political or cosmic thoughts were aired [p. 144].

Of interest is his point on a possible ethnocentric bias among foreign observers in Africa:

> ... whereas people in the West ... are likely to keep themselves occupied and to avoid long periods of complete solitude or, in contact with others, of silence, it may be that many Africans are perfectly content to be unoccupied except by their own feelings and thoughts and sense of well being [p. 144].

All the studies of conversation reported here have relied on a content analysis of the conversational samples gathered. The essential problems have been the representativeness of the sample collected. The unobserved observer (secreted under a bed or among a crowd), must be sensitive to the limitations of self-selection of subjects, a problem of external validity, and the limitations of the probable partial character of public-conversation samples. Any public conversation may be constrained because of the "danger" of being overheard. Many of the inaudible comments in public are likely to be drawn from a different population of topics than those loudly registered. Moreover, as we noted earlier, the method requires a careful selection of both place- and time-sampling units to increase representativeness, and these controls will not be the same over different geographic locales. Sampling bus conversations in Los Angeles and in Chicago yields a population of very different subjects. Moreover, these data are typically loosely packed, and it takes a substantial investment in time and labor to produce a large enough residual pool of relevant data. For all these limitations, however, there are research problems for which private commentary is not a significant worry, for which the adroit selection of locales and times can circumvent selective population characteristics, and for which the issue is of sufficient currency in the public mind to reduce the dross rate. For these situations, conversational sampling is a sensitive and faithful source of information.

TIME DURATION

The amount of attention paid by a person to an object has long been the source of inferences on interest. For research on infrahuman species, notoriously incompetent at filling out interest questionnaires, visual fixation has been a popular research variable, as in the recent work of Berkson and Fitz-Gerald (1963) on the effect of introducing novel stimuli into the visual world of infant chimps. With humans who can fill out questionnaires, time-duration measures have been less popular, but are not uncommon. Frequently, a duration variable is imbedded in a body of other measures. H. T. Moore (1917) measured anger, fear, and sex interests by giving a subject multiplication tasks and then exposing him to distraction of different types. The time taken to complete the tasks was the measure of interest: the longer the time, the greater the interest in the distracting content.

In a study of museum visitors, Melton (1935) hypothesized a positive relationship between the degree of interest shown by a visitor in the exhibits and the number and quality of the permanent educational results of the museum visit. Melton was very careful to study response-set biases and situational cues which would contaminate his measure of the duration of observed time spent in viewing an exhibit. He demonstrated the "right-turn" bias, and experimented with changing the number of exits and installing directional arrows — all elements which significantly affected the length of a visit.

In one finding, for example, he reports that the closer an exhibit is to an exit, the less time will be spent at it. He posits an "exit gradient." Going further, he talks of the number of paintings in a gallery, the proportion of applied or fine arts in the room, and comes up with findings on "museum satiation." As the number of paintings in a gallery increase, the average total time in the gallery also increases, the total number of paintings visited increases, *and* the time per painting visited does not decrease but increases. Melton's attention to these cues provides a model seldom followed in observational research.

Washburne (1928) reported on an experiment conducted in the Russian school system which conceivably could have used time for a measure. Each child in the school was given his own garden plot, and at the same time had joint responsibility for a common garden tended by all the children. It is reported that records were kept to show the relative amount of interest that each child had in the two types of work. Although no mention is made of the measure used to determine amount of interest, time might be an appropriate one. Because it can be assumed that for equal care a greater amount of time would have to be spent on the individual garden, adjustments would have to be made in comparing the times for the two gardens.

A number of theoretical variables may be linked to time duration and time perception. Cortes (cited in McClelland, 1961, p. 327) has shown that a significantly larger number of high-need achievers have watches that are fast than do low-need achievers. Do the high achievers also perceive time duration differentially?

The lack of general emphasis on time-duration methods is partly due to difficulty of measurement. For accurate observation, the hurly-burly conditions of a natural setting are damaging; the laboratory control over instrumentation is almost necessary if precise observations of small time units are to be reached.

Sometimes this can be circumvented by a measure in which time is scaled in grosser units than microseconds. Jacques (1956) defined "responsibility" by measuring how long a worker is allowed to commit the resources of his task without direct supervision. Observation yields "a time span of responsibility" and a descriptive measure of the worker. For a duration measure like this, it would be foolish to calibrate the measurement in seconds. Many researches demand ultrafine discrimination of time, and for them, natural observation is an awkward method. But where the unit is broader, observation in the natural setting becomes both feasible and desirable. Sometimes it is enough to say, "Professor X's interest in cutaneous sensation extended over a career of 38 years."

TIME SAMPLING AND OBSERVATION

For the permanent physical clues of observation—the scars, tattoos, and houses owned—the timing of when an observation is made may be relatively unimportant. It may be possible to conjure up conditions in which a tattoo may be so placed that it is differentially visible at various points in a day (with or without jacket, for example), but for the most part, the exterior signs are quite invulnerable to time-linked variance.

Many of the other simple observation materials — expressive movement, physical location, and language — are, however, subject to the objection that the critical behavior is variable over a day or some longer time period. The risk, or course, is that the timing of the data collection may be such that a selective population periodically appears before the observer, while another population, equally periodically, engages in the same behavior, but comes along only when the observer is absent. Similarly, the individual's behavior may shift as the hours or days of the week change. The best defense against this source of invalidity is to sample time units randomly.

Working in an industrial setting, Shepard and Blake (1962) observed employees and judged whether they were working or not. By a time-sampling design, they found a strong decline in percentage of workers working between 10:30 and 11:00 — the time of a daily supervisors' meeting which drew them away from direct control over employees.

> Hence, the composition of supervisors' meetings was changed so as to ensure continuous supervision in the shop . . . thus the managers are correct in their . . . conclusion that more consistent control and direction are needed to correct for their tendency to be irresponsible [pp. 88-89].

The technique has been extensively used in nursery settings, where there is a particular need for it because of the greater periodicity of behavior of infants and young children. Arrington (1943) has pointed out many of the factors which must be considered in assessing the results of time sampling recorded by the observer. The duration of the individual time sample must be chosen in accordance with behavior to be observed. Degree of sophistication, familiarity with the observer, previous experience in being observed, type of situation, and number of individuals in the situation are also thought to be factors contributing to "observation consciousness."

One of the important time-sampling studies of observation in a nursery setting was conducted by Thomas (1929). In recording the activities of the children, Thomas made use of a mapped floor plan and plotted movement against the plan. Olson (1929) used similar procedures, but concentrated on oral habits rather than movement patterns.

Barker and Wright (1951; 1954) have adopted an opposite strategy to time sampling. They sought to avoid the problem of selected behavior over time by a saturation method. Rather than sample behavior, they censused it. In their 1951 study, observations were made of one child for an entire day, with minute-by-minute notations. Eight observers were used in turn, each being wholly familiar with the child. For any child under ten, the authors feel the effects of observation are negligible. This may be subject to doubt, however, particularly in view of recorded statements detailing interaction between the observer and the child.

This strategy does solve a problem, but it provides other ones. It is practical for only relatively short periods of time (Imagine following a boy for a year!), and the method is predisposed to measurement of individuals, not groups. This latter point may be important for the probability of reactive effects creeping in, for, as we noted above, the size of the group may be an important factor in the degree of observation consciousness. A person tailing you about all day is quite different from one next to you in a theater lobby.

Yet these limitations are no more punishing than the limitations of other approaches, and the subtlety of links between behaviors can hardly be better described.[3] Either way, sampling or censusing, a measure of control is added over a usually uncontrolled variable.

[3]Edmond de Goncourt wrote of the goal of the *Goncourt Journal:* "What we have tried to do, then, is to bring our contemporaries to life for posterity in a speaking likeness, by means of the vivid stenography of a conversation, the physiological spontaneity of a gesture, those little signs of emotion that reveal a personality, those *imponderabilia* that render the intensity of existence, and, last of all, a touch of that fever which is the mark of the heady life of Paris" (p. xi). From *The Goncourt Journals: 1851-1870*, Edmond and Jules de Goncourt, translated by Lewis Galantiere. Copyright 1937 by Doubleday & Company, Inc. Reprinted by permission of the publisher.

OVER-ALL COMMENTS ON
SIMPLE OBSERVATION

The emphasis of this chapter has been on research in which
the observer is unobserved, and in settings where the investigator
has had no part in structuring the situation. The secretive nature of
the observer, whether hidden in a crowd or miles away before a
television screen, protects the research from some of the reactive
validity threats. The subject is not aware of being tested, there is
thereby no concomitant role-playing associated with awareness,
the measurement does not work as an agent of change, and the
interviewer (observer) effects are not an issue.

Moreover, there is the great gain that comes from getting the
data at first hand. In studies of archival records and in the
examination of trace and erosion evidence, there is always the
uncertainty that others who came between the data and the investigator, processing or pawing it, left their own indistinguishable
marks.

The first-hand collection of the data, usually of a contemporaneous event, also allows the gathering of other information to
reduce alternative hypotheses. One may note characteristics of the
subjects which permit a testing of rival hypotheses about the
selective composition of the sample. To be sure, these are mostly
limited to visual cues, but they can be extremely helpful. Similarly, the ability to observe the subjects in the act permits one to
designate the individual actors, either for follow-up observation, or
for study with other instruments like the questionnaire or interview.
Such follow-up of individuals is difficult or impossible with archival
and trace measures.

It would be difficult to overestimate the value of this potential
for follow-up. One of the singular gains of simple observation is
that it is a procedure which allows opportunistic sampling of
important phenomena. Because it is often opportunistic, there is
the attendant risk that the population under observation is an
atypical group, one unworthy to produce generalizations. The
follow-up studies may protect against this risk, as can adroit use of
locational and time sampling.

Against this impressive list of gains must be balanced some
possible sources of loss. Prime among these is the danger that the

data-gathering instrument, the human observer, will be variable over the course of his observations. He may become less conscientious as boredom sets in, or he may become more attentive as he learns the task and becomes involved with it. If there are any ambiguities about how the behavior is to be coded, the effect of time may be to reduce the variation of coding (increase intra-observer reliability) as he works out operating definitions of which behaviors go with which codes. All of these can work to produce spurious differences in comparisons.

Errors of the observer, however, are not random, but show systematic biases that can be predicted, and hence corrected for, from the observer's expectations of the experimental or field situation. Campbell (1959) has inventoried 21 systematic sources of error that apply to the human observer.

That this may apply to the principal investigator, as well as his aides, has been demonstrated by Rosenthal's (1963) "On the Social Psychology of the Psychological Experiment." The implication of these studies is the demand for a greater emphasis on the necessity for saturated training of observers, hopefully under a "blind" condition in which they do not know what a "good" result or behavior will be.

The one other significant issue under the label of reactive threats comes from response sets on those observed. To a large measure, these are knowable—either through application of research conducted in other settings, or through direct observation of behavior under different conditions. Hopefully, there will be enough variation in the settings available for sampling to examine whether any systematic response sets are at work, and whether these can be isolated from other possible sources of variance. This is awkward when one is not actively manipulating the environment, and becomes one of the strong arguments for the unobserved observer to alter the research environment surreptitiously and systematically in an undetectable way.

The populations available for observation fluctuate according to both time and location. Thus, some caution should be employed in generalizing from research which gathered observations at one time in one place. If generalizations about the subject matter of conversations are to all people, and content varies by age, then the "place" should be considered as a sampling universe including varying locations which are likely to draw on different populations. When the concern is generalized to more limited settings, say, a study of the effect of different treatment conditions in prisons, then the place sample should be more than one prison for each condition hypothesized to have an effect.

It is not always possible to draw elaborate locational samples, but that should not deter observational research. If the setting is circumscribed by practical conditions, a proper defense is to employ time-sampling methods. Limited to a population of "tour" visitors to a mental hospital, one must bear the cross of a self-selected population unlikely to be representative of much. Imposing a time-sampling design, observing different groups who come on different days or in different months, for example, would markedly improve the solidity of a shaky base.

Both time and locational sampling should be employed if possible, for empirical research and introspection suggest that population variation is a substantial issue in observation. An added gain is that the investigator can also vary his observers over the sampling units and randomly assign them to different times and locations, thus adding a badly needed control. Not all research possibilities afford this chance, but it is a goal to be reached for.

McCarroll and Haddon (1961) took care to ensure that location and time factors would not affect their study of the differences between fatally injured drivers in automobile accidents and noninvolved drivers. At each accident site, a team consisting of the authors, medical students, and from one to eight police stopped noninvolved cars proceeding in the same direction as the accident car on the same day of the week and at the same time of the day.

The same time- and locational-sampling strategy will also help to counteract some of the risks in selective content. The population varies over place and time, and the content of their behavior similarly varies. If one can broaden the sampling base, he can expand the character of material available for study. It is not possible to know all about college students if observations are limited to afternoons in the fall; when these observations fall on Saturday, worse yet.

But all the finesse of the skillful investigator will not solve some content limitations. Much of behavior is precluded from public display and is available only through unethical action, elaborate instrumentation, or some titanic combination of both. This is potentially a variable problem across cultures, as one notes members of certain societies willing to display classes of behavior that are hidden or taboo in others. Cross-cultural observational studies are thereby threatened not only by the ethnocentric attribution of meaning, but also by the lack of equivalence in observable behavior across societies. As one increases the number of societies, of course, the probability is greater that an incomplete set of observations of public behavior will be available over all.

Finally, being on the scene often means a necessary exposure to a large body of irrelevant information. Because one cannot often predict when a critical event will be produced, it is necessary to wait around, observe, and complain about the high dross rate of such a procedure. The payoff is often high, as in the case of one patient observer who knew critical signs and was immortalized in the song, "My Lover Was a Logger." The waitress sings,

> I can tell that you're a logger,
> And not just a common bum,
> 'Cause nobody but a logger
> Stirs his coffee with his thumb.

CHAPTER 6

Contrived Observation: Hidden Hardware and Control

This chapter discusses the investigator's intervention into the observational setting. In simple observational studies, research is often handicapped by the weaknesses of the human observer, by the unavailability of certain content, and by a cluster of variables over which the investigator has no control. To reduce these threats, a number of workers have elected to vary the setting actively or to substitute hardware devices for human record-keeping observers. We avoid here examples of the "speak clearly into the microphone, please" approach. The emphasis is on those investigations in which the scientist's intervention is not detectable by the subject and the naturalness of the situation is not violated.

HARDWARE: AVOIDING HUMAN INSTRUMENT ERROR

When the human observer is the recording agent, all the fallibilities of the organism operate to introduce extraneous variance into the data. People are low-fidelity observational instruments. We have already noted how recording and interpretation may be erratic over time, as the observer learns and responds to the research phenomena he observes.

The fluctuations of this instrument can be brought under some degree of control by random assignment of observers to locations and time units. Random assignment will not, however, create a capacity in the organism which is not there, nor eliminate response sets characteristic of all members of the society or subcultures from which the observers are drawn.

142

Osgood (1953) illustrates the capacity weakness of the human observer in his comments on studies of language behavior in the first four or five months of a human's life: ". . . from the total splurge of sounds made by an actively vocal infant, only the small sample that happens to strike the observer is recorded at all" (p. 684).

Not all observable behavior is so complex or so rapid, but there is enough to cause the consideration of a substitute mechanism for the observer. It might not be so bad if there were a random loss of material when the observer's perceptual system got overloaded. Unhappily, the nature of the material noted and not noted is likely to be a function of both the individual's idiosyncracies and the systematic response sets learned in a given society. Again speaking of speech studies of early childhood, Osgood comments,

> The inadequate recording methods employed in most of the early studies make the data of dubious validity. The typical procedure was merely to listen to the spontaneous vocalizations of an infant and write down what was heard. The selective factor of auditory perception — listeners "hear" most readily those sounds that correspond to the phonemes of their own language — was not considered [p. 684].

These same biases are at work with the recording of any language system that is unfamiliar to the observer — whether it be the occult language of a child, or the unfamiliar tones of a foreign language. Webb (in preparation) has noted this in his study of orthographies in African languages. His analysis was based on written records of the languages, many of which had been produced by missionaries, explorers, and other foreign nationals who came to Africa and learned the indigenous speech. In transcribing the sounds of these languages for others, there were selective approximations of the true sound, influenced by the tonal pattern of the characters in the observer's native language. Thus, German observers heard umlauts that evaded the British. There is some possibility of control over this particular bias, since for some of the languages there are written transcriptions of the same words by nationals of various countries; these can be matched against the known tonal characteristics of the European languages to correct for the selective hearing. When multi-national observations are missing, the task is much more difficult, and one must make inferences about the effect of perceptual biases based on the sound characteristics of the observer's native language.

A major gain from hardware recording, of course, is the permanence of this complete record. It is not subject to selective decay and can provide the stuff of reliability checks. Further, the same content can be the base for new hypothesis-testing not considered at the time the data were collected. Or material that was originally viewed as dross may become prime ore. For example, Bryan employs taped interviews in his study of call girls. Among other things, these are coded for the frequency of telephone calls received during the period of the interview. Such information serves as a partial check on the girl's self-report of business activity (Bryan, 1965).

Hardware, of varying degrees of flexibility, has been used throughout the history of scientific observation. To reduce the risk of forgetting, if nothing else, permanent records were made of observed behavior. They may have noted less than the total behavior, but they did serve to reduce reliance on human memory. Boring (1961) writes of Galton, "an indefatigable measurer."

> He used to carry a paper cross and a little needle point, arranged so that he could punch holes in the paper to keep count of whatever he was at that time observing. A hole at the head of the cross meant *greater*, on the arm *equal*, and on the bottom, *less* [p. 154].

Galton also contributed to that voluntary, self-descriptive reactive measure, the questionnaire, whose overuse William James anticipated: "Messrs. Darwin and Galton have set the example of circulars of questions sent out by the hundreds to those supposed able to reply. The custom has spread, and it will be well for us in the next generation if such circulars be not ranked among the common pests of life" (James, 1890, p. 194).

Evolving from such simple recording methods was the constriction of communication developed for work in small-group research in laboratory settings. Artificially, the participants were (or are) required to limit all communications to written notes, which are then saved by the investigator to provide a full record of all communication among participants. This is a very low-cost device, much cheaper than tape recording, but its stilted quality suggests a very high risk price for a very low dollar cost.

Other aids to the observer are pieces of apparatus which allow him to record his observations more quickly or more thoroughly. Sometimes the gain comes from forcing the observer into using a series of varied codes, sometimes it is just the gain of having a more permanent record of his perceptions of the behavior under study. Steiner and Field (1960), for example, timed vocal contributions to a group discussion by means of a polygraph, and a popular supplementary device has been the Interaction Chronograph, a recent use of which is reported in Chapple (1962).

A big boom exists, and properly, for audio tape recorders. With the development of superior omnidirectional and highly directional microphones, many of the former mechanical limitations have been resolved. The tape becomes the first source of data, and it is often considered the initial input into a hardware system. Thus, Andrew (1963) took tapes of sound patterns from primates (including man) and fed them into a spectograph for more detailed analyses.

Similarly, Heusler, Ulett, and their associates (Heusler, Ulett, and Blasques, 1959; Callahan et al., 1960; Heusler, Ulett, and Callahan, 1960; Ulett et al., 1961; Ulett, Heusler, and Callahan, 1961) developed what they termed a noise-level index for hospital wards. Their substantive concern was measuring the effects on drugs on hospital patients, and they planted tape recorders to pick up ward noises. These sounds are meshed in an integrator which provides a numerical total of the activity. Originally, this noise level had been rated by judges; in later work, however, the authors used a direct index of noise level, thus reducing biases, among them the possible confounding due to a judge's recognition of a patient's voice.

A highly opportunistic use of audiotapes was demonstrated by Matarazzo and his associates (Matarazzo et al., 1964) in their study of speech duration. The National Aeronautics and Space Administration made available to these investigators the audiotapes of conversations between astronauts and ground communicators for two orbital flights. From these tapes and the published transcripts of the communications (NASA Manned Spacecraft Center, 1962a; NASA Manned Spacecraft Center, 1962b) they coded the duration of each unit of speech by means of an Interaction Chronograph. These data provided a test of propositions developed in the experimental laboratories and previously reported (Matarazzo, 1962b; Matarazzo *et al.*, 1963). In space, as in the laboratory, the length of a response is positively correlated with the length of a question. It could hardly be claimed that the astronauts were thinking of Matarazzo's hypotheses at the time they were steering their craft, and the astronaut findings supported the work of the laboratory. This highly imaginative research dipped into archives that were available, archives known not to suffer from intermediary distortions.

The fidelity and breadth of content of the audiotapes give them an edge over written records for archival analysis. Not only are they uncontaminated by other hands, but they contain more pertinent material physically unavailable on the written record. Matarazzo, for example, could not have conducted so accurate a study had he been limited to transcripts alone. Interested in duration of speech, where the natural unit is a second of time, he would have had to make estimates of duration from word counts, which are pockmarked with substantial individual response-set errors in rate of speech, different levels of noncontent interjections (um-mm's), and the like.

There is a weighty mass of research material almost untouched by social scientists, although known and used by historians. It is found in the oral archives of the national radio and television networks, which have kept disc, film and tape recordings of radio and television shows over the years. The recent advent of video tape recordings has provided another dimension to these archives.

Videotapes are being used in some experimental research to validate the results of paper-and-pencil tests. A student of the effectiveness of television commercials has run some preliminary checks on an advertising exposure test. He called friends and asked them to send their secretaries to his office on the pretext of picking up a package. After arriving, the secretary was asked to wait in a reception room which contained newspapers, magazines, and a turned-on television set. A hidden television camera monitored her behavior as she turned to the printed material, watched television, or just sat. She left, unsuspecting, and was subsequently interviewed by standard questionnaire methods to determine her exposure to television commercials and magazines and newspapers. This is a more advanced variation of the obvious one-way mirror setting and provides a medium for a good check on observation and self-report data.

For some reason, still photography has never had much of a vogue as research hardware. Boring (1953) mentions that "Voliva supported his theory of the flat earth by a photograph of twelve miles of the shore line of Lake Winnebago: you could see, he argued, that the shore is horizontal and bowed."[1] Both still and movie films have been used in the study of eye behavior — direction, duration of looking, pupil dilation, and the like.

The physical *location* of eyes was used by Politz (1959) in a study of commercial exposure of advertising posters placed on the outside of buses. Politz' equipment was movie cameras placed in buses and automatically activated in a series of short bursts spread throughout a day. The camera was faced outward, over the poster under study, and, in a switch on the Bunker Hill advice, a person whose two eyes could be seen in the developed film was classified as "in" the advertising audience. This design, which used a random sample of both locations and time, is exemplary for its control of a large number of extraneous variables that could jeopardize external validity. The visibility of the camera raises a question. It occupied a bus seat, and there is the probability that it attracted some attention. That is, the eyes counted as looking at the poster were looking at the camera instead. This should result in an overestimate of the size of the bus-poster advertising audience. If one could assume that the novelty of the camera would wear off over time, one could test the hypothesis by making a longitudinal analysis of the material. If the test materials were controlled for novelty and extinction themselves, the estimated audience level should decline over the time period if a significant number of people were viewing the camera and not the poster.

Walters, Bowen, and Parke (1963) recorded the eye movements of male undergraduates viewing a series of pictures of nude or almost nude males and females. The men were told that a moving spot of light on the film indicated the eye movements of a previous subject. For about half the subjects, the light roved over

[1]In the same article, Professor Boring comments on changes in the human observer as an instrument. "I remember how a professor of genetics many years ago showed me published drawings of cell nuclei dated both before and after the discovery and description of chromosomes. Chromosomes kept showing up in the later drawings, not in the earlier" (p. 176).

the bodies portrayed in the film, while with the other half, the
light centered on the background of the pictures. The eye movement of the subjects was influenced, and

> Subjects who had been exposed to a supposedly sexually
> uninhibited model spent a significantly longer time looking at
> the nude and semi-nude bodies, and significantly less time
> looking at the background of the pictures [Walters, Bowen, and
> Parke, 1963, p. 77].

Another investigation showed that the presence of a female inhibited the interest of male students in "sexy" magazines. The
magazines were avoided with a woman present, but upon her
leaving, they were quickly retrieved (Sechrest, 1965b).

Zamansky (1956; 1959) used "time looking" at different types
of photos in his studies of homosexuality and paranoid delusions.
Exline (1963; 1964) and Exline and Winters (1964) worked behind
one-way mirrors to make controlled observations of mutual
glances, time spent looking at someone while speaking to him,
time spent looking when being spoken to, and the like.

Then, of course, there are the apparatus studies of pupil dilation. Gump (1962) reports that Chinese jade dealers were sensitive
to this variable and determined a potential buyer's interest in various stones by observing the dilation of his pupils as pieces were
shown (astute buyers countered this by wearing dark glasses).

Hess and Polt (1960) measured pupil dilation on 16-millimeter
film and related it to stimulus materials. The stimulus objects were
a series of pictures — a baby, a mother holding a child, a partially
nude woman, a partially nude man, and a landscape. The six
pictures elicited clear-cut differences in pupil size, and sex differences were present.

Commercial applications of this method have been based on
work under the direction of Hess. See Foote (1962); West (1962);
Anonymous (1964b); Krugman (1964).

The pupil-dilation studies have all been conducted in potentially reactive settings. Whether or not such a measure could be
employed without the subject's awareness is questionable. There
are technical difficulties with laboratory apparatus as is, and
resolving field-use problems might be too much to expect.

But certainly the eye-direction and duration-of-looking measures are amenable to naturalistic use. If Politz (1959) was able to

solve the technical problems of a jiggling bus, more stable situations should present little difficulty. Many of our laboratory experiences could be replicated in natural settings. Landis and Hunt's (1939) method of studying movement responses could easily be applied in nonlaboratory settings. Shooting off a gun, the authors filmed the subject's gestural response pattern, which included such movements as drawing the shoulders forward, contracting the abdomen, and bending the knees. Facial patterns included closing the eyes and widening the mouth. It will be remembered that Krout found that a gesture of placing the hand to the nose was correlated with fear. With the stimulus of an unexpected gunshot, the immediate response may be independent of any contaminants due to the experimental setting.

HARDWARE:
PHYSICAL SUPPLANTING OF THE OBSERVER

The hardware measures mentioned so far have been mainly concerned with reducing the risk associated with the human observer's fallibility as a measuring instrument — his selective perceptions and his lack of capacity to note all elements in a complex set of behaviors. Another use to which hardware has been put is to obtain research entrée into situations which are excluded by the usual simple observational method. Some of these content areas have been unattainable because of the privacy of the behavior, others because of the prohibitive costs of maintaining observational scrutiny over a substantial enough sample of time. Sitting in for the observer, hardware can help resolve both problems.[2]

[2]Galton, writing from Africa, sent the following letter to his brother: "I have seen figures that would drive the females of our native land desperate — figures that could afford to scoff at crinoline, nay more, as a scientific man and as a lover of the beautiful I have dexterously even without the knowledge of the parties concerned, resorted to actual measurement. Had I been a proficient in the language, I should have advanced, and bowed and smiled like Goldney, I should have explained the dress of the ladies of our country, I should have said that the earth was ransacked for iron to afford steel springs, that the seas were fished with consummate daring to obtain whalebone, that far distant lands were overrun to possess ourselves of caoutchou — that these three products were ingeniously wrought by competing artists, to the utmost perfection, that their handiwork was displayed in every street

"Blind bugging" via audiotapes is one such approach—a controversial one when applied in certain settings, and illegal in many. Jury deliberations are not observable because of standard legal restraints, but Strodtbeck and his colleagues (Strodtbeck & James, 1955; Strodtbeck & Mann, 1956; Strodtbeck, James, & Hawkins, 1957) received the approval of the court and counsel from both sides to place hidden microphones in the jury room. The use of concealed recording devices presents ethical questions that have been underlined by Amrine and Sanford (1956), Burchard (1957), and Shils (1959).

We may add as an aside that among the most astute devices for concealed recording is a microphone rigged in a mock hearing aid. It works extremely well in inducing the subject to lean over and shout directly into the recording apparatus. The presence of a dangling cord does not inhibit response.

The "cocktail-party effect" is an acoustical term for the process of listening to one among a multitude of talkers. First suggested by Pollack and Pickett (1957) and expanded by MacLean (1959), it was used by Legget and Northwood (1960) in conducting experiments at eight gatherings, relating recorded sound level to number of people attending and drawing on records for total consumption of food and drink. The experimenters found that the nature of the beverage served made no significant difference in the buildup of sound levels, that all-male gatherings were slightly quieter than mixed gatherings, and that the maximum sound levels were 80 to 85 decibels, ". . . not quite high enough to cause permanent impairment of hearing" (Legget & Northwood, 1960, p. 18). See also Hardy (1959) and Carhart (1965).

Riesman and Watson (1964) met with failure in their attempts to record party conversations on tape

---

corner and advertised in every periodical but that on the other hand, that great as is European skill, yet it was nothing before the handiwork of a bounteous nature. Here I should have blushed bowed and smiled again, handed the tape and requested them to make themselves the necessary measurement as I stood by and registered the inches or rather yards. This however I could not do—there were none but Missionaries near to interpret for me, they would never have entered into my feelings and therefore to them I did not apply—but I sat at a distance with my sextant, and as the ladies turned themselves about, as women always do, to be admired, I surveyed them in every way and subsequently measured the distance of the spot where they stood—worked out and tabulated the results at my leisure" (Pearson, 1914, p. 232).

. . . losses of comments lasting over one minute occurred at the
rate of about seven times per recorded hour . . . the critical
objection lay . . . in the tape's sometimes useful lack of selectivity: the record was a long-drawn-out tissue of inanities in
which the very diffuseness made analysis more difficult than
when one was dealing with the more condensed material of
recollection [p. 299].

Which are the "better" data—the true conversation or the
"condensed material of recollection"—is up to the investigator to
decide. The loss of content, however, is a severe limiting condition,
demonstrating the selective utility of some hardware. In this case,
the recorder would be adequate for recording sound level, but
inadequate for providing a complete record of conversations.

Many pieces of hardware have been developed for measuring
the level of physical activity, a variable that has been viewed as
symptomatic of many things. Perhaps the earliest mention of this
type of measure was made by Galton (1884), who was at that time
interested in the physical equivalents of metaphorical language.
He took as his example the "inclination of one person toward
another." This situation is clearly seen when two people are sitting
next to each other at a dinner table, according to Galton. To
demonstrate this empirically in quantitative terms (Galton, 1884;
Watson, 1959), he suggested a pressure gauge with an index and
dial to indicate changes in stress arranged on the legs of the chair
on the side nearest the other person. Galton specified three
necessary conditions for this type of experiment: the apparatus
must be effective; it must not attract notice; and it must be capable
of being applied to ordinary furniture. All of these criteria are
appropriate for contemporary apparatus studies.

It is obvious that such a device may be a substitute for human
observers when their presence might contaminate the situation,
and where no convenient hidden observation site is available.
Indeed, many of the studies discussed earlier as "simple observation" are amenable to mechanization, provided Galton's criteria
can be met.

There is F. Scott Fitzgerald's fictional account in *The Last
Tycoon*, of how the title character, a movie executive, evaluated
the quality of rushes (preliminary, unedited film "takes") by
observing how much they made him wiggle in his chair. The more
the wiggles, the poorer the movie scenes. Simple observational

measures could be made of twistings by a concealed observer, but they would clearly be inferior to a more mechanical device.

Galton (1885) suggested a fidget measure based on the amount of body sway among an audience. The greater the sway, the greater the boredom. "Let this suggest to observant philosophers, when the meeting they attend may prove dull, to occupy themselves in estimating the frequency, amplitude and duration of the fidgets of their fellow sufferers" (p. 175). The American playwright Robert Ardrey notes coughing as an audience response to boredom.

> One cougher begins his horrid work in an audience, and the cough spreads until the house is in bedlam, the actors in rage, and the playwright in retreat to the nearest saloon. Yet let the action take a turn for the better, let the play tighten up, and that same audience will sit in a silence unpunctuated by a single tortured throat [p. 85].[3]

A mechanical device has been employed by Kretsinger (1952; 1959). He used what he terms an electromagnetic movement meter to study gross bodily movement in theater audiences—a very difficult observational setting because of inadequate illumination. (See also Lyle, 1953.) Kretsinger claims that this method was "objective, essentially linear, and completely removed from the subject's awareness." The technique

> ... was based upon a capacity operated electronic system often used in burglar alarm applications. As modified by the author, it consisted of an oscillator detector, a D.C. amplifier, and an Esterline-Angus ink writing recorder. A concealed copper screen was located near the head of the S watching the film. As the S moved, the effective capacity of the oscillator circuit varied, changing the frequency of its oscillation. This frequency shift was converted to a change in D.C. voltage amplified sufficiently to drive an ink pen on a moving paper chart ... completely removed from the S's awareness [Kretsinger, 1959, p. 74].

The importance of heeding population characteristics is borne out by his conclusion, "There was some evidence that the presence of girls had a disquieting effect upon the boys ... " (p. 77).

Cox and Marley (1959) devised another movement measure in

---

[3]From *African Genesis*, by Robert Ardrey. Copyright©1961 by Literat S.A. Reprinted by permission of Atheneum Publishers.

their study of the restlessness of patients as a partial measure of the effect of various drugs. Their rather complex apparatus consists basically of a series of pulleys and springs, set under the springs of the bed, which record the displacement of the mattress. When the patient is perfectly motionless, the relay system does not operate, but the slightest movement will be recorded. A more simple device is possible with baby cribs: the activity level of the child is measured by shaving down one of the four crib legs and attaching a meter which records the frequency of jiggling. This is much less fine a measure than that of Cox and Marley, for the child could move without activating the meter. For studies which don't require such fine calibration, however, the simplicity of the device is appealing.

As beds, cribs, and chairs can be wired, so, too, can desks. Foshee (1958) worked on the hypothesis that a greater general drive state would manifest itself in greater activity. Here is a good theoretical proposition testable by a device appropriate for natural settings away from the laboratory. To measure activity, Foshee used a schoolroom desk which was supported at each corner by rubber stoppers. Attached to the platform which supported the desk was a mechanical level arrangement which amplified the longitudinal movements of the platform. Through an elaborate transmission system, the amplitude and frequency of the subject's movement could be measured. Foshee does not mention whether the subjects (in this case a group of mental defectives) were aware of the apparatus or not, but it would seem likely that the device could be constructed to evade detection.

To reach into the difficult setting of a darkened movie house for the study of expressive movement, several investigators have employed infrared photography (Siersted & Hansen, 1951; Bloch, 1952; Field, 1954; Greenhill, 1955; Gabriele, 1956). This type of filming eliminates almost entirely the element of subject awareness of the observational apparatus. It is clearly superior to unaided observation because of the advantage of working in the dark; the brighter the light in which to see the subject, the brighter the light for him to see you. This is illustrated in Leroy-Boussion's (1954) visible-observer study of emotional expressions of children during a comedy film. Although Leroy-Boussion claimed to be only a projection aide during the film, she did have to eliminate certain subjects who "seemed to be aware" of her presence as an observer. It would thus seem likely that there were other subjects who did not make their awareness known to the investigator. Putting aside the question of reducing the sample size, the more important issue is whether those who were aware (and discarded as subjects) were a selective group (the more suspicious or paranoid, for example). Infrared photography drastically reduces such selective loss. Further, it is possible to match the infrared camera with the regular projection machine so that in subsequent analysis the photographs of audience reaction can be matched easily to the specific film sequence.

The danger of relying solely on interview or questionnaire self-reports is sharply illustrated in the Siersted and Hansen (1951) study. They supplemented their filming by interviewing the children who had seen the film. There were marked differences between these interview responses and both the filmed reactions and verbal comments made during the film (recorded with hidden tape recorders).

For some reason, the French have been leaders in research on movie hardware. Toulouse and Mourgue (1948) worked with respiratory reactions in order to index reactions to films, and it has even been suggested that the temperature of the room in which a film is viewed might be monitored as an indicator.

The estimation of attendance at an event or an institution can be carried out by planting observers who count heads. Another way is to mechanize and count circuit breaks. The "electric eye," particularly when supplemented by a time recorder, provides a useful record of frequency of attendance and its pacing. The photoelectric cells are typically set up on either side of a doorway so that any break of the current will register a mark on an attached recording device. As Trueswell (1963) shrewdly pointed out, however, this apparatus is not free from mechanical or reactivity contaminants. Particularly when the device is first installed, it is common for people to step back and forth through the light or to wave arms and legs, thus registering three or four marks for a single entry. Another difficulty is the placement of the cells. If they are set too low, it is possible for each leg to register a separate mark as the person walks through. If the doorway is wide enough to admit two people, a couple may walk together and register only one mark. It is important to note that these are not random errors which balance out, but are constant for the method. Because of this, it is equally important that human observers be there with the mechanical device, particularly in its early period of installation, to study whether any such errors are admitted to the data.

Ellis and Pryer (1959) have demonstrated the complexities possible with photoelectric cells in their study of the movements of children with severe neuropathology. Their apparatus consisted of a square plywood enclosure in which the children played. Electronic devices were located on the outside surface of the walls and arranged so that the beams crisscrossed the enclosure at two-foot intervals. Interruption of a beam would be recorded, with each beam recorded separately.

With the light beams visible, the behavior of subjects may be modified—either because they dart back and forth in a playful game with the beam, or because it inhibits their movement to know that they are under observation. Ellis and Pryer suggest modifications of their technique to avoid such risks, among them installing infrared exciter lamps, noiseless relays, and soundproofing.

As a final example of the use of hardware to get otherwise difficult content, there is Weir's (1963) report of her audiotape recordings of a two-and-a-half-year-old boy falling to sleep. The child practices language, working with noun substitution and articulation. In the evening of the day when he was first offered raspberries, he says, "berries, *not* bayreez, berries." Maccoby (1964), who summarized the study, states: "These observations provide insight into language learning processes which are ordinarily covert and not accessible to observation" (p. 211).

THE INTERVENING OBSERVER

Most of the observation studies reported so far have been ones in which the observer is passive. He may take the behavior as it comes, or he may introduce mechanization to improve the accuracy and span of his observations, but he has not typically altered the cues in the environment to which the person or group is responding. This passivity has two costs. It is possible that the behavior under study occurs so infrequently that an inordinate amount of effort is expended on gathering large masses of data, only a small segment of which is useful. Or, paying the second cost, the naturally occurring behavior is not stimulated by events of sufficient discriminability. The investigator may want four or five levels of intensity of a condition, say, when the convenient simple observation approach can produce only two.

Rather than pay these costs, many investigators have actively stepped into the research environment and "forced" the data in a way that did not attract attention to the method. In some cases, this has meant grading experimental conditions over equivalent groups, with each group getting a different "natural" treatment. In a smaller number of studies, the conditions have been varied over the individual. Both classes are illustrated in this section.

Allen Funt of the television show "Candid Camera," perhaps the most visible of the hidden observers, gave up simple observation because of the high dross rate (Flagler, 1960). In the early years of the program, Funt's episodes consisted largely of studies of gestures and conversation (Hamburger, 1950; Martin, 1961). Particularly with conversation, Funt found that a large amount of time was required to obtain a small amount of material, and he turned to introducing confederates who would behave in such a way to direct attention to the topic of study.

In one magnificent sequence of film, Funt prepared a cross-cultural comparison of how men from different countries respond to the request of a female confederate to carry a suitcase to the corner. Filmed abroad, the episodes centered on the girl indicating she had carried the suitcase for a long time and would like a hand. The critical material is the facial expression and bodily gestures of the men as they attempted to lift the suitcase and sagged under the weight. It was filled with metal. The Frenchman shrugged; the Englishman kept at it. Funt has offered to open his extensive film library to social scientists. For students of response to frustration or unexpected stimuli, this is rich ground.

Obviously, experimental manipulation is not a contaminant. It is only when the manipulation is seen as such that reactivity enters to threaten validity. Carroll (1962) showed that active initiation of stimuli can have its comic side. In an exploratory venture, he sent out wires to 12 distant friends, congratulating each on his "recent achievement." Back came 11 acknowledgements of humble thanks. This approach lacks control, for we cannot know how many acknowledged in puzzled courtesy and how many felt Carroll had given them their due. If the study is replicated, it might be well to send a control sample a wire saying, "It doesn't matter. We're with you anyway." The wire was an efficient way to stimulate a response. An analogue may be an attempt to teach automobile driving by operant conditioning procedures. It is possible, but may take a hazardously long time contrasted to active control by the teacher (Bandura, 1962).

Simple observation, mechanized or not, is appropriate to a broad range of imaginative and useful research comparisons. Some of these we have mentioned. The advantage of contrived observation is to extend the base of simple observation and permit more subtle comparisons of the intensity of effect.

The early work of Hartshorne and May yields good examples of the manipulating observer. In *Studies in Service and Self Control* (Hartshorne, May, & Maller, 1929), they report on a long series of experiments—the first behavioral studies of "service." Employing "production methods of measurement," they indexed service or helpfulness by the subject's willingness to produce something—a toy in a shop, or the posting of a picture. Similarly, they employed "self sacrifice" techniques, measures on which the subject had to give up something.

The subjects were school children, and the active involvement of the experimenter (teacher) in defining alternatives of behavior was both expected and normal. The threat of subjects' awareness of being tested is less an issue in educational research, and the long line of studies on lecture versus discussion methods, as well as the current research on educational television, are a fine source of learning research because the risk of the contaminant is so reduced.

In the same way, it is not a patently false condition for a teacher to present students with the chance to help some other children in hospitals. Hartshorne and May graded the opportunities to help in an "envelope test." The student could put pictures, jokes, or stories in envelopes to give to hospitalized children, could promise to do so, or not do so. In another behavioral measure of sacrifice, one with more artificiality, however, the students were told they would be given some money. They were provided opportunities to bank it, give it to a charity, or keep it themselves. In another phase, one that presaged many small-group experiments, the children were given a choice of whether they would work for themselves or for the class in a spelling contest.

In Hartshorne and May's *Studies of Deceit* (1928), children were offered the opportunity not to return all of the coins distributed for arithmetic practice, to cheat by changing original answers in grading their own exam papers (which had previously been collected and then handed back with some excuse), to peek during "eyes-closed" tests and thus perform with unbelievable skill, to exaggerate the number of chin-ups when allowed to make their own records "unobserved." Forty separate opportunities were administered in whole or in part to about eight thousand pupils.

In one of their reports (May & Hartshorne, 1927) is found the first presentation of what is now known as Guttman scale analysis. The experimenters found high unidimensionality for a series of paper regrading opportunities: those students who cheated when an ink eraser was required cheated on *every* easier opportunity.

These studies of Hartshorne and May in the Character Education Inquiry are the classics of contrived observation, and nothing so thorough and ingenious has been done since. It is unfortunate for subsequent measurement efforts that interpretation of the cheating results was viewed as specific to the situation. To be sure, honesty was found to be relative to situation; for example, in one study (May & Hartshorne, 1927), only 2 per cent cheated when corrections required an ink eraser, while 80 per cent cheated when all that was needed was either erasing or adding a penciled digit. But this is not inconsistent with the six cheating opportunities forming a single-factored test or unidimensional scale. The data show a Guttman reproducibility coefficient of .96. Even though the measure was only six items long, there was a Kuder-Richardson reliability of .72 which becomes .84 when corrected for item-marginal ceiling effects as suggested by Horst (1953). Pooling all their disguised performance tests for a given trait, the experimenters checked the character tests against reputational scores from the so-called Guess-Who tests. The validities ranged from .315 to .374. Although very low values in terms of the standards of their day, they are now recognized to be reasonable values typical of those found for personality tests. Of course, the reputational measures contributed their full share of the error in validity.

Contrived observation, then, is observation in which the stimuli or the available responses are varied in an inconspicuous way. For Hartshorne and May, the variation was primarily of the response alternatives.

The recent series of studies by Fantz and associates (Fantz, 1961a; Fantz, 1961b; Fantz, Ordy, & Udelf, 1962; Fantz, 1963; Fantz, 1964) shows the more usual variation of the stimuli. They too, worked with subjects where the reactivity risk is low — newborn infants. The simple response measure was visual fix on a target, with the stimulus varied along such dimensions as novelty, color, and pattern. As far as a 48-hour-old infant is concerned, a series of concentric rings in his visual field is as natural as anything else.

Stechler (1964) also studied newborns, observing the effect of medication administered to the mother during labor on the baby's attentiveness. Each child received three stimuli, "held near the baby's face for a total of nine minutes . . . . An observer hidden from the babies recorded the total time they looked at and away from the stimuli" (p. 315).

A much more hardheaded group of subjects, automobile salesmen, were studied by Jung (1959; 1960; 1961; 1962) in his evaluations of the effect of various bargaining postures. The response measure was simple, the quoted price of an automobile with specified features, and three different bargaining postures were struck. In this well-designed series of experiments, confederates posed as customers and adopted one of these three poses: an eager, naive "I just got my license. Where do I sign?" approach, an engineering, price-sophisticated approach, and one in between. The differences among test conditions are smaller in absolute quotations than might have been expected — only $33 between the extremes in one study. Because the research was conducted in the heavily price-competitive Chicago area, the dollar differences may well be less than in areas in which competition is along other lines. The Chicago buyer, real or feigned, gets an automatic discount without any haggling. Jung has used the same feigned-shopper approach in studies of mortgage financing and the sale of mobile homes (Jung, 1963; Jung, 1964).

Brock (1965) turned the conditions around. His experimenter in a study of decision change was a paint salesman. After customers chose paint at a certain price, the salesman suggested either a

more or less expensive paint. The salesman was more successful
when he described himself as having recently bought the same
amount of paint at a different price.

Franzen (1950) conducted a sales experiment with pharmacists. The confederate was again a "customer," who related
various symptoms of illness to the pharmacist. The symptoms
were graded by their severity as told by the "customer," and it was
noted whether or not a visit to a physician was suggested. Examples of the symptoms, all of which could be related to early
cancer, were loss of voice, sore on lip, heartburn and stomach
trouble, and constipation.

Franzen also administered opinion questionnaires to an
equivalent, randomly selected group of pharmacists. The results
from the questionnaire are different from those of the field study.
The contrived observation results, we suspect, have a higher
predictive value than those from the questionnaires.

These findings recall the classic study comparing verbal
attitudes and overt acts: LaPiere's (1934) research on prejudice.
He and a Chinese couple visited 250 hotels and restaurants and
were refused service just once. Yet when questionnaires were sent
to those same places, asking if Chinese customers were welcome,
some 92 per cent answered negatively. As a control, LaPiere sent
identical questionnaires to 100 similar establishments which his
party had not visited, and the response was similar.

J. S. Adams (1963a; 1963b) has demonstrated in his important
work on wages what fine research can be undertaken with simple
productivity data. He conducted three experiments "to test how
people behave when they are working on a relatively highly paid
job for which they feel underqualified (that is, when they feel their
pay, or outcome, exceeds their qualifications or input)" (1963b, p.
10).

The subjects were students who were hired for part-time
temporary interviewing, not knowing they were part of an experiment. In the first experiment, they were paid $3.50 an hour and
divided into two groups. The experimental group was led to believe
that they were not qualified for the job as interviewers; they "were
treated quite harshly." The control group was told they had met all
qualifications for the job. With productivity the dependent variable, the experimental subjects produced significantly more than
the control subjects.

In the second experiment, interest was focused on the relationship between method of pay and dissonance. Thirty-six students were hired for the same interviewing job and randomly assigned to the four conditions:

1. Experimental dissonance condition—students were paid $3.50 an hour and made to feel overpaid.
2. Control condition—students were paid $3.50 an hour and made to feel it was an equitable wage.
3. Experimental dissonance condition—students were paid 30 cents an interview and made to feel overpaid on a piece rate.
4. Control condition—students were paid 30 cents an interview and made to feel payment was fair.

Adams' hypothesis was supported: "hourly workers in the dissonance condition had a higher mean productivity than their controls, whereas piece-workers in the dissonance condition had a lower mean productivity than their controls" (1963b, p. 13).

In the final experiment, Adams showed that pieceworkers who perceive that they are inequitably overpaid will perform better quality work at a lower productivity level than pieceworkers paid the same rate who believe that the wage is fair. The experimental subjects increased their "inputs" on each unit of work, thereby increasing the quality, but decreasing the quantity.

We have detailed this study because of the example that Adams provides of the shrewd hypothesis-testing potential of some of the rudimentary, but natural, measures available for experimental study.

The violation of prohibitions has offered the subject matter for several field studies of contrived observation. In these, the physical world of the observed was actively manipulated, and the dependent variables were simple motor acts.

Freed and his colleagues (Freed et al., 1955) experimented with sign violation. To what extent will students violate a sign urging the use of an inconvenient side door rather than the customary main door of a university building? The degree of prohibition was varied on the sign (high, medium, or low) with the interesting fillip of a confederate who conformed to the sign or violated it. In a control condition no confederate was present. Ninety subjects were assigned to nine different experimental groups, combinations of prohibition strength of the sign and a confederate's presence or behavior. They showed main effects for the two variables with no interaction between them. In an extension of these findings, another investigator (Sechrest, 1965b) found that a politely worded sign, "Please Do Not Use This Door," elicited fewer violations than the more abrupt "Use Other Door."

Violation of traffic signals was the dependent variable in a study by Lefkowitz, Blake, and Mouton (1955). An experimenter was again an active element in the setting—a male who dressed in either high- or low-status clothing. The confederate either conformed to or violated a traffic signal that ordered him to "wait" on a street corner. An observer a hundred feet from the corner noted the number of people on the corner who went along with the confederate. Would the difference in dress elicit differences in the number of pedestrians violating the light? Austin, Texas, was the locale, and pedestrians violated the sign more often in the presence of a model—significantly more often when the nonconforming model was in his higher-status dress.

Cratty (1962) attempted a replication of this study in Evanston, Illinois. He added observation of the race of violators and conformers, and his analysis suggests a significant difference between Negroes and whites on violations under *both* conditions. The racial composition of the sample could thus confound comparisons.[4] Cratty's findings also illustrate the problem of the cross-sectional stability of a research measure. To have good intersectional comparisons, the degree of usual conformity to the signs should be equivalent. Comparison of the Texas and Illinois data is muddied by a law-abiding difference. Only 1 per cent of the Texas sample violated the sign when the confederate was absent; over 60 per cent of the Illinois sample did.

Moore and Callahan (1943) conducted research in New Haven, concentrating on traffic and parking behavior. Three sets of studies are reported, all of them nonreactive, all examples of contrived observation. In the first set, the "parking" studies, observations were made over a four-year period. Moore and Callahan first observed the number and length of time parked of cars in areas where there was no formal ordinance against parking. Then

---

[4]It might be interesting to draw a sample of United States cities with varying degrees of reported racial tension and compare, by race, the extent to which minor violations such as walking on a red signal are committed.

a formal ordinance prohibiting parking was introduced, and the observation continued. Thus, there is a time-series analysis in which the baseline is the period preceding the introduction of signs.

In a second set of "administrative" studies, the militancy of enforcement of traffic violations was the independent variable. Parking was limited by ordinance (sign) to 30 minutes. In one condition, violations were tagged after 80 minutes and in a second condition, after 45 minutes. The frequency and duration of parking under these two conditions were compared to a control condition in which no tickets were given at all.

The third set centered on rotary traffic. All studies in this group used a large circular tract of pavement from which five streets radiated. Observation consisted of noting the path in which the area was crossed.

Five observation periods were employed. The first was before there was any ordinance regulating the direction of traffic. The second was before a formal ordinance was enacted, but in the presence of signs to "keep right." The third followed enactment of the ordinance. The fourth was while the ordinance was visibly in effect—barriers would not allow cars through the center of the circle. Finally, the barrier and signs were removed when the ordinance was still in effect. The observed directions of flow under the five conditions were compared.

Another driving study, reported by Sechrest (1965b), was concerned with willingness of drivers to accept a challenge to "drag" at stop signals. The investigators challenged by pulling alongside a car, gunning the engine of their car, and looking once at their "opponent." They used different stimulus cars and recorded several attributes of the responding cars. Results showed a strong decline in acceptance of the challenge with increasing age and with presence of passengers other than the driver in the respondent's car. As for the stimulus cars? Very few drivers wanted to drag with a Volkswagen.

Traffic behavior offers a splendid opportunity for naturalistic experimentation. A large body of control data is already available, produced for engineering studies or by market-research firms to document the exposure of outdoor advertising. It should be possible, for example, to study the effect of different degrees of threat in a persuasive message by studying the degree to which drivers slow down, if they do, after passing different classes of signs—say, those threatening legal enforcement or the danger to personal safety. Radar devices or filming from an overhead helicopter could provide the measure of speed. What might be of particular interest in such a study would be the extinction rate under the different conditions. Does an enforcement warning have a faster rate of decay than a personal safety message? What happens if both classes are equated for initial effect on speed?

Another study relating to legal processes is that of Schwartz and Skolnick (1962b). They investigated the effect of criminal records on the employment opportunities of unskilled workers. Four employment folders were prepared for an applicant; all folders were identical save for description of the criminal-court record of the applicant. Each of 100 employers was assigned one of four treatment folders, and the employer was asked whether he could "use" the man described in the folder. The employers were never given any indication that they were participating in an experiment. Even when the applicant was described as having been acquitted with an excusing letter from a judge or acquitted without a letter, the incidence of employers who thought they might use the applicant dropped.

Entrapment

Jones (1946) has provided an excellent summary of early behavioral studies of character development, many of which follow the entrapment strategy of Hartshorne and May. A recent example is the work of Freeman and Ataov (1960). They contrived a situation in which the subjects had a chance to cheat by grading their own examinations by a scoring sheet. Using three classes of questions—fill-in blanks, multiple-choice, and true-false—they found the number of changed answers for each class. The three formed a Guttman scale with a reproducibility coefficient of .94.

One of the more interesting studies on honesty has been reported by Merritt and Fowler (1948), who "lost" two kinds of stamped and addressed envelopes, one containing a trivial message, the other a lead slug of the dimensions of a fifty-cent piece. They dropped the letters "on many different days and in many different cities to insure a representative sample of the public at large" (p. 91). While 85 per cent of the control letters were returned, only 54 per cent of the test (containing slug) were, and some 13 per cent of the test letters that were returned had been opened. After the letters were dropped, there was a chance to work with auxiliary information on the unsuspecting subjects.

Watching the pickup of the letters proved to be a most entertaining pastime. Some were picked up and immediately posted at the nearest mailbox. Others were examined minutely, evidently precipitating quite a struggle between the finder and his conscience, before being pocketed or mailed. Some were carried a number of blocks before being posted, one person carrying a letter openly for nine blocks before mailing it. A lady in Ann Arbor, Michigan, found a letter and carried it six miles in her car to deliver it personally, although she was not acquainted with the addressee. One letter, picked up in Harrisburg, Pennsylvania was mailed from York, Pennsylvania. Another picked up in Toledo, Ohio was mailed in Cleveland. Still another from the Toledo streets was mailed from Monroe, Michigan. Two missives left on the steps of the cradle of liberty in Philadelphia failed to find their way into a mailbox. Two of five letters left on church steps during Sunday services failed to return [p. 93].

Grinder (1961; 1962) and Grinder and McMichael (1963) have reported studies using a "ray gun" type of apparatus. Like Hartshorne and May, their interest was in studying character, or "conscience development." Children operated a "ray gun" individually in a realistic game situation.

Seated seven feet from a target box, subjects were asked to shoot the ray gun pistol 20 times at a rotating rocket. With each pull of the ray gun trigger, prearranged scores from zero to five were registered by score lights also housed in the target box. High scores were rewarded with a marksman, sharpshooter, or expert badge ... subjects cumulated their scores on a paper score sheet. Subjects were judged to have resisted temptation if the scores recorded on their score sheets indicated that they had not earned a badge (they could not honestly). They were judged to have yielded to temptation if their score sheet showed that they had falsified their scores in order to earn one of the badges [Grinder & McMichael, 1963, p. 504].

Similar in its assumption of dishonesty by subjects is a study by Brock and Guidice (1963). The subjects were students ranging from the second to the sixth grade, and these children were individually asked if they would leave the class, go to another room, and participate in an experiment. Upon entering the room, the subject found the experimenter in a flustered state with her purse spilled and money lying on the floor. At this point the experimenter left, saying she would be back shortly, and asking the subject to pick up the contents of her purse while she was gone. The measure used was the amount of money stolen by the subject. There is a good risk that some of the children, having been told to go to another room for an "experiment," became suspicious. The effect of this is to make uncertain how many of those who took no money were honest and how many were acute. This bias could possibly interact with a practice effect on the part of the experimenter. Did she play her role differently over time, as she became more practiced or more bored? If professional actresses have problems "keeping fresh," it is reasonable to ask about amateurs.

The more complex the action of the confederate, the greater the risk of an experimenter effect, *and* the greater the possibility for more gradations in the experimental variable.

PETITIONS AND VOLUNTEERING

Petition-signing has been the dependent variable in observational studies by Blake, Mouton, and Hain (1956) and Helson, Blake, and Mouton (1958). In the first study, the strength of the plea to sign was varied, and frequency of signing was closely associated with this variable. A confederate was then introduced into this situation to provide varying reactions of another person. In some situations he signed readily, in others refused, and in still others his response was unknown to the person approached. The behavior of the confederate influenced signing, and an interesting finding was that both variables operated independently — the strength of the plea and endorsement by another.

The Helson, Blake, and Mouton (1958) study used petition-signing as a response behavior within a larger experimental setting. Students who had volunteered to participate in an experiment were taken by a guide to an experimental room. On the way, the pair was stopped, and a confederate asked the guide to sign a petition. After the guide (also a confederate) signed or did not sign, the subject was asked to sign. Four conditions were employed, with each student receiving one:

1. A petition on a proposal that had previously elicited 96 per cent positive response and confederate signed
2. The same 96 per cent positive proposal, but confederate refused to sign
3. A proposal that had received only a 15 per cent positive response and confederate signed
4. The same 15 per cent proposal; confederate did not sign.

Solicitation to sign a petition is a common enough event in academic settings, and may be becoming more common outside the cloistered world. Certainly it offers a broad freedom of movement in experimentation and structuring of contrived conditions. Searching for volunteers does, too, and several studies have used observation of the simple "volunteer-not volunteer" alternatives as the behavioral variable.

Schachter and Hall (1952) experimented with college students, employing different situational elements in eliciting volunteers for an experiment and then noting whether or not the volunteers did in fact show up for the experiment. Classes were divided into four groups and given different restraints. In one group, after a requesting speech, the listeners were asked to fill out a questionnaire, whether or not they wished to participate in the experiment. Those who did wish to participate were merely asked to check an appropriate place on the form. In a second group, the forms were passed around the room, and anyone who wanted to participate in the experiment could take one. A third group was asked to raise hands if interested; a fourth group also raised hands, but half of the class had been enlisted as confederates and "volunteered." Schachter and Hall's conclusion was that neither the high- nor low-constraint condition was particularly desirable in soliciting volunteers. If the experimenters made it easy to refuse, they got a high refusal rate, but high attendance among those who did volunteer. Contrariwise, placing high pressure on volunteering yielded a higher level of volunteers, but a smaller number who held to their promise.

Rosenbaum and Blake (1955) wanted to test the hypothesis that the act of volunteering is "a special case of conformance with social norms or standards, rather than . . . an individualistic act conditioned by an essentially unidentifiable complex of inner tensions, needs, etc." (p. 193). Subjects were plucked from students studying in the university library, and conditions were varied so that the subject saw either an acceptance or rejection of the request from a confederate. In a third group, the student accepted or rejected the volunteering request in the absence of a model. As predicted, acceptances were high with a conforming confederate, low with a nonconforming confederate, and in between on the control condition.

The University of Texas library was also the site of another study by Rosenbaum (1956). Volunteering was the dependent variable, and stimulus conditions included three request strengths (determined by a pilot study) and three background conditions employing confederates. The confederate entered the library, sat next to an unsuspecting student, and then the volunteer-seeker entered and started with the confederate.

Blake and his associates (Blake *et al.*, 1956) determined the effect on the level of volunteering of varying the attractiveness of alternatives to volunteering. The public or private character of the volunteering was also varied, with conditions altered so that a class might substitute volunteering time for time otherwise devoted to: (1) a pop quiz, (2) released time from class, (3) a control, with no time gained. It might be observed that under the pop-quiz alternative, 98.8 per cent of the subjects volunteered under the private-commitment situation and 100.0 per cent under public commitment. The 1.2 per cent above is accounted for by the single aberrant student who preferred a pop quiz to participation in an experiment.

Volunteering for social action was the subject of a study by Gore and Rotter (1963). The action in this case was the willingness of students in a southern Negro college to engage in different types of segregation-protest activity. This criterion measure was correlated with previously obtained scores on control of reinforcement and social desirability scales, these scales not specifically dealing with the segregation issue. A generalized attitude toward internal or external control was shown to predict the type and degree of behavior subjects were willing to perform in attempts at social change.

An Over-All Appraisal of Hidden Hardware and Control

As the discussion and examples of observational research have progressed over these past two chapters, the reader may have been sensitive to a movement along a passivity-activity dimension. In the studies reported in the chapter on simple observation methods, the observer was a non-intervening passive onlooker of behavior that came before his eyes or ears. He may have scrambled about in different locations to reduce some population restrictions, but his role was a quiet, receptive one. In many ways, this is appropriate for the covert character of the studies we have outlined.

With the hardware employed in the studies cited in this chapter, the investigator engaged his data more — actively expanding the possible scope of the content of research and achieving a more faithful record of what behaviors did go on. Yet the hardware varied, too. Some of the hardware devices are static, while others are mobile. To the degree that the hardware is mobile (say, a microphone in a mock hearing aid versus one secreted in a table), the experimenter has flexibility to make more economical forays into locational sampling. He could sample in a number of locations by installing more permanent recording devices, but commonly a more feasible method is to sample occasions and time with mobile equipment. As electronic technology develops, more opportunities arise. It isn't so long ago that television cameras had to be anchored in one spot.

When, through deliberate choice or no realistic alternative, the investigator was limited to a fixed instrument, he was forced to depend on the character of the population which flowed past that spot and the content appropriate to it. The waiting game can give accurate and complete measurement of a limited population and limited content, and the decision to use such an approach is posited on two criteria, one "theoretical," one "practical." Are the limitations likely to be selective enough to inhibit the generalizability of the findings? Can the investigator absorb the time and money costs of developing material with a low saturation of pertinent data for his comparisons?

In the contrived-observation studies, the experimenters took the next step and intervened actively in the production of the data, striding away from passive and critically placed observations. The effect was to produce very dense data, of which a high proportion was pertinent to the research comparisons. Further, a finer gradation of stimuli was then possible, and more subtle shadings of difference could be noted. By active intervention, as the petition and volunteering studies of conformity show, it was also possible to make estimates of the interaction of variables, an extremely difficult matter with passive observation.

As the experimenter's activity increases, and he achieves the gains of finer measurement and control, the price paid is the increased risk of being caught—that the subjects of the observation will detect the recording device, or will suspect that the confederate is really a "plant." This is a high price, for if he is detected, the experimenter's research is flooded with the reactive measurement errors which the hidden-observation approach, regardless of its simplicity or complexity, is designed to avoid. At the extreme end of contrivance, when a confederate is a visible actor in the subject's world, it requires the greatest finesse to protect against detection and against changes in the behavior of the confederate damaging to comparison. The best defense, as always, is knowledge, and almost all of the observational approaches have built into them the capacity to examine whether or not population or instrument contaminants are working to confound the data.

CHAPTER 7

A Final Note

> In the dialectic between impulsivity and restraint, the scientific
> superego became too harsh — a development that was particu-
> larly effective in intimidating adventurous research, because
> the young were learning more about methodological pitfalls
> than had their elders. . . .
>
> (Riesman, 1959, p. 11)

David Riesman's remarks on the evolution of communications research apply equally well to the broader panoply of the study of social behavior. As social scientists, we have learned much of the labyrinth that is research on human behavior, and in so doing discovered an abundance of cul-de-sacs. Learning the complexities of the maze shortened our stride through it, and often led to a pattern of timid steps, frequently retraced. No more can the knowledgeable person enjoy the casual bravura that marked the sweeping and easy generalizations of an earlier day.

The facile promulgation of "truth," backed by a few observations massaged by introspection, properly met its end — flattened by a more questioning and sophisticated rigor. The blackballing of verification by introspection was a positive advance, but an advance by subtraction. Partly as a reaction to the grandiosities of the past, partly as a result of a growing sophistication about the opportunities for error, the scope of individual research studies shrank, both in the range of content considered and in the diversity of procedures.

The shrinkage was understandable and desirable, for certainly no science can develop until a base is reached from which

171

reliable and consistent empirical findings can be produced.[1] But if reliability is the initial step of a science, validity is its necessary stride. The primary effect of improved methodological practices has been to further what we earlier called the internal validity of a comparison—the confidence that a true difference is being observed. Unfortunately, practices have not advanced so far in improving external validity—the confidence with which the findings can be generalized to populations and measures beyond those immediately studied.

Slowing this advance in ability to generalize was the laissez-faire intellectualism of the operational definition. Operational definitionalism (to use a ponderously cumbersome term) provided a methodological justification for the scientist not to stray beyond a highly narrow, if reliable, base. One could follow a single method in developing data and be "pure," even if this purity were more associated with sterility than virtue.

The corkscrew convolutions of the maze of behavior were ironed, by definitional fiat, into a two-dimensional T maze. To define a social attitude, for example, solely by the character of responses to a list of questionnaire items is eminently legitimate — so much so that almost everything we know about attitudes comes from such research. Almost everything we know about attitudes is also suspect because the findings are saturated with the inherent risks of self-report information. One swallow does not make a summer; nor do two "strongly agrees," one "disagree," and an "I don't know" make an attitude or social value.

Questionnaires and interviews are probably the most flexible and generally useful devices we have for gathering information. Our criticism is not against them, but against the tradition which allowed them to become the methodological sanctuary to which the myopia of operational definitionalism permitted a retreat. If one were going to be limited to a single method, then certainly the verbal report from a respondent would be the choice. With no other device can an investigator swing his attention into so many

[1]"Almost all experiments on the effects of persuasion communications, including those reported in the present volume, have been limited to investigating changes in opinion. The reason, of course, is that such changes can readily be assessed in a highly reliable way, whereas other components of verbalizable attitudes, although of considerable theoretical interest, are much more difficult to measure" (Janis and Hovland, 1959, p. 3).

different areas of substantive content, often simultaneously, and also gather intelligence on the extent to which his findings are hampered by population restrictions.

The power of the questionnaire and interview has been enormously enhanced, as have all methods, by the development of sensitive sampling procedures. With the early impetus provided by the Census Bureau to locational sampling, particularly to the theory and practice of stratification, concern about the population restrictions of a research sample has been radically diminished. Less well developed is the random sampling of time units — either over long periods such as months, or within a shorter period such as a day. There is no theoretical reason why time sampling is scarce, for it is a simple question of substituting time for location in a sampling design. Time sampling is of interest not only for its control over population fluctuations which might confound comparisons, but also because it permits control over the possibility of variable content at different times of the day or different months of the year.

The cost is high. And for that reason, government and commercial research organizations have led in the area, while academic research continues to limp along with conscripted sophomores. The controlled laboratory setting makes for excellent internal validity, as one has tight control over the conditions of administration and the internal structure of the questionnaire, but the specter of low generalizability is ever present.

That same specter is present, however, even if one has a national probability sample and the most carefully prepared questionnaire form or interview schedule. So long as one has only a single class of data collection, and that class is the questionnaire or interview, one has inadequate knowledge of the rival hypotheses grouped under the term "reactive measurement effects." These potential sources of error, some stemming from an individual's awareness of being tested, others from the nature of the investigator, must be accounted for by some other class of measurement than the verbal self-report.

It is too much to ask of any single class that it eliminate all the rival hypotheses subsumed under the population-, content-, and reactive-effects groupings. As long as the research strategy is based on a single measurement class, some flanks will be exposed, and even if fewer are exposed with the choice of the questionnaire method, there is still insufficient justification for its use as the only approach.

If no single measurement class is perfect, neither is any scientifically useless. Many studies and many novel sources of data have been mentioned in these pages. The reader may indeed have wondered which turn of the page would provide a commentary on some Ouija-board investigation. It would have been there had we known of one, and had it met some reasonable criteria of scientific worth. These "oddball" studies have been discussed because they demonstrate ways in which the investigator may shore up reactive infirmities of the interview and questionnaire. As a group, these classes of measurement are themselves infirm, and individually contain more risk (more rival plausible hypotheses) than does a well-constructed interview.

This does not trouble us, nor does it argue against their use, for the most fertile search for validity comes from a combined series of different measures, each with its idiosyncratic weaknesses, each pointed to a single hypothesis. When a hypothesis can survive the confrontation of a series of complementary methods of testing, it contains a degree of validity unattainable by one tested within the more constricted framework of a single method (Campbell & Fiske, 1959). Findings from this latter approach must always be subject to the suspicion that they are method-bound: Will the comparison totter when exposed to an equally prudent but different testing method? There must be a multiple operationalism. E. G. Boring (1953) put it this way:

> ... as long as a new construct has only the single operational definition that it received at birth, it is just a construct. When it gets two alternative operational definitions, it is beginning to be validated. When the defining operations, because of proven correlations, are many, then it becomes reified [p. 222].

This means, obviously, that the notion of a single "critical experiment" is erroneous. *There must be a series of linked critical experiments, each testing a different outcropping of the hypothesis.* It is through triangulation of data procured from different measurement classes that the investigator can most effectively strip of plausibility rival explanations for his comparison. The usual procedural question asked is: Which of the several available data-collection methods will be best for my research problem? We suggest the alternative question: Which set of methods will be best? — with "best" defined as a series which provides data to test the most significant threats to a comparison with a reasonable expenditure of resources.

There are a number of research conditions in which the sole use of the interview or questionnaire leaves unanswerable rival explanations. The purpose of those less popular measurement classes emphasized here is to bolster these weak spots and provide intelligence to evaluate threats to validity. The payout for using these measures is high, but the approach is more demanding of the investigator. In their discussion of statistical records, Selltiz and her associates (Selltiz *et al.*, 1959) note:

> The use of such data demands a capacity to ask many different questions related to the research problem.... The guiding principle for the use of available statistics consists in keeping oneself flexible with respect to the form in which research questions are asked [p. 318].

This flexibility of thought is required to handle the reactive measurement effects which are the most systematic weakness of all interview and questionnaire studies. These error threats are also systematically present in all observation studies in which the presence of an observer is known to those under study. To varying degrees, measurements conducted in natural settings, without the individual's knowledge, control this type of error possibility. In all of them — hidden observation, contrived observation, trace analysis, and secondary records — the individual is not aware of being tested, and there is little danger that the act of measurement will itself serve as a force for change in behavior or elicit role-playing that confounds the data. There is also minimal risk that biases coming from the physical appearance or other cues provided by the investigator will contaminate the results.

In the observational studies, however, hiding the observer does not eliminate the risk that he will change as a data-collecting instrument over time. Any change, for the better or worse, will introduce shifts that might be erroneously interpreted as stemming from the causal variable. This source of error must be guarded against in the same way that it is in other measurement classes — by careful training of the observer (interviewer), by permitting practice effects to take place before the critical data are collected, and by "blinding" the observer to the hypothesis. There is no way of knowing, of course, whether all reasonable precautions have worked. For this, the only solution is an internal longitudinal analysis of data from a single observer and cross-analysis of data from different observers at various times during the data collection.

Finally, none of the methods emphasized here, by themselves, can eliminate response sets which might strongly influence the character of the data. These must be brought under experimental control by manipulation of the setting itself (as in contrived field experimentation) or by statistical operations with the data if the character of the response sets is known well enough to permit adjustments. With archival records, it may be extremely difficult to know if response sets were operating at the time the data were produced.

These methods also may counter a necessary weakness of the interview and questionnaire — dependence upon language. When one is working within a single society, there is always the question whether the differential verbal skills of various subcultures will mislead the investigator. It is possible, if groups vary in articulateness, to overgeneralize the behavior or attitudes of the group or individuals with the greater verbal fluency. This risk is particularly marked for the interpretation of research reports which employ quotations liberally. The natural tendency of the writer is to choose illustrative quotations which are fluent, dramatic, or engaging. If the pool of good quotations is variable across the subcultures, the reader may mistakenly overvalue the ideas in the quotations, even though the writer himself does not. This is a question of presentation, but an important one because of the disproportionate weight that may be placed on population segments.

The differential capacity to use the language artfully is one source of error, while the absolute capacity of the language to convey ideas is another.[2] This is an issue strongly present in cross-cultural comparisons, where different languages may vary radically as a medium of information transfer. The effect of this is to limit the content possible for study with questionnaries or inter-

[2] In a similar note on observers, Heyns and Lippitt (1954) ask if the "observer lacks the sensitivity or the vocabulary which the particular observation requires" (p. 372).

views. If one worked in New Guinea, for example, and had to depend upon the *lingua franca* pidgin widely spoken there, he would find it adequate to indicate an answer to "Where do you keep your fishing nets?" but too gross a filter to study the ethnocentricism of a tribe. Pidgin simply does not possess the subtle gradients required to yield textured responses to questions on attitudes toward neighboring tribes or one's own tribe. Although it is theoretically possible to learn all the regional dialects well enough to be competent in a language, in practice this does not occur. A more pragmatic approach is to search for observational or trace evidence which will document aspects of ethnocentrism (e.g., reactions to outsiders, disposition and use of weapons) and then relate it to the verbal responses in the inadequate pidgin.

One more weakness of the dependence on language is that sometimes there is silence. So long as a respondent talks, glibly or not, in a rich language or not, checks and controls can be worked on the reported content.[3] There are, however, situations in which refusals to cooperate preclude any chance of correcting distorted information. This usually results in a biased research population and not a rejection of all findings, because it is almost always possible to find some people who will discuss any topic. But it can also result in a complete stalemate if only the verbal report is considered as the research instrument.

An amusing example of this inability to get data by verbal report, and a nonreactive circumvention, is provided by Shadegg (1964). In his book on political campaign methods, Shadegg writes of a campaign manager who used every available means to learn the plans of his opponent, who, reasonably enough, was unwilling to grant a revealing interview. One method arranged for procuring the contents of his opponent's wastebasket: "He came into possession of carbon copies of letters . . . memos in the handwriting of his opponent's manager." Admittedly a less efficient method than the interview, it admirably met the criterion of being workable: "It took a lot of digging through the trash to come up with the nuggets. But . . . daily panning produced some very fine gold." The "investigator" did not limit himself to inferences drawn from observations of his opponent's public acts, but was able to develop

[3]For an extended discussion of this issue, see Hyman *et al.* (1954) and Kahn and Cannell (1957).

ingeniously (although perhaps not ethically) a trace measure to complement the observation. Each aided the other, for the observations give a validity check on the nuggets among the trash (Was misleading material being planted?), and the nuggets gave a more accurate means of interpreting the meaning of the public acts.

Evidence of how others are sensitive to wastebaskets is seen in the practice in diplomatic embassies of burning refuse under guard, the discussion of refuse purchase by industrial spies (Anonymous, 1964c), and the development of a new electric wastebasket that shreds discarded paper into unreadable bits.

Generally speaking, then, observational and trace methods are indicated as supplementary or primary when language may serve as a poor medium of information—either because of its differential use, its absolute capacity for transfer, or when significant elements of the research population are silent.

The verbal methods are necessarily weak along another dimension, the study of past behavior or of change. For historical studies, there is no alternative but to rely mainly on records of the past time. Behavioral research on the distant past is rare, however; more common are studies which center on experiences within the lifetime of respondents. For example, there is a large literature on child-rearing practices, in which mothers recollect their behavior of years past. A sole dependence on this type of data-gathering is highly suspect. It may be enough to note that Thomas Jefferson, in his later years, observed that winters weren't as cold as they used to be. Available records could be used to check both Mr. Jefferson and other observers of secular changes in winter's fierceness.

For more current evidence on the fallibility of such recall data, see Pyles, Stolz, and Macfarlane, 1935; McGraw and Molloy, 1941; Smith, 1958; Weiss and Dawis, 1960—all of whom comment on, or test, the validity of mothers' recall of child-rearing practices. Weiss and Dawis wrote, "It is indefensible to assume the validity of purportedly factual data obtained by interview" (p. 384). The work of Haggard, Brekstad, and Skard (1960) and Robbins (1963) suggests that it is a problem of differentially accurate recall. In Haggard's phrase, the interviews "did not reflect the mothers' earlier experiences and attitudes so much as their current picture of the past" (p. 317).

When, through death or refusal, reports of past behavior are unavailable, a proper contingent strategy is to interview others who have had access to the same information, or who can report at second hand. This is very shaky information, but useful if other intelligence is available as a check. For many investigations, of course, the nature of the distortion is itself an important datum and can become a central topic of study when a reliable baseline is possible.[4] If other materials are present, and they usually are in a record-keeping society, the best way to estimate past behavior is to combine methods of study of archival records, available traces, and verbal reports, even if secondhand. Clearly, direct observational methods are useless for past events.

With studies of social change, the most practical method is to rely on available records, supplemented by verbal recall. If one wanted more control over the data, it would be possible to conduct a continuing series of field experiments extending over a long period of years. But the difficulty of such an approach is evidenced by the scarcity of such longitudinal, original-data studies in social science. Forgetting the number of years required, there is the problem of unstable populations over time, a growing problem as the society becomes more mobile. Potential errors lie in both directions as one moves forward or backward in time, and the more practical approach of the two is to analyze data already collected—making the ever present assumption that such are available.

A more integrative approach for studying change is to develop two discrete time series—one based on available records, the other freshly developed by the investigator. With this strategy, it is necessary to have an overlap period in which the relationships between the two series are established. Given knowledge of the relationships, the available records can be studied retrospectively, thereby providing more intelligence than would be possible if they existed alone. Again, there is a necessary assumption: one must be able to reject the plausibility of an interaction between time and the method. If there is any content or population fluctuation

[4]The courts have handled secondary information by excluding it under the "hearsay" rule (Wigmore, 1935; Morgan, 1963). Epically put, "Pouring rumored scandal into the bent ear of blabbering busybodies in a pool room or gambling house is no more disreputable than pronouncing it with clipped accents in a courtroom" (Donnelly, Goldstein, & Schwartz, 1962, p. 277). The case from which this is cited is *Holmes*, 379 Pa. 599 (1954).

beyond chance, such a method is invalid. Diagrammatically, where O is an observation and the subscript n equals new data and a available data:

$$O_{a1}O_{a2}O_{a3}O_{a4}O_{a5}O_{a6}O_{a7}O_{a8}O_{a9}O_{a10}$$

$$O_{n6}O_{n7}O_{n8}O_{n9}O_{n10}$$

A final gain from the less reactive methods is frequently the lower cost of data collection. Many scholars know how to conduct massive surveys which effectively control major sources of error; few do so. This knowledge is an underdeveloped resource. With survey interviews often costing $10 or more apiece, the failure is understandable, however regrettable. When the interview or questionnaire is viewed as the only method, the researcher is doomed to either frustration or a studied avoidance of thoughts on external validity. Peace of mind will come if the investigator breaks the single-method mold and examines the extent to which other measurement classes can substitute for verbal reports. The price of collecting each unit of data is low for most of the methods we have stressed. In some cases, the dross rate is high, and it may be necessary to observe a hundred cases before one meets the research specifications. Nonetheless, even under these high dross-rate conditions, the cost per usable response is often lower than that of a completed interview or returned questionnaire. The lower cost permits flexibility to expand into content and population areas otherwise precluded, and the result of this is to increase the confidence one has in generalizing findings. Just as in the case of studying social change, it may be possible to generate different data series, some based on verbal reports, others based on secondary or observational data. Providing for enough cases of the more expensive procedures to yield a broad base for linkage, the larger number of cases can be allocated to the usually less expensive observational or secondary methods. It is important to note that we add "usually" before "less expensive." The savings are centered in data-collection costs, and it may be that all the savings are vitiated by the elaborate corrections or transformations that a particular data series may require. The cost of materials and analysis is an equivocal area indeed.

In the multimethod pattern of testing, the primary gains coming from the less popular methods are protection against reactive measurement threats, auxiliary data in content areas where verbal reports are unreliable, an easier method of determining long-term change, and a potentially lower-cost substitute for some standard survey practices.

Offsetting these gains, there are associated problems for each of the less popular measurement classes — indeed, if they were less problematic, we would be writing an argument in favor of an increased use of the interview.

The most powerful aspect of the verbal methods — their ability to reach into all content areas — is a soft spot in the hidden-observation, trace, and archival analysis procedures. We have noted remarkably adept and nonobvious applications of data from these sources, but for some content areas, the most imaginative of investigators will have trouble finding pertinent material. Individually, those methods are simply not as broad gauged.

Often missing, too, is complete knowledge of the conditions under which the data were collected, the definitions of important terms used in classification, and the control or lack of it over error risks that may be salient. This is particularly disturbing when dealing with comparisons of public records from different areas or from widely different times. The variation in definitions of "suicide" versus "accidental death," or the differential thoroughness with which marriages are entered in official records are examples of this issue. In general, for trace evidence and archival records, a dominant concern is the possibility of selective deposit and selective survival of the research data. Through supporting research designed to learn of these errors, it is sometimes possible to apply corrections to what is available. At other times, the researcher must remain in ignorance and make assumptions. If he restricts himself to working with *only* such data, he remains helpless before their vagaries. If he uses other measurement classes, the process of triangulating all the different data may provide a test of his assumptions and reveal the presence or extent of error. The comparison of data from the different classes can always add intelligence unavailable from comparisons of data from within the single class.

Because of the risks of error and the danger of unknown

biases, we have stressed the importance of careful data sampling. Wherever feasible, locational sampling should be employed, extending over regions as well as areas within a single locality. Similarly, time sampling should be considered not only as a device employed within a single day or week, but applied over months and years. By such effort, we are able to protect against both population and content restrictions, and very often produce interesting data from comparisons of results from different locations or times.[5] The need for time and location sampling is no less for observational or archival data than it is for interviews or questionnaires, for sampling is a problem that transcends the class of measurement.

Another common demand, this one not so applicable to the verbal-report approaches, is that for data adjustment and conversion. The need comes from the experimenter's decreased control over the production of his materials. The exception to this is the contrived field experiment, where the investigator can have full control, but the data from archives, trace sources, and observations are frequently too raw to be used as is. The need is underlined because of one of the major advantages of the secondary data — their ability to produce fine time-series information. In time series, it is usually necessary to account for extraneous sources of variation, such as secular trends or cyclical patterns. Thus, the "score" which is the basis of comparison is some transformed measure which is a residual of the total "score." In other studies, the absolute number of cases varies from unit time to unit time, and the only reasonable comparison score is one which is related in some way, through an average or percentage, for example, to the variable baseline. The investigator may have no control over the flow of an observed population, but he can obtain a count of that flow and use this intelligence as the basis for modifying his comparison score.

The more sophisticated forms of transformation, such as index numbers based on multiple components, demand more

[5]See, for example, Caplow and McGee's (1958) discussion of variation in salaries in American universities — particularly the relationship between beginning salaries and the prestige of the institution. In a related report, the head of an employment agency reported, "The Chicago advertising man on the average makes 10 per cent more than his New York counterpart, 25 per cent more than he would make on the West Coast, and 40 per cent more than he would make in a small town or in the south" (Baxter, 1962, p. 65).

information, particularly as one assigns relative weights to components collected into a single score. This is not as awesome as it sounds, and if the investigator is sensitive to the potential usefulness of index numbers, he often finds enough secondary data available for the task, or may obtain new information without extraordinarily high marginal costs. Insofar as these transformations demand time and labor to make the raw data more precise, they are disadvantageous compared with standard questionnaire procedures. There are, however, as we have suggested in various points in the text, indications that index numbers and more simple transformations could be used properly in all classes of measurement. The *Zeitgeist* may as yet be inappropriate, but an important work will someday link index-number theory and literature to social-science measurement theory and practice.

These, then, are the gains; these the losses. There are no rewards for ingenuity as such, and the payoff comes only when ingenuity leads to new means of making more valid comparisons. In the available grab bag of imperfect research methods, there is room for new uses of the old.

Max Eastman once suggested that books should start with a first section consisting of a few sentences, the second section a few pages, and so on. He even wrote one like that—*The Enjoyment of Laughter*. Since this has been an unconventional monograph on unconventional research procedures, it is proper that it should have an unconventional close. We reverse Eastman's formula and offer a one-phrase final chapter and a one-paragraph penultimate chapter.

CHAPTER 8

A Statistician on Method

We must use all available weapons of attack, face our problems realistically and not retreat to the land of fashionable sterility, learn to sweat over our data with an admixture of judgment and intuitive rumination, and accept the usefulness of particular data even when the level of analysis available for them is markedly below that available for other data in the empirical area.

(Binder, 1964, p. 294)

CHAPTER 9

Cardinal Newman's Epitaph

From symbols and shadows to the truth.

References

Adams, J. S. Toward an understanding of inequity. *Journal of Abnormal and Social Psychology*, 1963, *67*, 422-436. (a)

Adams, J. S. Wage inequities, productivity, and work quality. In *Psychological research on pay*. Reprint No. 220. Berkeley: Univer. of California, Institute of Industrial Relations, 1963, pp. 9-16. (b)

Advertising Service Guild. *The press and its readers*. London: Art & Technics, 1949.

Alger, C. F. Interaction in a committee of the United Nations General Assembly. In J. D. Singer (ed.), *International yearbook of behavior research*, *6*. New York: The Free Press, 1965. (In press.)

Allport, G. W. *The use of personal documents in psychological science*, New York: Social Science Research Council, 1942.

Amrine, M., & Sanford, F. In the matter of juries, democracy, science, truth, senators, and bugs. *American Psychologist*, 1956, *11*, 54-60.

Amthauer, R. Ergebnisse einer studie über krankheitsbedingte Fehlzeiten. *Psychologische Rundschau*, 1963, *14*, 1-12.

Anastasi, A. *Differential psychology*. (3rd ed.) New York: Macmillan, 1958.

Andrew, R. J. The origin and evolution of the calls and facial expressions of the primates. *Behavior*, 1963, *20*, 1-109.

Angell, R. C. The moral integration of American cities. *American Journal of Sociology*, 1951, *57*, 123-126.

Anonymoi. Hair style as a function of hard-headedness *vs.* long-hairedness in psychological research, a study in the personology of science. Unprepared manuscript, Northwestern Univer. & Univer. of Chicago, 1953-1960.

Anonymous. Z-Frank stresses radio to build big Chevy dealership. *Advertising Age*, 1962, *33*, 83.

Anonymous. Help wanted ads in September hit new high, NICB reports. *Advertising Age*, November 2, 1964, *35*, 74. (a)

Anonymous. In the eye of the beholder. *Sponsor*, December 28, 1964, *18*, 25-29. (b)

Anonymous. Litter bugged. *Advertising Age*, November 2, 1964, *35*, 74. (c)

Anonymous. Senator Salinger? *Newsweek*, August 10, 1964, *63*, 28. (d)

Anonymous. Civil rights: by the book. *Newsweek*, March 1, 1965, *65*, 37.

Ardrey, R. *African genesis*. New York: Delta, 1961.

Aronson, E. The need for achievement as measured by graphic expres-

187

sion. In J. W. Atkinson (Ed.), *Motives in fantasy, action, and society.* Princeton: Van Nostrand, 1958. Pp. 249-265.

Arrington, R. Time sampling in studies of social behavior: a critical review of techniques and results with research suggestions. *Psychological Bulletin,* 1943, *40,* 81-124.

Arsenian, J. M. Young children in an insecure situation. *Journal of Abnormal and Social Psychology,* 1943, *38,* 225-249.

Ashley, J. W. Stock prices and changes in earnings and dividends: some empirical results. *Journal of Political Economy,* 1962, *70,* 82-85.

Athey, K. R., Coleman, J. E., Reitman, A. P., & Tang, J. Two experiments showing the effect of the interviewer's racial background on responses to questionnaires concerning racial issues. *Journal of Applied Psychology,* 1960, *44,* 244-246.

Babchuk, N., & Bates, A. P. Professor or producer: the two faces of academic man. *Social Forces,* 1962, *40,* 341-348.

Back, K. W. The well-informed informant. In R. N. Adams & J. J. Preiss (Eds.), *Human organization research.* Homewood, Ill.: Dorsey Press, 1960. Pp. 179-187.

Bain, H. M., & Hecock, D. S. *Ballot position and voter's choice: the arrangement of names on the ballot and its effect on the voter.* Detroit: Wayne State Univer. Press, 1957.

Bain, R. K. The researcher's role: a case study. In R. N. Adams & J. J. Preiss (Eds.), *Human organization research.* Homewood, Ill.: Dorsey Press, 1960. Pp. 140-152.

Bales, R. F. *Interaction process analysis.* Cambridge: Addison-Wesley, 1950.

Bandura, A. Lecture on imitation learning, Northwestern Univer., 1962.

Bandura, A., & Walters, R. *Social learning and personality development.* New York: Holt, Rinehart & Winston, 1963.

Barch, A. M., Trumbo, D., & Nangle, J. Social setting and conformity to a legal requirement. *Journal of Abnormal and Social Psychology,* 1957, *55,* 396-398.

Barker, R. G., & Wright, H. F. *One boy's day: a specimen record of behavior.* New York: Harper & Bros., 1951.

Barker, R. G., & Wright, H. F. *Midwest and its children: the psychological ecology of an American town.* Evanston, Ill.: Row, Peterson, 1954.

Barry, H. Relationships between child training and the pictorial arts. *Journal of Abnormal and Social Psychology,* 1957, *54,* 380-383.

Barzun, J. *The delights of detection.* New York: Criterion Books, 1961.

Bass, B. M. Ultimate criteria of organizational worth. *Personnel Psychology,* 1952, *5,* 157-173.

Baxter, J. Chicago shops pay better than N. Y.: big agencies pay more too. *Advertising Age,* May 28, 1962, *33,* 65.

Baumrind, D. Some thoughts on ethics of research: after reading Milgram's "Behavioral Study of Obedience," *American Psychologist,* 1964, *19,* 421-423.

Becker, H. S. Problems of inference and proof in participant observation. *American Sociological Review*, 1958, *23*, 652-660.

Belknap, G. M. A method for analyzing legislative behavior. *Midwest Journal of Political Science*, 1958, *2*, 377-402.

Beloff, J., & Beloff, H. The influence of valence on distance judgments of human faces. *Journal of Abnormal and Social Psychology*, 1961, *62*, 720-722.

Benney, M., Riesman, D., & Star, S. Age and sex in the interview. *American Journal of Sociology*, 1956, *62*, 143-152.

Berelson, B. *Content analysis in communication research*. Glencoe, Ill.: Free Press, 1952.

Berger, C. S. An experimental study of doodles. *Psychological Newsletter*, 1954, *6*, 138-141.

Berkson, G., & Fitz-Gerald, F. L. Eye fixation aspect of attention to visual stimuli in infant chimpanzees. *Science*, 1963, *139*, 586-587.

Berlyne, D. E. Emotional aspects of learning. In P. R. Farnsworth, O. McNemar, & Q. McNemar (Eds.), *Annual Review of Psychology*, 1964, *15*, 115-142.

Bernberg, R. E. Socio-psychological factors in industrial morale: I. the prediction of specific indicators. *Journal of Social Psychology*, 1952, *36*, 73-82.

Bernstein, E. M. *Money and the economic system*. Chapel Hill.: Univer. of North Carolina Press, 1935.

Berreman, J. V. M. Factors affecting the sale of modern books of fiction: a study of social psychology. Unpublished doctoral dissertation, Stanford Univer., 1940.

Binder, A. Statistical theory. In P. R. Farnsworth, O. McNemar, & Q. McNemar (Eds.), *Annual Review of Psychology*, 1964, *15*, 277-310.

Birdwhistell, R. Kinesics and communication. In E. Carpenter (Ed.), *Exploration in communication*. Boston: Beacon Hill, 1960. Pp. 54-64.

Birdwhistell, R. The kinesic level in the investigations of emotions. In P. Knapp (Ed.), *The expression of emotions in man*. New York: International Universities Press, 1963. Pp. 123-140.

Blake, R. R., Berkowitz, H., Bellamy, R. Q., & Mouton, J. S. Volunteering as an avoidance act. *Journal of Abnormal and Social Psychology*, 1956, *53*, 154-156.

Blake, R. R., Mouton, J. S., & Hain, J. D. Social forces in petition signing. *Southwest Social Science Quarterly*, 1956, *36*, 385-390.

Blau, P. M. *The dynamics of bureaucracy*. Chicago: Univer. of Chicago Press, 1955.

Blau, P. The research process in the study of *The dynamics of bureaucracy*. In P. E. Hammond (Ed.), *Sociologists at work*. New York: Basic Books, 1964. Pp. 16-49.

Bloch, V. L'étude objective du comportement des spectateurs. *Revue Internationale de Filmologie*, 1952, *3*, 221-222.

Blomgren, G. W., & Scheuneman, T. W. Psychological resistance to seat belts. Research Project RR-115, Northwestern Univer., Traffic Institute, 1961.

Blomgren, G. W., Scheuneman, T. W., & Wilkins, J. L. Effects of exposure to a safety poster on the frequency of turn signalling. *Traffic Safety*, 1963, *7*, 15-22.

Boring, E. G. The role of theory in experimental psychology. *American Journal of Psychology*, 1953, *66*, 169-184. (Reprinted in E. G. Boring, *History, psychology, and science.* Ed. R. I. Watson & D. T. Campbell, New York: Wiley, 1963. Pp. 210-225.)

Boring, E. G. The beginning and growth of measurement in psychology. *Isis*, 1961, *52*, 238-257. (Reprinted in E. G. Boring, *History, psychology, and science.* Ed. R. I. Watson & D. T. Campbell, New York: Wiley, 1963. Pp. 140-158.)

Boring, E. G. *History, psychology and science.* Ed. R. I. Watson & D. T. Campbell, New York: Wiley, 1963.

Boring, E. G., & Boring, M. D. Masters and pupils among the American psychologists. *American Journal of Psychology*, 1948, *61*, 527-534. (Reprinted in E. G. Boring, *History, psychology, and science.* ₀Ed.₀, R. I. Watson & D. T. Campbell, New York: Wiley, 1963. Pp. 132-139.)

Brayfield, A. H., & Crockett, W. H. Employee attitudes and employee performance. *Psychological Bulletin*, 1955, *52*, 396-424.

Bridgman, P. W. *The logic of modern physics.* New York: Macmillan, 1927.

Brock, T. C. Communicator-recipient similarity and decision change. *Journal of Personality and Social Psychology*, 1965, *1*, 650-654.

Brock, T. C., & Guidice, C. D. Stealing and temporal orientation. *Journal of Abnormal and Social Psychology*, 1963, *66*, 91-94.

Brogden, H., & Taylor, E. The dollar criterion — applying the cost accounting concept to criterion construction. *Personnel Psychology*, 1950, *3*, 133-154.

Brookover, L. A., & Back, K. W. Time sampling as a field technique. *Human Organization*, 1965, in press.

Brown, J. W. A new approach to the assessment of psychiatric therapies. Unpublished manuscript, 1960.

Brown, J. W. The use of the single case study with actuarial and indirect indices in psychiatric research. Unpublished manuscript, 1961.

Brozek, J. Recent developments in Soviet psychology. In P. R. Farnsworth, O. McNemar, & Q. McNemar (Eds.), *Annual Review of Psychology*, 1964, *15*, 493-594.

Bryan, J. Personal communication, 1965.

Bugental, J. F. T. An investigation of the relationship of the conceptual matrix to the self-concept. Unpublished doctoral dissertation, Ohio State Univer., 1948.

Burchard, W. W. A study of attitudes towards the use of concealed devices in social science research. *Social Forces*, 1957, *36*, 111.

Burchinal, L. G., & Chancellor, L. E. Ages at marriage, occupations of grooms and interreligious marriage rates. *Social Forces*, 1962, *40*, 348-354.

Burchinal, L. G., & Chancellor, L. E. Survival rates among religiously homogamous and interreligious marriages. *Social Forces*, 1963, *41*, 353-362.

Burchinal, L. G., & Kenkel, W. F. Religious identification and occupational status of Iowa grooms. *American Sociological Review*, 1962, *27*, 526-532.

Burma, J. H. Self-tattooing among deliquents: a research note. *Sociology and Social Research*, 1959, *43*, 341-345.

Burwen, L., & Campbell, D. T. The generality of attitudes toward authority and nonauthority figures. *Journal of Abnormal and Social Psychology*, 1957, *54*, 24-31.

Callahan, J. D., Morris, J. C., Seifried, S., Ulett, G. A., & Heusler, A. F. Objective measures in psychopharmacology: baseline observations. *Missouri Medicine*, 1960, *57*, 714-718.

Campbell, D. T. The informant in quantitative research. *American Journal of Sociology*, 1955, *60*, 339-342.

Campbell, D. T. Leadership and its effects upon the group. *Ohio Studies in Personnel*, Research Monograph 83. Columbus: Ohio State Univer., Bureau of Business Research, 1956.

Campbell, D. T. Factors relevant to the validity of experiments in social settings. *Psychological Bulletin*, 1957, *54*, 297-312.

Campbell, D. T. Systematic error on the part of human links in communication systems. *Information and Control*, 1959, *1*, 334-369.

Campbell, D. T. Recommendations for APA test standards regarding construct trait or discriminant validity. *American Psychologist*, 1960, *15*, 546-553.

Campbell, D. T. The mutual methodological relevance of anthropology and psychology. In F. L. K. Hsu (Ed.), *Psychological anthropology approaches to culture and personality*. Homewood, Ill.: Dorsey Press, 1961. Pp. 333-352.

Campbell, D. T. Administrative experimentation, institutional records and nonreactive measures. In B. G. Chandler, E. F. Carlson, F. Bertolaet, C. Byerly, J. Lee, R. Sperber (Eds.), *Research Seminar on Teacher Education*, Report on Cooperative Research Project No. G-011 supported by the Cooperative Research Program of the Office of Education, U. S. Department of Health, Education, and Welfare, Northwestern Univer., August, 1963. Pp. 75-120. (Duplicated.) (a)

Campbell, D. T. From description to experimentation: interpreting trends as quasi-experiments. In C. W. Harris (Ed.), *Problems in measuring change*. Madison, Wis.: Univer. of Wisconsin Press, 1963. Pp. 212-242. (b)

Campbell, D. T. Social attitudes and other acquired behavioral dispositions. In S. Koch (Ed.), *Psychology: a study of a science*, Vol. 6, *Investigations of man as socius*. New York: McGraw-Hill, 1963. Pp. 94-176. (c)

Campbell, D. T. Pattern matching as an essential in distal knowing. In K. R. Hammond (Ed.), *The psychology of Egon Brunswik*. New York: Holt, Rinehart & Winston, 1965. (a)

Campbell, D. T. On the use of both pro and con items in attitude scales. Unpublished manuscript, 1965. (b)

Campbell, D. T., & Fiske, D. W. Convergent and discriminant validation by the multitrait-multimethod matrix. *Psychological Bulletin*, 1959, *56*, 81-105.

Campbell, D. T., Kruskal, W. H., & Wallace, W. P. Seating aggregation as an index of attitude. *Sociometry*, 1966, *29*, 1-15.

Campbell, D. T., & Mack, R. W. The steepness of interracial boundaries as a function of the locus of social interaction. In preparation.

Campbell, D. T., & McCormack, T. H. Military experience and attitudes toward authority. *American Journal of Sociology*, 1957, *62*, 482-490.

Campbell, D. T., & Stanley, J. C. Experimental and quasi-experimental designs for research on teaching. In N. L. Gage (Ed.), *Handbook of research on teaching*. Chicago: Rand McNally, 1963. Pp. 171-246.

Cane, V. R., & Heim, A. W. The effects of repeated testing: III. further experiments and general conclusions. *Quarterly Journal of Experimental Psychology*, 1950, *2*, 182-195.

Cantril, H. *Gauging public opinion*. Princeton: Princeton Univer. Press, 1944.

Caplow, T., & McGee, R. *The academic marketplace*. New York: Basic Books, 1958.

Capra, P. C., & Dittes, J. E. Birth order as a selective factor among volunteer subjects. *Journal of Abnormal and Social Psychology*, 1962, *64*, 302.

Carhart, R. The binaural reception of meaningful materials. Unpublished manuscript, Northwestern Univer., 1965. To appear in A. B. Graham (Ed.), *Sensorineuro hearing processes and disorders*. Boston: Little, Brown, in press.

Carlson, J., Cook, S. W., & Stromberg, E. L. Sex differences in conversation. *Journal of Applied Psychology*, 1936, *20*, 727-735.

Carroll, P. F. Personal communication, 1962.

Chapman, L. J., & Bock, R. D. Components of variance due to acquiescence and content in the F-scale measure of authoritarianism. *Psychological Bulletin*, 1958, *55*, 328-333.

Chapple, E. D. Quantitative analysis of complex organizational systems. *Human Organization*, 1962, *21*, 67-80.

Christensen, H. T. Cultural relativism and premarital sex norms. *American Sociological Review*, 1960, *25*, 31-39.

Clark, K. *America's psychologists*. Washington, D. C.: American Psychological Association, 1957.

Clark, W. H. A study of some of the factors leading to achievement and creativity with special reference to religious skepticism and belief. *Journal of Social Psychology*, 1955, *41*, 57-69. (Abstracted in M. I. Stein & S. J. Heinze [Eds.], *Creativity and the individual*. Glencoe, Ill.: Free Press, 1960. Pp. 147-148.)

Cogley, J. Cited in D. McCahill, Parleys to evaluate Catholic status. *Chicago Sun-Times*, June 8, 1963, *16*, 12.

Coleman, J., Katz, E., & Menzel, H. The diffusion of an innovation among physicians. *Sociometry*, 1957, *20*, 253-270.

Coleman, R. P., & Neugarten, B. *Social class in the city*. In preparation.

Conrad, B. *The death of Manolete*. Cambridge: Houghton Mifflin, 1958.

Cook, S. W., & Selltiz, C. A multiple-indicator approach to attitude measurement. *Psychological Bulletin*, 1964, *62*, 36-55.

Coombs, C. *A theory of data*. New York: Wiley, 1963.

Cooper, S. L. Random sampling by telephone: a new and improved method. *Journal of Marketing Research*, 1964, *1*, 45-48.

Couch, A., & Keniston, K. Yeasayers and naysayers: agreeing response set as a personality variable. *Journal of Abnormal and Social Psychology*, 1960, *60*, 151-174.

Couch, A., & Keniston, K. Agreeing response set and social desirability. *Journal of Abnormal and Social Psychology*, 1961, *62*, 175-179.

Cox, C. M. *The early mental traits of three hundred geniuses*. Stanford, Calif.: Stanford Univer. Press, 1926. (Abstracted in M. I. Stein & S. J. Heinze, [Eds.], *Creativity and the individual*. Glencoe, Ill.: Free Press, 1960. Pp. 128-133.)

Cox, G. H., & Marley, E. The estimation of motility during rest or sleep. *Journal of Neurology, Neurosurgery and Psychiatry*, 1959, *22*, 57-60.

Craddick, R. A. Size of Santa Claus drawings as a function of time before and after Christmas. *Journal of Psychological Studies*, 1961, 12, 121-125.

Craddick, R. A. Size of witch drawings as a function of time before, on, and after Halloween. *American Psychologist*, 1962, *17*, 307. (Abstr.)

Cratty, J. Conformity behavior as a function of dress and race. Unpublished manuscript, Northwestern Univer., 1962.

Crespi, L. P. The interview effect on polling. *Public Opinion Quarterly*, 1948, *12*, 99-111.

Cronbach, L. J. Response sets and test validity. *Educational and Psychological Measurement*, 1946, *6*, 475-494.

Cronbach, L. J. Proposals leading to analytic treatment of social perception scores. In R. Tagiuri & L. Petrullo (Eds.), *Person perception and interpersonal behavior*. Stanford, Calif.: Stanford Univer. Press, 1958. Pp. 353-379.

Crowald, R. H. Soviet grave markers indicate how buried rated with regime. *El Universal* (Mexico City), August 15, 1964, *196*, 12.

Dalton, M. Preconceptions and methods in *Men Who Manage*. In P. E. Hammond (Ed.), *Sociologists at work*. New York: Basic Books, 1964. Pp. 50-95.

Darwin, C. *The expression of the emotions in man and animals*. London: Murray, 1872.

Davis, R. C. Physiological responses as a means of evaluating information. In A. D. Biderman & H. Zimmer (Eds.), *The manipulation of human behavior*. New York: Wiley, 1961. Pp. 142-168.

Dearborn, D. C., & Simon, H. A. Selective perception: a note on the departmental identification of executives. *Sociometry*, 1958, *21*, 140-144.

DeCharms, R., & Moeller, G. Values expressed in American children's readers: 1800-1950. *Journal of Abnormal and Social Psychology*, 1962, *64*, 136-142.

DeFleur, M. L., & Petranoff, R. M. A televised test of subliminal persuasion. *Public Opinion Quarterly*, 1959, *23*, 168-180.

Dempsey, P. Liberalism-conservatism and party loyalty in the U. S. Senate. *Journal of Social Psychology*, 1962, *56*, 159-170.

Deutsch, M. An experimental study of the effects of cooperation and competition upon group process. *Human Relations*, 1949, *2*, 199-231.

Dexter, L. A. What do congressmen hear? In N. Polsby, R. Dentler, & P. Smith (Eds.), *Politics and social life*. Boston: Houghton Mifflin, 1963. Pp. 485-495.

Dexter, L. A. Communications — pressure, influence or education? In L. A. Dexter & D. M. White (Eds.), *People, society and mass communications*. New York: Free Press, 1964. Pp. 394-409.

Diamond, S. Some early uses of the questionnaire. *Public Opinion Quarterly*, 1963, *27*, 528-542.

Digman, J., & Tuttle, D. An interpretation of an election by means of obverse factor analysis. *Journal of Social Psychology*, 1961, *53*, 183-194.

Dittman, A. T., & Wynne, L. C. Linguistic techniques and the analysis of emotionality in interviews. *Journal of Abnormal and Social Psychology*, 1961, *63*, 201-204.

Dollard, J., & Mowrer, O. H. A method for measuring tension in written documents. *Journal of Abnormal and Social Psychology*, 1947, *42*, 3-32.

Donnelly, R. C., Goldstein, J., & Schwartz, R. D. *Criminal law*. New York: Free Press, 1962.

Doob, L. W. *Communication in Africa*. New Haven: Yale Univer. Press, 1961.

Dornbusch, S., & Hickman, L. Other-directedness in consumer goods advertising: a test of Riesman's historical theory. *Social Forces*, 1959, *38*, 99-102.

DuBois, C. N. Time Magazine's fingerprints' study. *Proceedings: 9th Conference, Advertising Research Foundation*. New York: Advertising Research Foundation, 1963.

Duncan, C. P. Personal communication, 1963.

Durand, J. Mortality estimates from Roman tombstone inscriptions. *American Journal of Sociology*, 1960, *65*, 365-373.

Durkheim, E. *Suicide*. Trans. J. A. Spaulding & G. Simpson, Glencoe, Ill.: Free Press, 1951.

Edwards, A. L. *The social desirability variable in personality assessment and research*. New York: Dryden Press, 1957.

Edwards, A. L., & Walker, J. N. A note on the Couch and Keniston measure of agreement response set. *Journal of Abnormal and Social Psychology*, 1961, *62*, 173-174.

Ehrle, R. A., & Johnson, B. G. Psychologists and cartoonists. *American Psychologist*, 1961, *16*, 693-695.

Ekelblad, F. A. *The statistical method in business.* New York: Wiley, 1962.

Ellis, N. R., & Pryer, R. S. Quantification of gross bodily activity in children with severe neuropathology. *American Journal of Mental Deficiency*, 1959, *63*, 1034-1037.

Enciso, J. *Design motifs of ancient Mexico.* New York: Dover, 1953.

Evan, W. M. Peer-group interaction and organizational socialization: a study of employee turnover. *American Sociological Review*, 1963, *28*, 429-435.

Exline, R. V. Explorations in the process of person perception: visual interaction in relation to competition, sex and affiliation. *Journal of Personality*, 1963, *31*, 1-20.

Exline, R. V. *Affective phenomena and the mutual glance: effects of evaluative feedback and social reinforcement upon visual interaction with an interviewer.* Technical Report No. 12, Office of Naval Research Contract No. Nonr-2285(02), 1964.

Exline, R. V., Gray, D., & Schuette, D. Visual behavior in a dyad as affected by interview content and sex of respondent. *Journal of Personality and Social Psychology*, 1965, *1*, 201-209.

Exline, R. V., & Winters, L. C. *Interpersonal preference and the mutual glance.* Technical Report No. 13, Office of Naval Research Contract No. Nonr-2285(02), 1964.

Fairbanks, H. The quantitative differentiation of samples of spoken language. *Psychological Monographs*, 1944, *56*, No. 2 (Whole No. 255), 19-38.

Fantz, R. L. A method for studying depth perception in infants under six months of age. *Psychological Record*, 1961, *11*, 27-32. (a)

Fantz, R. L. The origin of form perception. *Scientific American*, May 1961, *204*, 66-72. (b)

Fantz, R. L. Pattern vision in newborn infants. *Science*, 1963, *140*, 296-297.

Fantz, R. L. Visual experience in infants: decreased attention to familiar patterns relative to novel ones. *Science*, 1964, *146*, 668-670.

Fantz, R. L., Ordy, J. M., & Udelf, M. S. Maturation of pattern vision in infants during the first six months. *Journal of Comparative and Physiological Psychology*, 1962, *55*, 907-917.

Farris, C. D. A method of determining ideological groupings in the Congress. *Journal of Politics*, 1958, *20*, 308-338.

Feshbach, S., & Feshbach, N. Influence of the stimulus object upon the complementary and supplementary projection of fear. *Journal of Abnormal and Social Psychology*, 1963, *66*, 498-502.

Festinger, L., & Katz, D. *Research methods in the behavioral sciences.* New York: Holt, Rinehart & Winston, 1953.

Fiedler, F. E. The nature of teamwork. *Discovery*, February 1962.

Fiedler, F. E., Dodge, J. S., Jones, R. E., & Hutchins, E. B. Interrelations among measures of personality adjustment in non-clinical populations. *Journal of Abnormal and Social Psychology*, 1958, *56*, 345-351.

Field, M. *Children and films: a study of boys and girls in the cinema.* Dunfermline, Fife: Carnegie United Kingdom Trust, 1954.

Fisher, I. *The making of index numbers.* Boston: Houghton Mifflin, 1923.

Fiske, D. W. Values, theory and the criterion problem. *Personnel Psychology*, 1951, *4*, 93-98.

Flagler, J. M. Profiles: student of the spontaneous. *New Yorker*, December 10, 1960, *36*, 59-92.

Flugel, J. C. *Psychology of clothes.* London: Hogarth, 1930.

Foote, E. Pupil dilation — new measurement of ad's effectiveness. *Advertising Age*, March 5, 1962, *33*, 12.

Forshufvud, S. *Vem mordade Napoleon?* Stockholm: A. Bonnier, 1961.

Foshee, J. G. Studies in activity level: I. simple and complex task perform-ances in defectives. *American Journal of Mental Deficiency*, 1958, *62*, 882-886.

Fowler, E. M. Help-wanted ads show sharp rise. *New York Times*, May 13, 1962, *III*, 1.

Franzen, R. Scaling responses to graded opportunities. *Public Opinion Quarterly*, 1950, *14*, 484-490.

Freed, A., Chandler, P. J., Mouton, J. S., & Blake, R. R. Stimulus and background factors in sign violation. *Journal of Personality*, 1955, *23*, 499. (Abstract.)

Freeman, L. C., & Ataov, T. Invalidity of indirect and direct measures of attitude toward cheating. *Journal of Personality*, 1960, *28*, 443-447.

French, E. G. Some characteristics of achievement motivation. *Journal of Experimental Psychology*, 1955, *50*, 232-236.

French, N. R., Carter, C. W., & Koenig, W. The words and sounds of telephone conversations. *Bell System Technical Journal*, 1930, *9*, 290-324.

Freud, S. *Psychopathology of everyday life.* London: Unwin, 1920.

Fry, C. L. The religious affiliations of American leaders. *Scientific Monthly*, 1933, *36*, 241-249. (Abstracted in M. I. Stein & S. J. Heinze [Eds.], *Creativity and the individual.* Glencoe, Ill.: Free Press, 1960. Pp. 148-149.)

Gabriele, C. T. *The recording of audience reactions by infrared photography,* Technical Report, NAVTRADEVCEN 269-7-56, 1956.

Gage, N. L., & Shimberg, B. Measuring senatorial progressivism. *Journal of Abnormal and Social Psychology*, 1949, *44*, 112-117.

Galton, F. *Hereditary genius.* New York: D. Appleton, 1870. (Abstracted in M. I. Stein, & S. J. Heinze [Eds.], *Creativity and the individual.* Glencoe, Ill.: Free Press, 1960. Pp. 85-90.)

Galton, F. Statistical inquiries into the efficacy of prayer. *Fortnightly Review*, 1872, *12*, 125-135.

Galton, F. Measurement of character. *Fortnightly Review,* 1884, *36,* 179-185.

Galton, F. The measure of fidget. *Nature,* 1885, *32,* 174-175.

Garner, W. R. Context effects and the validity of loudness scales. *Journal of Experimental Psychology,* 1954, *48,* 218-224.

Garner, W. R., Hake, H. W., & Eriksen, C. W. Operationism and the concept of perception. *Psychological Review,* 1956, *63,* 149-159.

Gearing, F. The response to a cultural precept among migrants from Bronzeville to Hyde Park. Unpublished master's thesis, Univer. of Chicago, June, 1952.

Ghiselli, E. E., & Brown, C. W. *Personnel and industrial psychology.* (2nd. ed.) New York: McGraw-Hill, 1955.

Goncourt, Edmond de. *The Goncourt Journals: 1851-1870.* Ed. & trans. by Louis Galantière from *Journal of Edmond & Jules de Goncourt.* New York: Doubleday, Doran, 1937.

Good, C. V., & Scates, D. E. *Methods of research, educational, psychological, sociological.* New York: Appleton-Century-Crofts, 1954.

Goode, W. J., & Hatt, P. K. *Methods in social research.* New York: McGraw-Hill, 1952.

Gordon, T. The development of a method of evaluating flying skill. *Personnel Psychology,* 1950, *3,* 71-84.

Gore, P. M., & Rotter, J. B. A personality correlate of social action. *Journal of Personality,* 1963, *31,* 58-64.

Gosnell, H. F. *Getting out the vote: an experiment in the stimulation of voting.* Chicago: Univer. of Chicago Press, 1927.

Gottschalk, L. A., & Gleser, G. C. An analysis of the verbal content of suicide notes. *British Journal of Medical Psychology,* 1960, *33,* 195-204.

Gould, J. Costello TV's first headless star; only his hands entertain audience, *New York Times,* March 4, 1951, *100* (34), 1. Cited in I. Doig, Kefauver and crime; the rise of television news and a senator. Unpublished master's thesis. Northwestern Univer., 1962.

Grace, H., & Tandy, M. Delegate communication as an index of group tension. *Journal of Social Psychology,* 1957, *45,* 93-97.

Gratiot-Alphandery, H. L'enfant et le film. *Revue Internationale de Filmologie,* 1951, *2,* 171-172. (a)

Gratiot-Alphandery, H. Jeunes spectateurs. *Revue Internationale de Filmologie,* 1951, *2,* 257-263. (b)

Green, E. *Judicial attitudes in sentencing.* New York: St. Martin's Press, 1961.

Green, H. B., & Knapp, R. H. Time judgment, aesthetic preference, and need for achievement. *Journal of Abnormal and Social Psychology,* 1959, *58,* 140-142.

Greenhill, L. P. The recording of audience reactions by infrared photography. Technical report from Pennsylvania State Univer. to U.S.

Navy, Special Devices Center, SPECDEVCEN 269-7-56, September 20, 1955, pp. 1-11.

Griffin, J. R. Coia "catch," kicking draw much criticism. *Chicago Sun-Times*, October 27, 1964, *17*, 76.

Griffith, R. M. Odds adjustments by American horse race bettors. *American Journal of Psychology*, 1949, *62*, 290-294.

Grinder, R. E. New techniques for research in children's temptation behavior. *Child Development*, 1961, *32*, 679-688.

Grinder, R. E. Parental child learning practices, conscience, and resistance to temptation of sixth grade children. *Child Development*, 1962, *33*, 803-820.

Grinder, R. E., & McMichael, R. E. Cultural influence on conscience development: resistance to temptation and guilt among Samoans and American caucasians. *Journal of Abnormal and Social Psychology*, 1963, *66*, 503-507.

Grusky, O. Organizational goals and the behavior of informal leaders. *American Journal of Sociology*, 1959, *65*, 59-67.

Grusky, O. The effects of formal structure on managerial recruitment: a study of baseball organization. *Sociometry*, 1963, *26*, 345-353. (a)

Grusky, O. Managerial succession and organizational effectiveness. *American Journal of Sociology*, 1963, *69*, 21-31. (b)

Guilford, J. P. *Psychometric methods*. New York: McGraw-Hill, 1954.

Guilford, J. P. The relation of intellectual factors to creative thinking in science. In C. Taylor (Ed.), *The 1955 University of Utah research conference on the identification of creative scientific talent*. Salt Lake City: Univer. of Utah Press, 1956. Pp. 69-95.

Guion, R. M. Criterion measurement and personnel judgments. *Personnel Psychology*, 1961, *14*, 141-149.

Gullahorn, J., & Strauss, G. The field worker in union research. In R. N. Adams & J. J. Preiss (Eds.), *Human organization research*. Homewood, Ill.: Dorsey Press, 1960. Pp. 153-165.

Gump, R. *Jade: stone of heaven*. New York: Doubleday, 1962.

Gusfield, J. R. Field work reciprocities in studying a social movement. In R. N. Adams & J. J. Preiss (Eds.), *Human organization research*. Homewood, Ill.: Dorsey Press, 1960. Pp. 99-108.

Hafner, E. M., & Presswood, Susan. Strong inference and weak interactions. *Science*, 1965, *149*, 503-510.

Haggard, E. A., Brekstad, A., & Skard, A. G. On the reliability of the anamnestic interview. *Journal of Abnormal and Social Psychology*, 1960, *61*, 311-318.

Halbwachs, M. *Les causes de suicide*. Paris: Felix Alcan, 1930.

Hall, E. T. Silent assumption in social communication. *Disorders of Communication*, 1964, *42*, 41-55.

Hall, R. L., & Willerman, B. The educational influence of dormitory roommates. *Sociometry*, 1963, *26*, 294-318.

Hamburger, P. Peeping Funt. *New Yorker*, January 7, 1950, *25*, 72-73.

Hamilton, T. Social optimism in American protestanism. *Public Opinion Quarterly*, 1942, *6*, 280-283.

Hansen, A. H. Cycles of prosperity and depression in the United States. *Univer. of Wisconsin Studies in Social Sciences and History.* Madison, 1921.

Hanson, N. R. *Patterns of discovery.* Cambridge: Cambridge Univer. Press, 1958.

Hardy, H. C. Cocktail party acoustics. *Journal of the Acoustical Society of America,* 1959, *31,* 535.

Hartmann, G. W. A field experiment on the comparative effectiveness of "emotional" and "rational" political leaflets in determining election results. *Journal of Abnormal and Social Psychology,* 1936, *31,* 99-114.

Hartshorne, H., & May, M. A. *Studies in the nature of character.* Vol. 1. *Studies in deceit.* New York: Macmillan, 1928.

Hartshorne, H., May, M. A., & Maller, J. B. *Studies in the nature of character.* Vol. 2. *Studies in service and self control.* New York: Macmillan, 1929.

Hartshorne, H., May, M. A., & Shuttleworth, F. K. *Studies in the nature of character.* Vol. 3. *Studies in the organization of character.* New York: Macmillan, 1930.

Harvey, J. The content characteristics of best-selling novels. *Public Opinion Quarterly,* 1953, *17,* 91-114.

Haworth, M.R. An exploratory study to determine the effectiveness of a filmed puppet show as a group projective technique for use with children. Unpublished doctoral dissertation, Pennsylvania State Univer., 1956. University Microfilms, Ann Arbor, Mich. No. 19305.

Helson, H., Blake, R. R., & Mouton, J. S. Petition-signing as adjustment to situational and personal factors. *Journal of Social Psychology,* 1958, *48,* 3-10.

Hemphill, J. K., & Sechrest, L. B. A comparison of three criteria of aircrew effectiveness in combat over Korea. *Journal of Applied Psychology,* 1952, *36,* 323-327.

Henle, M., & Hubble, M. B. "Egocentricity" in adult conversation. *Journal of Social Psychology,* 1938, *9,* 227-234.

Henry, H. *Motivation research: its practice and uses for advertising, marketing, and other business purposes.* London: Crosby Lockwood, 1958.

Herbinière-Lebert, S. Pourquoi et comment nous avons fait "Mains Blanches": premières experiences avec un film educatif realisé spécialement pour les mins de sept ans. *Revue Internationale de Filmologie,* 1951, *2,* 247-255.

Hess, E. H., & Polt, J. M. Pupil size as related to interest value of visual stimuli. *Science,* 1960, *132,* 349-350.

Heusler, A., Ulett, G., & Blasques, J. Noise-level index: an objective measurement of the effect of drugs on the psychomotor activity of patients. *Journal of Neuropsychiatry,* 1959, *1,* 23-25.

Heusler, A. F., Ulett, G. A., & Callahan, J. D. Comparative EEG studies of tranquilizing drugs. Research Laboratories of the St. Louis State

Hospital, St. Louis, Mo. Paper read at Pan-American Medical Congress, Mexico City, May 3, 1960.

Heyns, R., & Lippitt, R. Systematic observational techniques. In G. Lindzey (Ed.), *Handbook of social psychology*. Vol. 1. Cambridge: Addison-Wesley, 1954. Pp. 370-404.

Hildum, D. C., & Brown, R. W. Verbal reinforcement and interviewer bias. *Journal of Abnormal and Social Psychology*, 1956, *53*, 108-111.

Hillebrandt, R. H. Panel design and time-series analysis. Unpublished master's thesis, Northwestern Univer., 1962.

Holmes, L. D. *Ta'u: Stability and change in a Samoan village*. Reprint No. 7. Wellington, N.Z.: Polynesian Society, 1958.

Horst, P. Correcting the Kuder-Richardson reliability for dispersion of item difficulties. *Psychological Bulletin*, 1953, *50*, 371-374.

Houseman, E. E., & Lipstein, B. Observation and audit techniques for measuring retail sales. *Agricultural Economics*, 1960, *12*, 61-72.

Hovland, C. I., Lumsdaine, A. A., & Sheffield, F. D. *Experiments on mass communication*. Princeton: Princeton Univer. Press, 1949.

Howells, L. T., & Becker, S. W. Seating arrangement and leadership emergence. *Journal of Abnormal and Social Psychology*, 1962, *64*, 148-150.

Hughes, E. C. *Men and their work*. Glencoe, Ill.: Free Press, 1958.

Humphreys, L. G. Note on the multitrait-multimethod matrix. *Psychological Bulletin*, 1960, *57*, 86-88.

Hyman, H. H., Cobb, W. J., Feldman, J. J., Hart, C. W., & Stember, C. H. *Interviewing in social research*. Chicago: Univer. of Chicago Press, 1954.

Ianni, F. A. Residential and occupational mobility as indices of the acculturation of an ethnic group. *Social Forces*, 1957-58, *36*, 65-72.

Imanishi, K. Social organization of subhuman primates in their natural habitat. *Current Anthropology*, 1960, *1*, 393-407.

Jackson, D. N., & Messick, S. J. A note on "ethnocentrism" and acquiescent response sets. *Journal of Abnormal and Social Psychology*, 1957, *54*, 132-134.

Jacques, E. *Measurement of responsibility*. Cambridge: Harvard Univer. Press, 1956.

Jaffe, A. J., & Stewart, C. D. *Manpower, resources and utilizations*. New York: Wiley, 1951.

Jahoda-Lazarsfeld, M., & Zeisel, H. *Die Arbeitslösen von Marienbad*. Leipzig: Hirzel, 1932.

James, J. A preliminary study of the size determinant in small group interaction. *American Sociological Review*, 1951, *16*, 474-477.

James, R. W. A technique for describing community structure through newspaper analysis. *Social Forces*, 1958, *37*, 102-109.

James, W. *The principles of psychology*. New York: Holt, 1890.

Janis, I. L., & Hovland, C. I. An overview of persuasibility research. In I. L. Janis & C. I. Hovland (Eds.), *Personality and persuasibility*. New Haven: Yale Univer. Press, 1959. Pp. 1-26.

Janowitz, M. Inferences about propaganda impact from textual and documentary analysis. In W. E. Daugherty & M. Janowitz (Eds.), *A psychological warfare casebook*. Baltimore: Johns Hopkins Press, 1958. Pp. 732-735.

Jay, R., & Copes, J. Seniority and criterion measures of job proficiency. *Journal of Applied Psychology*, 1957, *41*, 58-60.

Jecker, J., Maccoby, N., Breitrose, H. S., & Rose, E. D. Teacher accuracy in assessing cognitive visual feedback from students. *Journal of Applied Psychology*, 1964, *48*, 393-397.

Jones, R. W. Progressivism in Illinois communities as measured by library services. *Transactions of the Illinois State Academy of Science*, 1960, *53*, 166-172.

Jones, V. Character development in children: an objective approach. In L. Carmichael (Ed.), *Manual of child psychology*. New York: Wiley, 1946. Pp. 707-751.

Jung, A. F. Price variations among automobile dealers in Chicago, Illinois. *Journal of Business*, 1959, *32*, 315-326.

Jung, A. F. Prices of Falcon and Corvair cars in Chicago and selected cities. *Journal of Business*, 1960, *33*, 121-126.

Jung, A. F. Impact of the compact cars on new-car prices. *Journal of Business*, 1961, *34*, 167-182.

Jung, A. F. Impact of the compact cars on new-car prices: a reappraisal. *Journal of Business*, 1962, *35*, 70-76.

Jung, A. F. Dealer pricing practices and finance charges for new mobile homes. *Journal of Business*, 1963, *36*, 430-439.

Jung, A. F. Mortgage availability and terms in Florida. *Journal of Business*, 1964, *37*, 274-279.

Kadish, S. On the tactics of police-prosecution oriented critics of the courts. *Cornell Law Quarterly*, 1964, *49*, 436-477.

Kahn, R. L., & Cannell, C. F. *The dynamics of interviewing: theory, technique and cases*. New York: Wiley, 1957.

Kaminski, G., & Osterkamp, U. Untersuchungen über die Topologie sozialer Handlungsfelder. *Zeitschrift für experimentelle und angewandte Psychologie*, 1962, *9*, 417-451.

Kane, F. Clothing worn by out-patients to interviews. *Psychiatric Communications*, 1958, *1* (2).

Kane, F. Clothing worn by an out-patient: a case study. *Psychiatric communications*, 1959, *2* (2).

Kane, F. The meaning of the form of clothing. *Psychiatric Communications*, 1962, *5* (1).

Kanfer, F. H. Verbal rate, eyeblink and content in structured psychiatric interviews. *Journal of Abnormal and Social Psychology*, 1960, *61*, 341-347.

Kappel, J. W. Book clubs and the evaluation of books. *Public Opinion Quarterly*, 1948, *12*, 243-252.

Katz, D. Do interviewers bias poll results? *Public Opinion Quarterly*, 1942, *6*, 248-268.

Kavanau, J. L. Behavior: confinement, adaptation, and compulsory regimes in laboratory studies. *Science*, 1964, *143*, 490.

Kendall, L. M. The hidden variance: what does it measure? *American Psychologist*, 1963, *18*, 452.

Kerlinger, F. N. *Foundations of behavioral research: educational and psychological inquiry.* New York: Holt, Rinehart & Winston, 1964.

Kimbrell, D. L., & Blake, R. R. Motivational factors in the violation of a prohibition. *Journal of Abnormal and Social Psychology*, 1958, *56*, 132-133.

Kinsey, A. C., Pomeroy, W. B., Martin, C. E., & Gebhard, P. H. *Sexual behavior in the human female.* Philadelphia: W. B. Saunders, 1953.

Kintz, B. L., Delprato, D. J., Mettee, D. R., Persons, C. E., & Schappe, R. H. The experimenter effect. *Psychological Bulletin*, 1965, 63, 223-232.

Kirk, P. L. Criminalistics. *Science*, 1963, *140*, 367-370.

Kitsuse, J. I., & Cicourel, A. V. A note on the uses of official statistics. *Social Problems*, 1963, *11*, 131-139.

Knox, J. B. Absenteeism and turnover in an Argentine factory. *American Sociological Review*, 1961, *26*, 424-428.

Kort, F. Predicting Supreme Court decisions mathematically: a quantitative analysis of "right to counsel" cases. *American Political Science Review*, 1957, *51*, 1-12.

Kort, F. Reply to Fisher's "Mathematical Analysis of Supreme Court Decisions." *American Political Science Review*, 1958, *52*, 339-348.

Kramer, E. Judgment of personal characteristics and emotions from nonverbal properties of speech. *Psychological Bulletin*, 1963, *60*, 408-420.

Kramer, E. Elimination of verbal cues in judgments of emotion from voice. *Journal of Abnormal and Social Psychology*, 1964, *68*, 390-396.

Krasner, L. Studies of the conditioning of verbal behavior. *Psychological Bulletin*, 1958, *55*, 148-170.

Kretsinger, E. A. An experimental study of gross bodily movement as an index to audience interest. *Speech Monographs*, 1952, *19*, 244-248.

Kretsinger, E. A. An experimental study of restiveness in preschool educational television audiences. *Speech Monographs*, 1959, *26*, 72-77.

Krislov, S. Amicus curiae brief: from friendship to advocacy. *Yale Law Journal*, 1963, *72*, 694-721.

Krout, M. H. *Major aspects of personality.* Chicago: College Press, 1933.

Krout, M. H. Further studies on the relation of personality and gestures: a nosological analysis of autistic gestures. *Journal of Experimental Psychology*, 1937, *20*, 279-287.

Krout, M. H. Gestures and attitudes: an experimental study of the verbal equivalents and other characteristics of a selected group of manual autistic gestures. Unpublished doctoral dissertation, Univer. of Chicago, 1951.

Krout, M. H. An experimental attempt to determine the significance of unconscious manual symbolic movements. *Journal of General Psychology*, 1954, *51*, 121-152. (a)

Krout, M. H. An experimental attempt to produce unconscious manual symbolic movements. *Journal of General Psychology*, 1954, *51*, 93-120. (b)

Krueger, L. E. & Ramond, C. K. References. In M. Mayer, *The intelligent man's guide to sales measures of advertising*. New York: Advertising Research Foundation, 1965. Pp. 29-71.

Krugman, H. E. Some applications of pupil measurement. *Journal of Marketing Research*, 1964, *1*, 15-19.

Kuhn, T. *The structure of scientific revolutions*. Chicago: Univer. of Chicago Press, 1962.

Kupcinet, I. Kup's column. *Chicago Sun-Times*, March 9, 1965, *18*, 46.

Lander, B. *Towards an understanding of juvenile delinquency*. New York: Columbia Univer. Press, 1954.

Landis, C. National differences in conversation. *Journal of Abnormal and Social Psychology*, 1927, *21*, 354-357.

Landis, C., & Hunt, W. A. *The startle pattern*. New York: Farrar & Rinehart, 1939.

Landis, M. H., & Burtt, H. E. A study of conversations. *Journal of Comparative Psychology*, 1924, *4*, 81-89.

Lang, K., & Lang, G. E. Decisions for Christ: Billy Graham in New York City. In M. Stein, A. J. Vidich, & D. M. White (Eds.), *Identity and anxiety*. Glencoe, Ill.: Free Press, 1960. Pp. 415-427.

LaPiere, R. T. Attitudes vs. actions. *Social Forces*, 1934, *13*, 230-237.

Lasswell, H. D. The world attention survey. *Public Opinion Quarterly*, 1941, *5*, 456-462.

Lea, T. *The brave bulls*. Boston: Little, Brown, 1949.

Lefkowitz, M., Blake, R. R., & Mouton, J. S. Status factors in pedestrian violation of traffic signals. *Journal of Abnormal and Social Psychology*, 1955, *51*, 704-706.

Legget, R. F., & Northwood, T. D. Noise surveys of cocktail parties. *Journal of the Acoustical Society of America*, 1960, *32*, 16-17.

Lehman, H. C., & Witty, P. A. Scientific eminence and church membership. *Scientific Monthly*, 1931, *36*, 544-549. (Abstracted in M. I. Stein, & S. J. Heinze, *Creativity and the individual*. Glencoe, Ill.: Free Press, 1960. Pp. 149-150.)

Leipold, W. D. Psychological distance in a dyadic interview as a function of introversion-extraversion, anxiety, social desirability and stress. Unpublished doctoral dissertation, Univer. of North Dakota, 1963.

Lenski, G. E., & Leggett, J. C. Caste, class, and deference in the research interview. *American Journal of Sociology*, 1960, *65*, 463-467.

Leroy-Boussion, A. Etude du comportement émotional enfantin au cours de la projection d'un film comique. *Revue Internationale de Filmologie*, 1954, *5*, 105-123.

Lewin, H. S. Hitler youth and the Boys Scouts of America. *Human Relations*, 1947, *1*, 206-227.

Lewis, O. *The children of Sanchez.* New York: Random House, 1961.

Libby, W. I. Accuracy of radio-carbon dates. *Science*, 1963, *140*, 278-280.

Lippmann, W. *The public philosophy.* New York: New American Library, 1955.

Lodge, G. T. Pilot stature in relation to cockpit size: a hidden factor in Navy jet aircraft accidents. *American Psychologist*, 1963, *17*, 468. (Abstr.)

Lombroso, C. *The man of genius.* London: Walter Scott, 1891. (Abstracted in M. I. Stein, & S. J. Heinze, *Creativity and the individual.* Glencoe, Ill.: Free Press, 1960. Pp. 350-353.)

Loomis, C. P. Political and occupational changes in a Hanoverian village, Germany. *Sociometry*, 1946, *9*, 316-333.

Lucas, D. B., & Britt, S. H. *Advertising psychology and research.* New York: McGraw-Hill, 1950.

Lucas, D. B., & Britt, S. H. *Measuring advertising effectiveness.* New York: McGraw-Hill, 1963.

Lustig, N. I. The relationships between demographic characteristics and pro-integration vote of white precincts in a metropolitan southern community. *Social Forces*, 1962, *40*, 205-208.

Lyle, H. M. An experimental study of certain aspects of the electromagnetic movement meter as a criterion to audience attention. *Speech Monographs*, 1953, *20*, 126. (Abstr.)

Mabie, E. A study of the conversation of first-grade pupils during free play periods. *Journal of Educational Research*, 1931, *24*, 135-138.

Mabley, J. Mabley's report. *Chicago American*, January 22, 1963, *62*, 3.

McCarroll, J. R., & Haddon, W. A controlled study of fatal accidents in New York City. *Journal of Chronic Diseases*, 1961, *15*, 811-826.

McCarthy, D. A comparison of children's language in different situations and its relation to personality traits. *Journal of Genetic Psychology*, 1929, *36*, 583-591.

Maccoby, E. E. Developmental psychology. In P. R. Farnsworth, O. McNemar, & Q. McNemar (Eds.), *Annual Review of Psychology*, 1964, *15*, 203-250.

McClelland, D. C. *The achieving society.* Princeton: Van Nostrand, 1961.

McGranahan, D., & Wayne, I. German and American traits reflected in popular drama. *Human Relations*, 1948, *1*, 429-455.

McGrath, J. E. The influence of positive interpersonal relations on adjustment and effectiveness in rifle teams. *Journal of Abnormal and Social Psychology*, 1962, *65*, 365-375.

McGraw, M., & Molloy, L. B. The pediatric anamnesis: inaccuracies in eliciting developmental data. *Child Development*, 1941, *12*, 255-265.

MacKinney, A. C. What should ratings rate? *Personnel*, 1960, *37*, 75-78.

MacLean, W. R. On the acoustics of cocktail parties. *Journal of the Acoustical Society of America.* 1959, *31*, 79-80.

MacRae, D. The role of the state legislator in Massachusetts. *American Sociological Review,* 1954, *19,* 185-194. (a)

MacRae, D. Some underlying variables in legislative roll call votes. *Public Opinion Quarterly,* 1954, *18,* 191-196. (b)

MacRae, D., & MacRae, E. Legislators' social status and their votes. *American Journal of Sociology,* 1961, *66,* 599-603.

Madge, J. *The tools of social science.* New York: Doubleday Anchor, 1965.

Mahl, G. Disturbances and silences in the patient's speech in psychotherapy. *Journal of Abnormal and Social Psychology,* 1956, *53,* 1-15.

Maller, J. B. The effect of signing one's name. *School and Society,* 1930, *31,* 882-884.

Manago, B. R. Mad: out of the comics rack and into satire. *Add One,* 1962, *1,* 41-46.

Marsh, R. M. Formal organization and promotion in a pre-industrial society. *American Sociological Review,* 1961, *26,* 547-556.

Martin, P. I call on the Candid Camera man. *Saturday Evening Post,* May 27, 1961, *234,* 26-27.

Matarazzo, J. D. Control of interview behavior. Paper read at American Psychological Association, St. Louis, September, 1962. (a)

Matarazzo, J. D. Prescribed behavior therapy: suggestions from noncontent interview research. In A. J. Bachrach (Ed.), *Experimental foundations of clinical psychology.* New York: Basic Books, 1962. Pp. 471-509. (b)

Matarazzo, J. D., Weitman, M., Saslow, G., & Wiens, A. N. Interviewer influence on duration of interviewee speech. *Journal of Verbal Learning and Verbal Behavior,* 1963, *1,* 451-458.

Matarazzo, J. D., Wiens, A. N., Saslow, G., Dunham, R. M., & Voas, R. B. Speech durations of astronaut and ground communicator. *Science,* 1964, *143,* 148-150.

Matthews, T. S. *The sugar pill.* New York: Simon & Schuster, 1957.

May, M. A., & Hartshorne, H. First steps toward a scale for measuring attitude. *Journal of Educational Psychology,* 1927, *17,* 145-162

Mechanic, D., & Volkart, E. H. Stress, illness behavior and the sick role. *American Sociological Review,* 1961, *26,* 51-58.

Melbin, M. Organization practice and individual behavior: absenteeism among psychiatric aides. *American Sociological Review,* 1961, *26,* 14-23.

Melton, A. W. Some behavior characteristics of museum visitors. *Psychological Bulletin,* 1933, *30,* 720-721. (a)

Melton, A. W. Studies of installation at the Pennsylvania Museum of Art. *Museum News,* 1933, *11,* 508. (b)

Melton, A. W. Problems of installation in museums of art. *Studies in museum education.* Washington, D.C.: American Association of Museums, 1935.

Melton, A. W. Distribution of attention in galleries in a museum of science and industry. *Museum News,* 1936, *13,* 3, 5-8.

Melton, A. W., Feldman, N. G., & Mason, C. W. Experimental studies of the education of children in a museum of science. *Publications of the American Association of Museums*, New Series, No. 15, 1936.

Merritt, C. B., & Fowler, R. G. The pecuniary honesty of the public at large. *Journal of Abnormal and Social Psychology*, 1948, *43*, 90-93.

Middleton, R. Fertility values in American magazine fiction: 1916-1956. *Public Opinion Quarterly*, 1960, *24*, 139-143.

Miller, G. A. Population, distance and the circulation of information. *American Journal of Psychology*, 1947, *60*, 276-284.

Mills, F. C. *The behavior of prices*. New York: National Bureau of Economic Research, 1927.

Mindak, W. A., Neibergs, A., & Anderson, A. Economic effects of the Minneapolis newspaper strike. *Journalism Quarterly*, 1963, *40*, 213-218.

Mitchell, W. C. *Index numbers of wholesale prices in the U.S. and foreign countries: I. the making and using of index numbers*. Bulletin No. 284. Washington, D.C.: U.S. Department of Labor, Bureau of Labor Statistics, 1921.

Moore, H. T. Laboratory tests of anger, fear, and sex interest. *American Journal of Psychology*, 1917, *28*, 390-395.

Moore, H. T. Further data concerning sex differences. *Journal of Abnormal and Social Psychology*, 1922, *17*, 210-214.

Moore, U., & Callahan, C. *Law and learning theory: a study in legal control*. New Haven: Yale Law Journal Co., 1943.

Moore, W. E. The exploitability of the "labor force" concept. *American Sociological Review*, 1953, *18*, 68-72.

Morgan, E. M. *Basic problems of evidence*. New York: Joint Committee on Continuing Legal Education of the American Law Institute and the American Bar Association, 1963.

Morgenstern, O. *On the accuracy of economic observations*. (2nd ed.) Princeton: Princeton Univer. Press, 1963.

Mosteller, F. Use as evidenced by an examination of wear and tear on selected sets of ESS. In K. Davis *et al.*, A study of the need for a new encyclopedic treatment of the social sciences. Unpublished manuscript, 1955. Pp. 167-174.

Mosteller, F., & Wallace, O. L. Inference in an authorship problem: a comparative study of discrimination methods applied to the authorship of *The Federalist Papers. Journal of the American Statistical Association*, 1963, *58*, 275-309.

Mudgett, B. D. *Index numbers*. New York: Wiley, 1951.

Murphy, G., & Murphy, L. Soviet life and Soviet psychology. In R. A. Bauer (Ed.), *Some views on Soviet psychology*. Washington, D.C.: American Psychological Association, 1962. Pp. 253-276.

Murray, E. J., & Cohen, M. Mental illness, milieu therapy, and social organization in ward groups. *Journal of Abnormal and Social Psychology*, 1959, *58*, 48-54.

Nagel, S. Ethic affiliations and judicial propensities. *Journal of Politics*, 1962, *24*, 92.

Naroll, R. The preliminary index of social development. *American Anthropologist*, 1956, *58*, 687-715.

Naroll, R. Controlling data quality. In Series Research in Social Psychology. *Symposia Studies Series*, No. 4, September, 1960. Pp. 7-12.

Naroll, R. Two solutions to Galton's problems. *Philosophy of Science*, 1961, *28*, 15-39.

Naroll, R. *Data quality control.* Glencoe, Ill.: Free Press, 1962.

Naroll, R., & Naroll, F. On bias of exotic data. *Man*, 1963, *25*, 24-26.

NASA Manned Spacecraft Center. *Results of the first United States manned orbital space flight, February 20, 1962.* Washington, D.C.: U.S. Government Printing Office, 1962. (a)

NASA Manned Spacecraft Center. *Results of the second United States manned orbital space flight, May 24, 1962.* Washington, D.C.: U.S. Government Printing Office, 1962. (b)

National Advertising Company. *Shopping center research study.* Bedford Park, Ill.: Author, 1963.

Nixon, H. K. Attention and interest in advertising. *Archives of Psychology*, 1924, *11*, 1-68.

North, R. C., Holsti, O. R., Zaninovich, M. G., & Zinnes, D. A. *Content analysis.* Evanston, Ill.: Northwestern Univer. Press, 1963.

O'Connor, N. (Ed.) *Recent Soviet psychology.* Trans. Ruth Kish, R. Crawford, & H. Asher. New York: Pergamon, 1961.

Olson, W. C. *The measurement of nervous habits in normal children.* Minneapolis: Univer. of Minnesota Press, 1929.

Orne, M. T. The nature of hypnosis: artifact and essence. *Journal of Abnormal and Social Psychology*, 1959, *58*, 277-299.

Orne, M. T. On the social psychology of the psychological experiment: with particular reference to demand characteristics and their implications. *American Psychologist*, 1962, *17*, 776-783.

Orne, M. T. & Evans, F. J. Social control in the psychological experiment: antisocial behavior and hypnosis. *Journal of Personality and Social Psychology*, 1965, *1*, 189-200.

Orne, M. T., & Scheibe, K. E. The contribution of nondeprivation factors in the production of sensory deprivation effects: the psychology of the "panic button." *Journal of Abnormal and Social Psychology*, 1964, *68*, 3-12.

Osgood, C. E. *Method and theory in experimental psychology.* New York: Oxford Univer. Press, 1953.

Osgood, C. E. & Walker, E. Motivation and language behavior: a content analysis of suicide notes. *Journal of Abnormal and Social Psychology*, 1959, *59*, 58-67.

OSS Assessment Staff. *Assessment of men.* New York: Rinehart, 1948.

Paisley, W. J. Identifying the unknown communicator in painting, literature and music: the significance of minor encoding habits. *Journal of Communication*, 1964, *14*, 219-237.

Parker, E. B. The effects of television on public library circulation. *Public Opinion Quarterly*, 1963, *27*, 578-589.

Parker, E. B. The impact of a radio book review program on public library circulation. *Journal of Broadcasting*, 1964, *8*, 353-361.

Pearson, K. *The life, letters and labours of Francis Galton.* Vol. 1. Cambridge: Cambridge Univer. Press, 1914.

Perrine, M., & Wessman, A. W. Disguised public opinion interviewing with small samples. *Public Opinion Quarterly*, 1954, *18*, 92-96.

Pettigrew, T. *A profile of the Negro American.* Princeton: Van Nostrand, 1964.

Phillips, R. H. Miami goes Latin under Cuban tide. *New York Times*, March 18, 1962, *111*, 85.

Platt, J. R. Strong inference. *Science*, 1964, *146*, 347-353.

Polansky, N., Freeman, W., Horowitz, M., Irwin, L., Paponia, N., Rapaport, D., & Whaley, F. Problems of interpersonal relations in research on groups. *Human Relations*, 1949, *2*, 281-291.

Politz Media Studies. *The readers of "The Saturday Evening Post."* Philadelphia: Curtis Publishing Co., 1958.

Politz Media Studies. *A study of outside transit poster exposure.* New York: Alfred Politz, 1959.

Pollack, I., & Pickett, J. M. Cocktail party effect. *Journal of the Acoustical Society of America*, 1957, *29*, 1262.

Pool, Ithiel de Sola (Ed.). *Trends in content analysis.* Urbana: Univer. of Illinois Press, 1959.

Popper, K. *Logic der Forschung.* Wien: Springer, 1935.

Popper, K. *The logic of scientific discovery.* New York: Basic Books, 1959.

Popper, K. *Conjectures and refutations.* New York: Basic Books, 1962.

Prosser, W. L. *Handbook of the law of torts.* (3rd ed.) St. Paul: West, 1964.

Pyles, M. K., Stolz, H. R., & Macfarlane, J. W. The accuracy of mothers' reports on birth and developmental data. *Child Development*, 1935, *6*, 165-176.

Quine, W. V. *From a logical point of view.* Cambridge: Harvard Univer. Press, 1953.

Rashkis, H., & Wallace, A. F. C. The reciprocal effect. *Archives of General Psychiatry*, 1959, *1*, 489-498.

Ray, M. L. Cross-cultural content analysis: its promise and its problems. Unpublished manuscript, Northwestern Univer., 1965.

Reddy, J. Heady thieves find Wheeling their Waterloo. *Chicago Sun-Times*, February 28, 1965, *18*, 66.

Riesman, D. Orbits of tolerance, interviewers and elites. *Public Opinion Quarterly*, 1956, *20*, 49-73.

Riesman, D. Comment on "The State of Communication Research." *Public Opinion Quarterly*, 1959, *23*, 10-13.

Riesman, D., & Ehrlich, J. Age and authority in the interview. *Public Opinion Quarterly*, 1961, *25*, 39-56.

Riesman, D., & Watson, J. The sociability project: a chronicle of frustration and achievement. In P. E. Hammond (Ed.), *Sociologists at work.* New York: Basic Books, 1964. Pp. 235-321.

Riker, W., & Niemi, D. The stability of coalitions on roll calls in the House of Representatives. *American Political Science Review*, 1962, *56*, 58-65.

Riley, M. W. *Sociological research: I. a case approach.* New York: Harcourt, Brace & World, 1963.

Robbins, L. C. The accuracy of parental recall of aspects of child development and of child rearing practices. *Journal of Abnormal and Social Psychology*, 1963, *66*, 261-270.

Robins, L. N., Hyman, H., & O'Neal, P. The interaction of social class and deviant behavior. *American Sociological Review*, 1962, *27*, 480-492.

Robinson, D., & Rohde, S. Two experiments with an anti-semitism poll. *Journal of Abnormal and Social Psychology*, 1946, *41*, 136-144.

Robinson, E. S. The behavior of the museum visitor. *Publications of the American Association of Museums*, New Series, No. 5, 1928.

Roens, B. B. New findings from Scott's special advertising research study. In *Proceedings: 7th Annual Conference, Advertising Research Foundation.* New York: Advertising Research Foundation, 1961. Pp. 65-70.

Rogow, A. A., & Lasswell, H. D. *Power, corruption and rectitude.* Englewood Cliffs, N.J.: Prentice-Hall, 1963.

Rorer, L. G. The great response-style myth. *Psychological Bulletin*, 1965, *63*, 129-156.

Rosenbaum, M. E. The effect of stimulus and background factors on the volunteering response. *Journal of Abnormal and Social Psychology*, 1956, *53*, 118-121.

Rosenbaum, M. E., & Blake, R. R. Volunteering as a function of field structure. *Journal of Abnormal and Social Psychology*, 1955, *50*, 193-196.

Rosenthal, A. M. Japan, famous for politeness, has a less courteous side, too. *New York Times*, February 25, 1962, *111*, 20.

Rosenthal, R. On the social psychology of the psychological experiment: the experimenter's hypothesis as unintended determinant of experimental results. *American Scientist*, 1963, *51*, 268-283.

Rosenthal, R. Experimenter outcome-orientation and the results of the psychological experiment. *Psychological Bulletin*, 1964, *61*, 405-412.

Rosenthal, R., & Fode, K. L. Psychology of the scientist: V. three experiments in experimenter bias. *Psychological Reports*, 1963, *12*, 491-511.

Rosenthal, R., & Lawson, R. A longitudinal study of the effects of experimenter bias on the operant learning of laboratory rats. *Journal of Psychiatric Research,* 1963, *2*, 61-72.

Rosenthal, R., Persinger, G. W., Vikan-Kline, L., & Fode, K. L. The effect of early data returns on data subsequently obtained by outcome-biased experimenter. *Sociometry,* 1963, *26*, 487-498.

Ross, H. L. The inaccessible respondent: a note on privacy in city and country. *Public Opinion Quarterly,* 1963, *27*, 269-275.

Ross, H. L., & Campbell, D. T. Time series data in the quasi-experimental analysis of the Connecticut speeding crackdown. Unpublished manuscript, 1965.

Rotter, J. B., Liverant, S., & Crowne, D. P. The growth and extinction of expectancies in chance, controlled and skilled tasks. *Journal of Psychology,* 1961, *52*, 161-177.

Ruesch, J., & Kees, W. *Nonverbal communication: notes on the visual perception of human relations.* Berkeley: Univer. of California Press, 1956.

Rush, C. A factorial study of sales criteria. *Personnel Psychology,* 1953, *6*, 9-24.

Salzinger, K. A method of analysis of the process of verbal communication between a group of emotionally disturbed adolescents and their friends and relatives. *Journal of Social Psychology,* 1958, *47*, 39-53.

Sawyer, H. G. The meaning of numbers. Speech before the American Association of Advertising Agencies, 1961.

Schachter, S. *The psychology of affiliation.* Stanford, Calif.: Stanford Univer. Press, 1959.

Schachter, S., & Hall, R. Group derived restraints and audience persuasion. *Human Relations,* 1952, *5*, 397-406.

Schanck, R. L., & Goodman, C. Reactions to propaganda on both sides of a controversial issue. *Public Opinion Quarterly,* 1939, *3*, 107-112.

Schneidman, E. S., & Farberow, N. L. Some comparisons between genuine and simulated suicide notes in terms of Mowrer's concepts of discomfort and relief. *Journal of General Psychology,* 1957, *56*, 251-256.

Schubert, G. *Quantitative analysis of judicial behavior.* Glencoe, Ill.: Free Press, 1959.

Schubert, G. *Judicial decision-making.* New York: Free Press, 1963.

Schulman, J. L., Kasper, J. C., & Throne, J. M. *Brain damage and behavior.* Springfield: W. I. Thomas, 1965.

Schulman, J. L., & Reisman, J. M. An objective measure of hyperactivity. *American Journal of Mental Deficiency,* 1959, *64*, 455-456.

Schwartz, M. S., & Stanton, A. H. A social psychological study of incontinence. *Psychiatry,* 1950, *13*, 399-416.

Schwartz, R. D. Field experimentation in sociolegal research. *Journal of Legal Education,* 1961, *13*, 401-410.

Schwartz, R. D., & Skolnick, J. H. Television and tax compliance. In L. Arons & M. A. May (Eds.), *Television and human behavior.* New York: Appleton-Century-Crofts, 1962. (a)

Schwartz, R. D., & Skolnick, J. H. Two studies of legal stigma. *Social Problems*, 1962, *10*, 133-142. (b)

Sebald, H. Studying national character through comparative content analysis. *Social Forces*, 1962, *40*, 318-322

Sechrest, L. Handwriting on the wall: a view of two cultures. Unpublished manuscript, Northwestern Univer., 1965. (a)

Sechrest, L. Situational sampling and contrived situations in the assessment of behavior. Unpublished manuscript, Northwestern Univer., 1965. (Mimeographed.) (b)

Sechrest, L., & Flores, L. The occurrence of a nervous mannerism in two cultures. *Journal of Nervous and Mental Disease*, in press.

Sechrest, L., Flores, L., & Arellano, L. Social distance and language in bilingual subjects. Unpublished manuscript, Northwestern Univer., 1965.

Sechrest, L., & Wallace, J. Figure drawing and naturally occurring events: elimination of the expansive euphoria hypothesis. *Journal of Educational Psychology*, 1964, *55*, 42-44.

Selltiz, C., Jahoda, M., Deutsch, M., & Cook, S. W. *Research methods in social relations*. New York: Holt, Rinehart & Winston, 1959.

Severin, D. The predictability of various kinds of criteria. *Personnel Psychology*, 1952, *5*, 93-104.

Shadegg, S. C. *How to win an election*. New York: Toplinger, 1964.

Shepard, H. R., & Blake, R. R. Changing behavior through cognitive change. *Human Organization*, 1962, *21*, 88-92. Published by the Society for Applied Anthropology.

Shils, E. A. Social inquiry and the autonomy of the individual. In D. Lerner (Ed.), *The human meaning of the social sciences*. Cleveland: Meridian, 1959. Pp. 114-157.

Siersted, E., & Hansen, H. L. Réaction des petits enfants au cinema: resumé d'une serie d'observations faites au Danemark. *Revue Internationale de Filmologie*, 1951, *2*, 241-245.

Singh, P. H., & Huang, S. C. Some socio-cultural and psychological determinants of advertising in India: a comparative study. *Journal of Social Psychology*, 1962, *57*, 113-121.

Sleeper, C. B. Samplings of leisure-time conversations to find sex differences in drives. Unpublished, cited in G. Murphy & S. L. Murphy, *Experimental social psychology*. New York: Harper, 1931.

Sletto, R. F. *A construction of personality scales by the criterion of internal consistency*. Hanover, N.H.: Sociological Press, 1937.

Smedslund, J. Educational psychology. In P. R. Farnsworth, O. McNemar, & Q. McNemar (Eds.), *Annual Review of Psychology*, 1964, *15*, 251-276.

Smith, H. T. A comparison of interview and observation methods of mother behavior. *Journal of Abnormal and Social Psychology*, 1958, *57*, 278-282.

Snyder, E. C. Uncertainty and the Supreme Court's decisions. *American Journal of Sociology*, 1959, *65*, 241-245.

Snyder, R., & Sechrest, L. An experimental study of directive group therapy with defective delinquents. *American Journal of Mental Deficiency*, 1959, *63*, 117-123.

Solley, C. M., & Haigh, G. A. A note to Santa Claus. *Topeka Research Papers, The Menninger Foundation*, 1957, *18*, 4-5.

Solomon, R. L. An extension of control group design. *Psychological Bulletin*, 1949, *46*, 137-150.

Sommer, R. Studies in personal space. *Sociometry*, 1959, *22*, 247-260.

Sommer, R. Personal space. *Canadian Architect*, 1960, pp. 76-80.

Sommer, R. Leadership and group geography. *Sociometry*, 1961, *24*, 99-110.

Sommer, R. The distance for comfortable conversations: further study. *Sociometry*, 1962, *25*, 111-116.

Spiegel, D. E., & Neuringer, C. Role-of dread in suicidal behavior. *Journal of Abnormal and Social Psychology*, 1963, *66*, 507-511.

Stechler, G. Newborn attention as affected by medication during labor. *Science*, 1964, *144*, 315-317.

Stein, M. I., & Heinze, S. J. *Creativity and the individual.* Glencoe, Ill.: Free Press, 1960.

Steiner, G. A. *The people look at television.* New York: Knopf, 1963.

Steiner, I. D. Group dynamics. In P. R. Farnsworth, O. McNemar, & Q. McNemar (Eds.), *Annual Review of Psychology*, 1964, *15*, 421-446.

Steiner, I. D., & Field, W. L. Role assignment and interpersonal influence. *Journal of Abnormal and Social Psychology*, 1960, *61*, 239-245.

Stephan, F. F., & McCarthy, P. J. *Sampling opinions.* New York: Wiley, 1958.

Stern, R. *Golk.* New York: Criterion Books, 1960.

Stewart, J. Q. Empirical mathematical rules concerning the distinction and equilibrium of population. *Geographical Review*, 1947, *37*, 461-485.

Stoke, S. M., & West, E. D. Sex differences in conversational interests. *Journal of Social Psychology*, 1931, *2*, 120-126.

Stouffer, S. A. Problems in the application of correlation to sociology. *Journal of the American Statistical Association*, 1934, *29*, 52-58. (Reprinted in S. A. Stouffer, *Social research to test ideas.* Glencoe, Ill.: Free Press, 1962. Pp. 264-270.)

Stouffer, S. A. *Social research to test ideas.* Glencoe, Ill.: Free Press, 1962. (Reprinted from P. F. Lazarsfeld, *Radio and the printed page.* New York: Duell, Sloan and Pearce, 1940. Pp. 266-272.)

Stouffer, S. A., Lumsdaine, A. A., Lumsdaine, M. H. Williams, R., Smith, M., Janis, I., Star, S., & Cottrell, L. *The American soldier: combat and its aftermath.* Vol. 2. Princeton: Princeton Univer. Press, 1949.

Strodtbeck, F. L., & James, R. M. Social process in jury deliberations. Paper read at American Sociological Society, 1955.

Strodtbeck, F. L., James, R. M, & Hawkins, C. Social status in jury deliberations. *American Sociological Review*, 1957, *22*, 713-719.

Strodtbeck, F. L., & Mann, R. D. Sex role differentiation in jury deliberations. *Sociometry*, 1956, *19*, 3-11.

Stuart, I. R. Minorities vs. minorities: cognitive, affective and conative
components of Puerto Rican and Negro acceptance and rejection.
Journal of Social Psychology, 1963, *59*, 93-99.

Sussman, L. Mass political letter writing in America. *Public Opinion
Quarterly*, 1959, *23*, 203-212.

Sussman, L. *Dear F. D. R.* New York: Bedminster, 1963.

Swift, A. L., Jr. *The survey of the YMCA of the City of New York.*
(Limited ed.) New York: Association Press, 1927.

Tannenbaum, P. H., & Noah, J. E. Sportugese: a study of sports page
communication. *Journalism Quarterly*, 1959, *36*, 163-170.

Tarde, G. *L'Opinion et la foule.* Paris: Felix Alcan, 1901.

Terman, L. M. The intelligence quotients of Francis Galton in childhood.
American Journal of Psychology, 1917, *28*, 209-215.

Thomas, D. S. *Some new techniques for studying social behavior.* New
York: Columbia Univer. Press, 1929.

Thomas, W. I., & Znaniecki, F. *The Polish peasant in Europe and
America: monograph of an immigrant group.* Vol. 1. Chicago:
Univer. of Chicago Press, 1918.

Thorndike, E. L. *Your City.* New York: Harcourt, Brace, 1939.

Thorndike, R. L. *Personnel selection.* New York: Wiley, 1949.

Toulouse, M. M., & Mourgue, R. Des réactions respiratoires au cours de
projections cinématographiques. *Revue Internationale de Filmologie*, 1948, *2*, 77-83.

Trueswell, R. W. A survey of library users' needs and behavior as related
to the application of data processing and computer technique. Unpublished doctoral dissertation, Northwestern Univer., 1963.

Turner, W. Dimensions of foreman performance: a factor analysis of
criterion measures. *Journal of Applied Psychology*, 1960, *44*,
216-223.

Udy, S. H. Cross-cultural analysis: a case study. In P. E. Hammond (Ed.),
Sociologists at work. New York: Basic Books, 1964. Pp. 161-183.

Ulett, G. A., Heusler, A., Callahan, J. Objective measures in psychopharmacology (methodology). In E. Rothlin (Ed.), *Neuro-psycho-
pharmacology*, 1961, *2*, 401-409.

Ulett, G. A., Heusler, A., Ives-Word, V., Word, T., & Quick, R. Influence of chlordiozepoxide on drug-altered EEG patterns and behavior.
Medicina Experimentalis, 1961, *5*, 386-390.

Ulmer, S. S. Quantitative processes: some practical and theoretical
applications. In Hans W. Baade (Ed.), *Jurimetrics.* New York: Basic
Books, 1963.

Underwood, B. J. *Psychological research.* New York: Appleton-Century-
Crofts, 1957.

Vernon, D. T. A., & Brown, J. The utilization of secondary or less
preferred sources of information by persons in potentially stressful
situations. Unpublished manuscript, 1963.

Vidich, A. J., & Shapiro, G. A. A comparison of participant observation and survey data. *American Sociological Review*, 1955, *20*, 28-33.

Vincent, C. E. Socioeconomic status and familial variables in mail questionnaire responses. *American Journal of Sociology*, 1964, *69*, 647-653.

Vose, C. E. *Caucasions only.* Berkeley: Univer. of California Press, 1959.

Walters, R. H., Bowen, Norma V., & Parke, R. D. Experimentally induced disinhibition of sexual responses. Unpublished manuscript, Univer. of Waterloo, 1963. Cited in A. Bandura & R. H. Walters, *Social learning and personality development.* New York: Holt, Rinehart, & Winston, 1964. Pp. 76-79.

Warner, W. L. *The living and the dead.* New Haven: Yale Univer. Press, 1959.

Warner, W. L., Meeker, M., & Eells, K. *Social class in America.* Chicago: Science Research Associates, 1949.

Washburne, C. The good and bad in Russian education. *New Era*, 1928, *9*, 8-12.

Watson, J., Breed, W., & Posman, H. A study in urban conversation: sample of 1001 remarks overheard in Manhattan. *Journal of Social Psychology*, 1948, *28*, 121-123.

Watson, R. I. Historical review of objective personality testing: the search for objectivity. In B. M. Bass & I. A. Berg (Eds.), *Objective approaches to personality assessment.* Princeton: Van Nostrand, 1959. Pp. 1-23.

Wax, R. H. Reciprocity in field work. In R. N. Adams & J. J. Preiss (Eds.), *Human organization research.* Homewood, Ill.: Dorsey Press, 1960. Pp. 90-98.

Webb, E. J. *Men's clothing study.* Chicago: Chicago Tribune Co., 1957.

Webb, E. J. How to tell a columnist: I. *Columbia Journalism Review*, 1962, *1*, 23-25. (a)

Webb, E. J. Television programming and the effect of ratings. Paper read at Association for Education in Journalism, Chapel Hill, N.C., 1962. (b)

Webb, E. J. How to tell a columnist: II. *Columbia Journalism Review*, 1963, *2*, 20.

Webb, E. J. The orthographies of seven African languages. In preparation.

Wechsler, H. Community growth, depressive disorders and suicide. *American Journal of Sociology*, 1961, *67*, 9-16.

Weir, R. H. *Language in the crib.* The Hague: Mouton, 1963.

Weiss, D. J., & Dawis, R. V. An objective validation of factual interview data. *Journal of Applied Psychology*, 1960, *44*, 381-385.

Weitz, J. Selecting supervisors with peer ratings. *Personnel Psychology*, 1958, *11*, 25-35.

Werner, H., & Wapner, S. Changes in psychological distance under conditions of danger. *Journal of Personality*, 1953, *24*, 153-167.

West, D. V. In the eye of the beholder. *Television Magazine*, 1962, *19*, 60-63.

Whisler, T. L., & Harper, S. F. *Performance appraisal: research and practice*. New York: Holt, Rinehart & Winston, 1962.

White, R. K. Hitler, Roosevelt and the nature of war propaganda. *Journal of Abnormal and Social Psychology*, 1949, *44*, 157-174.

Whyte, W. H. *The organization man*. New York: Simon & Schuster, 1956.

Wigmore, J. H. *A student's textbook of the law of evidence*. Brooklyn: Foundation Press, 1935.

Wigmore, J. H. *The science of judicial proof as given by logic, psychology, and general experience and illustrated in judicial trials*. (3rd ed.) Boston: Little, Brown, 1937.

Williams, R. Probability sampling in the field: a case history. *Public Opinion Quarterly*, 1950, *14*, 316-330.

Wilson, E. B. *An introduction to scientific research*. New York: McGraw-Hill, 1952.

Windle, C. Test-retest effect on personality questionnaires. *Educational and Psychological Measurement*, 1954, *14*, 617-633.

Winick, C. Thoughts and feelings of the general population as expressed in free association typing. *The American Imago*, 1962, *19*, 67-84.

Winship, E. C., & Allport, G. W. Do rosy headlines sell newspapers? *Public Opinion Quarterly*, 1943, *7*, 205-210.

Winston, S. Birth control and the sex-ratio at birth. *American Journal of Sociology*, 1932, *38*, 225-231.

Wolff, C. *A psychology of gesture*. London: Methuen, 1948.

Wolff, C. *The hand in psychological diagnosis*. London: Methuen, 1951.

Wolff, W., & Precker, J. A. Expressive movement and the methods of experimental depth psychology. In H. H. Anderson & G. L. Anderson (Eds.), *An introduction to projection techniques*. New York: Prentice-Hall, 1951. Pp. 457-497.

Wolfson, R. Graphology. In H. H. Anderson & G. L. Anderson (Eds.), *An introduction to projection techniques*. New York: Prentice-Hall, 1951. Pp. 416-456.

Yates, F. *Sampling methods for censuses and surveys*. New York: Hafner, 1949.

Yule, G. U., & Kendall, M. G. *An introduction to the theory of statistics*. (14th ed.) New York: Hafner, 1950.

Zamansky, H. S. A technique for assessing homosexual tendencies. *Journal of Personality*, 1956, *24*, 436-448.

Zamansky, H. S. An investigation of the psychoanalytic theory of paranoid delusions. *Journal of Personality*, 1958, *26*, 410-425.

Zeisel, H. *Say it with figures*. (4th ed.) New York: Harper, 1957.

Zipf, G. K. Some determinants of the circulation of information. *American Journal of Psychology*, 1946, *59*, 401-421.

Zipf, G. K. *Human behavior and the principle of least effort*. Cambridge: Addison-Wesley, 1949.

Index

Ability to replicate, 33-34
Access to descriptive cues, 33, 85, 138
Accretion measures, controlled, 44-46
Accretion measures, natural, 38-43
Acquiescent response set, 19-20
Actuarial records, 57-65
Adams, J. S., 160, 161
Advertising Service Guild, 123
Alger, C. F., 89, 126
Allport, G. W., 79, 95, 104
Amrine, M., 150
Amthauer, R., 101
Anastasi, A., 19
Anderson, A., 73, 97
Andrew, R. J., 145
Angell, R. C., 73
Anonymity guarantees, 15
Archival records, 14, 175, 179: advantages of, 53, 87; biases of, 54-55, 84; selective deposit of, 54-55; selective survival of, 54-55
Archives, continuous: bedside records, 81, 82; birth records, 57, 59; book sales, 80, 81; cartoons, 77, 78; city budgets, 73; Congressional Record, 68; death records, 73; directories, 63, 64, 65; divorce records, 59; election statistics, 69, 70; freight shipments, 76; horse race betting, 80; journal articles, 82; judicial voting, 70, 71; legislative voting, 65-67; library withdrawals, 81; magazine fiction, 58; marriage records, 59, 60; moon phases, 72; newspaper circulation, 76, 79, 80; obituaries, 63; park acreage, 73; parking meter collections, 73; patents, 75; photographs, 78, 79; plays, 78; political speeches, 67, 68, 78; population change, 61; power failures, 74, 75; press conferences, 77; sales records, 76; school attendance, 73;

society news, 77; songbooks, 78; sports records, 76; tax payments, 70; television repair, 78; tombstones, 53, 54, 55, 61, 62; traffic fatalities, 73; travel rates, 76; water pressure, 73, 74; weather data, 72
Archives, episodic and private: absenteeism, 100, 101, 102; advertising, 97, 98; air travel, 90; alcohol consumption, 89, 90; art, 109; autograph prices, 93; book sales, 92, 97; children's drawings, 109; college grades, 102, 103; courts-martial, 103; desk calendars, 94; diaries, 106; drug adoption, 93, 94; drug sales, 94; economic forecasts, 94, 95; height of pilots, 89; insurance purchases, 90, 91; job promotion, 101; job seniority, 101; job turnover, 100, 101; laundry activity, 104; letters, 104, 105, 106, 107, 108; medical visits, 102, 103; pay increases, 101; peanut sales, 91; re-enlistment rates, 100; seat belt sales, 96; soap consumption, 89; stamp sales, 93; stock sales, 95; suicide notes, 108, 109; tardiness, 102; thievery, 90; ticket sales, 97; union grievances, 102; work production, 99
Ardrey, R., 152
Arellano, Lourdes, 125
Armstrong, R., 80
Arrington, R., 136
Arsenian, J. M., 113
Ashley, J. W., 95
Ataov, T., 164
Athey, K. R., 21
Awareness of being tested, 13-16, 50, 175
Audiotapes, 144, 145, 146, 150, 151, 155

217

THE BORROWED HOUSE

OTHER BOOKS BY HILDA VAN STOCKUM

The "Bantry Bay" Series
The Cottage at Bantry Bay
Francie on the Run
Pegeen

The "Mitchells" Series
The Mitchells: Five for Victory
Canadian Summer
Friendly Gables

Others
A Day on Skates
Kersti and St. Nicholas
Gerrit and the Organ
The Angels' Alphabet
Patsy and the Pup
King Oberon's Forest
Little Old Bear
The Winged Watchman
Jeremy Bear
Bennie and the New Baby
New Baby is Lost
Mogo's Flute
Penegro
Rufus Round and Round

The
The Borrowed House

House

Hilda van Stockum

BETHLEHEM BOOKS · IGNATIUS PRESS
BATHGATE, ND   SAN FRANCISCO

Cover art © 2000 by Lydia Halverson
Cover design by Davin Carlson

First Printing, April 2000

ISBN 1–883937–46–9
Library of Congress Card Number: 00-101258

Bethlehem Books • Ignatius Press
10194 Garfield Street South
Bathgate, ND 58216
www.bethlehembooks.com

Printed in the United States on acid free paper

Table of Contents

To my twin cousin, Nella,
in memory of happy childhood days

ONE

The Ring of Power

THE BARN SMELLED of stale hay, chicken droppings, and cabbage. Lorelei, the white hen, cackled. With a swift glance over her shoulder, Janna took the broom and chased the bird off her nest. Sure enough, there was an egg. Janna slid it into her apron pocket. The barn door creaked as Frau Kopp came in, towering over Janna, a mountain of authority.

"Kill me a couple of chickens, Janna, quick," she said. "I've unexpected company." Janna looked around in dismay. What she saw were not chickens but Lorelei and Ilsebill, the leghorns; Wilhelm, the rooster; Fritz and Franz, the cockerels; Lieschen, Gretchen, and all the other cackling, scratching friends she knew by name. How could you kill something that had a name? But what could you do against a grownup? Janna began to sweep vigorously.

"Johanna," repeated Frau Kopp, "did you hear me?"

Janna looked up, shaking the hair out of her eyes. "I can't," she said, trembling at her own audacity.

"You *can*," Frau Kopp insisted. "I showed you. You wring their necks, like that . . . it's easy. What a fool they have sent me—and the other one so good, so willing! Why did she have to leave?"

"I'm on duty," said Janna desperately. "We have a Youth meeting."

"But it isn't Wednesday," protested Frau Kopp. "I know

on Wednesdays you have your *Heim Abend* and have to leave early. But today is Tuesday and you can help in the kitchen, can't you?"

"It's a special meeting," said Janna, noticing the frustrated expression on Frau Kopp's face. No one was allowed to interfere with the Hitler Youth meetings: not the church, or the school, parents or employers.

"A special meeting, a special meeting," grumbled Frau Kopp. "You are always having these special meetings and I think it's just to escape work. What's this meeting for, then?"

Janna's face lit up. "It's a rehearsal," she said. "We're going to do a play our group leader has written. And *imagine* . . . they've chosen *me* to be Brunhilde!"

"And who is Brunhilde?" asked Frau Kopp sourly.

"Don't you know? She is Siegfried's bride. He gives her the magic ring, which was stolen from the Rhine maidens. But there is a curse on it. Siegfried drinks an evil potion, forgets Brunhilde, and marries someone else. Brunhilde is furious and causes him to die, but she is sorry afterward, and when she lights his funeral pyre she jumps on it herself, and as they burn all the gods burn with them."

Frau Kopp had listened open-mouthed. "Where do you get all that heathenish nonsense?"

"Oh, it isn't nonsense," said Janna. "It's all in Wagner's operas."

"It's heathenish anyway," sputtered Frau Kopp. "And for that they keep you from honest work!"

"Learning a part is work too. My parents have to do it all the time. They're famous actors, their pictures are often in the papers, and Hitler has praised them. It's in an article . . . I'll show it to you. . . . He says they are an outstanding example of true Aryan culture."

"I know, I know," Frau Kopp interrupted, "you've told me before. Isn't it early for you to go? Your meetings are always later."

"Not this one," said Janna.

Frau Kopp looked at her suspiciously, opened her mouth to say something, and then closed it again. It was not wise to tangle with the Youth groups; she'd heard stories. . . . Adjusting her black shawl, she shrugged her shoulders. "All right, go if you must and leave me with all the work." She bent and made a grab at the unsuspecting Lieschen. Janna lifted her coat from a nail and fled.

It was the last half of February. The thick blanket of snow was raveled and torn, showing patches of earth and yellow vegetation. Streams rushed singing down the hills, sweeping mud and pebbles along. The mountains, wrapped in fog, loomed like ghosts. Janna's boots picked up the sticky snow as she clumped along. A stiff wind tore at her hair and slapped her cheeks. She passed Frau Kopp's farmhouse with its steep, overhanging roof, half straw, half shingle. Bruno, the mongrel dog, almost choked himself on his chain trying to get to her. She patted his shaggy head, climbed a fence, and stood on the road, where puddles gleamed between ridges of mud. In the distance the church steeple lifted a warning finger at a flock of crows that seemed to be weaving swastikas against the sky.

Janna took a deep breath. She had managed to evade the cruel task Frau Kopp had laid on her because she was a Hitler Youth. Frau Kopp was afraid of Hitler. All grown-ups were.

She thought about the play again, still wondering at her luck to be chosen for such a big role when she was only a junior. Of course it was a responsibility too. Her mother always said that to be good you had to *live* the part. Janna tried to imagine herself as Brunhilde while she trudged along the sleety road. . . . Brunhilde the Valkyrie, flying through the sky on a magic horse with her sisters, wearing full armor, with helmets on their streaming hair and spears in their hands. They directed all battles, taking care that the just won. Sometimes, when clouds massed on the horizon and Janna looked through her eyelashes, she fancied she saw them. They were warrior maidens, pure and immaculate. No one could touch them, they were free as the wind. If she were really Brunhilde, thought Janna, she'd be rid of grownups who always made her do what they wanted, who had their own kind of magic. She thought about Gisela in the village. Last year she'd been in school, doing lessons like everyone else. Now she was grown up, wore pretty dresses, and walked like a queen. Any boys or men still left in the village flocked around her. People thought she was beautiful, but Janna didn't like her fat lips and the way she flapped her eyelashes. She was cruel too, often teasing her admirers. Janna hoped she wouldn't be like that when she grew up. It was better to be a Valkyrie, proud and stern, wielding a spear.

But Brunhilde disobeyed Wotan, the chief god, who wanted her to back the wrong side in a fight. Wotan punished her by chaining her to a rock in the middle of a ring of fire. There she had to sleep till Siegfried woke her. When he did, she went all soft and loved him. Janna wasn't sure she'd be able to lie absolutely still, without blinking. She wondered who would play the noble blond hero who had fearlessly slain a dragon yet trembled at the sight of Brunhilde's beauty. And that was another problem: Janna knew she was no beauty. Well, maybe they could do things with stage lights.

What would it be like to have a magic ring that gave you power over everybody? thought Janna. And why hadn't Brunhilde used it to save Siegfried and conquer her enemies? Why had she given it back to the Rhine maidens? They had hidden the ring and now no one could get it, though some people said it had been given to Hitler and that that was why he had conquered all those countries.

A girl hailed Janna from a neighboring farm. She came running across the fields, darting around rocks and shrubs, her long braids dancing on her back. It was Greta, a classmate.

"Wait for me, Janna!"

"You got away early too," said Janna.

"I said we had a Youth meeting."

"So did I!" The girls burst into laughter.

"They'll think it's funny when we have our rehearsal on Friday. They'll say we have too many special meetings!"

"They can't do anything," said Greta. "We're allowed as many meetings as we like."

"As long as our group leader doesn't tell on us."

"She won't. Hildegarde is nice. The other group leader we had, Hannelore, was awful, really strict. She used to make us march with heavy packs and take cold baths in freezing weather because she said we should be as tough as the boys. We were going to be the mothers of future German soldiers and she wasn't having any weaklings."

"Did you bag anything today?" asked Janna.

"Not much. I think Frau Hahn is noticing. But if she says anything, I'll tell on her. I'll tell she slaughtered a pig illegally."

"Did she?" asked Janna.

"Of course. They're always doing it, those farmers. They don't care if our soldiers starve. I got some onions anyway. They're good in soup."

"I got an egg," said Janna.

"An egg? But they count those!" exclaimed Greta.

"I got it before it was counted." They walked for a moment in silence, listening to a robin chirping on a bare branch.

The old mailman, his brown leather bag over his shoulder, was bicycling past. He was bent over the handlebars against the wind, treading down the pedals heavily with his big boots. Slush sprayed up and the girls jumped back.

"*Grüss Gott!*" said the mailman, nodding at them.

"Heil Hitler!" answered the girls, arms outstretched. Janna thoughtfully picked her way among the puddles.

"Did you ever see Hitler?" she asked.

"Yes, once," said Greta, "at that Youth rally we went to."

"There were too many people, I couldn't see a thing."

"I climbed a tree," said Greta, enjoying Janna's look of admiration. "But I didn't see much," she confessed. "Only the back of his head and his raised arm. And do you know, he didn't raise it high enough, not even as high as his shoulder!" Hildegarde made the girls raise their arms well above their heads, and no matter how long the occasion lasted, you were never allowed to rest your arm on the girl in front.

But of course Hitler didn't have to raise his arm at all; the greeting was *to* him. Besides, laws were for other people, not for Hitler.

"Why did *you* want to go home early today?" Janna asked.

"Because of the test tomorrow," said Greta, looking worried. "They keep us working so late, I'm too tired to do my homework. I did badly all this term. Race science is our most important subject and I want to do as well as I can, but I can't memorize all that stuff. Those terribly long words!"

"I know, like 'brachycephalic,'" said Janna. "That's a kind of skull. There are round, square, and long ones, and it's very important which kind you have. The Aryan ones are the best."

"Why?"

"It has something to do with room for your brains. Monkeys don't have much. Aryans have the most. We're Aryans, the only true race. We're supposed to become supermen."

"What other races are there?"

"Oh, Slavs and Mongolians and Semites . . . that's the Jews. When you don't know the answer to a question, just say something bad about the Jews and they'll give you a good mark. They'll forget what they asked."

"Really?"

"Sure, I tried it. It sometimes works with Slavs too, they're almost as bad as the Jews . . . that's the Russians, you know. But the Jews are the worst. They made us lose the First World War. We were winning the war, the soldiers were winning it—and Hitler was a soldier then so he knows—but the Jews in Berlin made us sign the Treaty of Versailles and that made us lose the war. We lost a lot of territory so we hadn't enough *Lebensraum* and we had to pay so much money to our enemies that we became poor. We even used our paper money in the toilets!"

"Why?" asked Greta.

"Because it was worth less than toilet paper. No one

had work and people fell dead in the streets with hunger, but the democratic government did nothing. When Hitler came, he got back our lost territories and everyone had work. We had an army again and enough food. That's why we have to thank Hitler before and after meals."

"But what has that got to do with race?"

"Don't you see, Greta? It's race that makes the Jews so bad. They've got the wrong blood. We were pure Aryans before the Jews came and we must become pure Aryans again. That's why our boys have written on their daggers: 'Blood and honor.' It's shameful to let your race deteriorate by mixing it with inferior races. In the ancient days of Atlantis the Aryans had magic powers. The swastika is a magic Aryan sign, you know. But the Jews have weakened us and we've lost those powers. Hitler wants to give them back to us, but he can do it only if we stamp out the evil influence of the Jews."

"Did you ever see a Jew?" asked Greta.

"No, only in pictures."

"A Jew used to visit our village before you came," said Greta. "Every Friday he stood in the marketplace, selling a pig. He had a big yellow star on his coat. But there was always something wrong with the pig. We were glad when he didn't come any more."

"I think they're like the *Nibelungen* dwarfs in our play . . . sly and dangerous," said Janna. "It's the Jews in England and America that are fighting us. All the Aryan people would like to belong to us. And the Jews gave us Christianity, which is making us weak. Christians have to love their enemies, do good to those who hate them, and give more to those who steal from them. If you believe that, how can you be a strong nation and conquer the world? Hitler says it's impossible to be a good German and a Christian at the same time."

"Do you believe that?" asked Greta.

"Hitler says so," said Janna.

"And why are the Slavs bad?"

"They're Communists; the Jews gave them Communism. They say that everyone is equal, and that's a lie. There's a master race, that's us, and inferior races. The inferior races must serve the master race."

"You make it sound so simple, Janna. I wonder how you do it . . . all those long chapters in *Mein Kampf* . . ."

"I suppose it's because of my parents," said Janna. "They're famous, you know. Hitler said . . ."

"Yes, you told me," Greta broke in. The only thing she disliked about Janna was the way she boasted about her parents. "Here's my road. See you tomorrow."

Greta lived in a hut in the mountains, while Janna's home was in the village with her nurse Erna and Erna's mother. The celebrated Mechtild and Otto Oster, Janna's parents, had been traveling about for over two years, entertaining troops in foreign countries. They kept writing Janna that they would get a house soon and send for her, but so far it hadn't happened. Janna consoled herself by writing them long letters and talking about them to anyone who would listen. They were always present to her, an admiring audience for all she did.

Erna took great interest in Janna's Youth meetings, but the old mother, who mumbled away her last days in a rocking chair beside the huge blue porcelain stove, a rosary in perpetual motion between her fingers, disapproved of the Youth movement. She said it was wicked to hold meetings on Sunday mornings so that Janna could not go to church. She warned Janna not to listen to the pagan things she was being taught. She would go on to mutter threats against a mysterious being called Antichrist and predict all manner of evil for Germany, till Erna made her be quiet.

"Don't mind her," Erna would say contemptuously. "The old one is crazy."

Janna loved her Youth group. It was the only pleasant thing in her life. All the rest was grim. School from eight to twelve, much of the time taken up preparing bandages or doing other work for the soldiers, as well as writing letters to them. Then midday dinner, which consisted of potatoes with a flavor of meat. Then farm work in the afternoons. When there was no Youth meeting, Janna often had to work late, so that her homework suffered. The farmers forgot how young their helpers were and they piled on the work. If it had not been for the Hitler Youth, Janna didn't think she could have stood it.

The Youth meetings were delightful—except for readings from *Mein Kampf* or lectures on early Germanic tribes, which were dull. But the girls also learned handicrafts, practiced on musical instruments, played games, acted in plays, held songfests, and went on hikes. In the summer there were camping trips and excursions to Youth rallies. Those were the high points. When Janna was on a camping trip with her group, she felt confident, strong, and alive. The fresh air, the lovely woods and mountains, the comradeship of the other girls: it was glorious. They all felt they mattered, their country needed them—and what a beautiful, beautiful country it was!

In the evenings, tired out, they would gather around a leaping bonfire. Then Hildegarde would tell stories: old tales grown from the soil they sat on. They heard of the great Norse gods and their fiery matings, of curses and spells, of heroes with magic powers and of their malicious foes . . . till their eyelids pricked and the fire dwindled to a few glimmering worms. Then the night wind would blow them into their tents to dream of blond gods.

Janna loved it all. She sang enthusiastically with the rest:

> *"Today we own Germany,*
> *Tomorrow the world."*

She was nearing the village and looked forward to Erna's face when she saw the egg. Erna would tell her to thank Frau Kopp. Janna grinned. Frau Kopp would as soon part with her false teeth as with her eggs!

She had passed the first pastel-colored village houses with their wooden latticework, smoke curling from their chimneys. Usually Hans, the shoemaker, sat in front of his window, nodding at her, but today the window was empty. A bit farther on lived the clockmaker. His shop was full of interesting, carved wooden clocks, ticking and wheezing away, but Janna did not linger to look. She saw an ambulance standing before the little hotel. Frau Bauer, the hotelkeeper's wife, was opening the door for two men, who were carrying out Frau Bauer's old aunt on a stretcher. She was covered with a blanket and her face looked pale and anxious as she clutched the blanket with emaciated fingers.

"Now remember, Aunt Hedwig, it's for your own good. They are going to make you better," said Frau Bauer.

"I know . . ." quavered Aunt Hedwig. "They have this new treatment . . . but . . ."

"You don't want to go on having those pains," said Frau Bauer.

"But it's so far . . ." complained Aunt Hedwig. "You won't be able to visit me!"

"I wouldn't be able to anyway. The hotel . . ."

"I know, I know . . ." Aunt Hedwig's voice trailed off.

A group of villagers had gathered around the ambulance. The men carrying the stretcher had no expression on their faces. They did not talk to Aunt Hedwig or to Frau Bauer. They waited till the goodbyes were over; then they pushed the stretcher into the ambulance and slammed the doors shut. They climbed into the front seat. A stink came from the exhaust pipe as the ambulance sputtered into action, its wheels spraying slush, and growled off. The villagers watched it getting smaller and smaller till it disappeared down the hill. Frau Bauer sobbed and hurried into the hotel, her handkerchief pressed against her face.

"If she had to have new treatment, why not send her to the hospital in Freiburg? Why to Hademan? It's so far away," said a woman.

"I think that's decided by the government," another voice remarked.

"Hademan is for the aged and for incurables and feebleminded," said Hans, the shoemaker. "It's a special place."

"That's true," the postmistress chipped in. "My sister's boy wasn't right in the head and they took him there, but he died soon after. They said it was pneumonia."

"Grandpa went there with a sore foot, and he died of pneumonia too," said a messenger boy. "It must be drafty in that place."

"He was old; perhaps the change was too much for him."

"Maybe," said the postmistress grimly. "But has any of you ever heard of anyone who came back from Hademan alive?" There was a silence. Somewhere a radio blared:

"Adolf Hitler's favorite flower
Is the simple edelweiss."

Janna shivered. Was something wrong? Was something dreadful going to happen to Aunt Hedwig? Gentle Aunt Hedwig, always lying on her long chair in front of the window and welcoming children with a box of homemade candy. She had been like a grandmother to Janna, telling her stories of long ago, when women wore long skirts and men had whiskers. Together they had pored over albums with stiff pages full of dried ferns and faded brown snapshots. If Aunt Hedwig had been in pain she had never shown it.

The tall youth standing beside Janna saw her distress. He belonged to the Jung Volk, the older boys' group. His name was Kurt Engel.

"Don't listen to those gossips," he said, putting his hand on Janna's shoulder as he walked beside her. That was a great honor.

"Do you think she'll be all right?" asked Janna timidly, gazing up at him. Kurt looked away into the distance. The main street was sloping down steeply now, and they could see the misted valley with row upon row of snowcapped mountains melting into a haze of purple.

"Does it matter?" he asked. "Aunt Hedwig is a useless old woman of no further value to our nation. Why worry about her? Don't you realize what is happening to our young people, our soldiers in Russia? Have you seen the list of the dead? Why don't you worry about them?" He was gazing at the sky where the last rays of the sun slanted down like spears from a gap in the clouds.

"We're in a crisis," he said. "Only four times in history was there a similar crisis in Europe: when the Greeks warded off the Persians, when Charles Martel defended France against Islam, when Vienna held out against the Turks, and when the Teutonic knights stopped the hordes of Genghis Khan at Liegnitz. Now, once again Europe is threatened by barbarians from the East and we Germans are called to save it." Kurt's closely cropped head, lifted against the sky, looked stern and noble, thought Janna.

"There is a prophecy," Kurt went on, "that after the gods were killed, the horn of Heimdall, the guardian of the border line between gods and men, would sound one day to awaken the Germanic race. I think it has happened: Hitler is that horn. He has special powers and is sent to lead us to a great victory, which will be spoken of for centuries to come. We must trust him and follow him, even unto death."

"Oh, I hope not *death*," cried Janna.

Kurt looked down at her as if he had just discovered her. His smile lit up his face. "You're all right, Janna," he said. "Don't worry. Hitler is invincible, a man of destiny. With him we can do anything. See you Friday. I suppose you know I'm playing Siegfried . . ." Nodding affably at her, he strode off, tall and handsome in his leather jacket. Janna stared after him. So *he* was to be Siegfried! What a stunning Siegfried he would make! She began to think about her costume: a flowing white dress with silver breast-plates, a girdle studded with jewels, and a helmet on her head. She also needed silver sandals and a spear. She wondered where she'd get all that, but Hildegarde would help, she always did. Janna was almost home before she remembered the egg.

"See what I've got for you, Erna!" she cried, bursting into the kitchen. Erna looked around. She was holding a letter.

"Janna!" she exclaimed, scarcely noticing the egg. "I'm so glad you are early! We just got this special-delivery letter. Your father and mother have found a house in Amsterdam. They want you to join them as soon as possible. You'll be traveling with a Frau Mueller, an officer's wife who is visiting her husband. So much to do, I don't know where to start! But . . . what's the matter? Don't you *want* to go to your parents?"

✠ TWO ✠

Crossing the Rhine

JANNA TRUDGED ALONG the platform beside Frau Mueller, a thin, nervous woman who kept asking questions without listening to the answers. Janna had already told her three times that yes, she was glad to be going to her parents, and no, she had never visited Holland before.

"You'll like it," Frau Mueller promised. "Wait till I fix this parcel, it keeps slipping. Oh, could you? Thanks, that's better." For Janna, who carried only a small suitcase and a bag, had relieved her of some of her packages.

"You can't get anything in the Dutch shops any more," Frau Mueller complained. "The few things that are left are all imitation, just as over here. In 1940, ah, what riches! What luxuries! Things we hadn't seen here for *years!* But that is all over now," she ended sadly.

They were walking alongside a dingy-looking train with a clumsy, wood-burning engine. The Freiburg station was like a madhouse: people running about, people embracing, people sitting patiently on suitcases, porters shouting at everybody to get out of the way. There were many soldiers with duffel bags. The train was packed. People were standing in the aisles, but at the very back Frau Mueller managed to find an almost empty car. It was filling up last because it was unheated. It was also dirty and had a damp smell. The floor had not been swept, newspapers lay about, and several windowpanes were broken.

16

Frau Mueller chose two opposite window seats near the door to the next compartment. She began to distribute her luggage in the overhead racks. Janna noticed the name Edeltraut Mueller on the labels. So she was called Edeltraut. Grownups should not have first names, thought Janna. It made them ridiculous. Except royalty, of course, or actors.

"I hope we won't be bombed," said Edeltraut Mueller, pushing one of her parcels farther back.

"Bombed?" asked Janna.

"Yes, the last time I went to Amsterdam we had to get out of the train and take shelter in a ditch. Glass got sprayed all over my best suit. I could never wear it again. Some people were killed."

This was a shock to Janna. It was all right to sit on a plush seat in a movie theater and watch your own heroic pilots bombing foreign cities. It was quite different, somehow, when it happened to you. She looked around. The carriage was filling up with soldiers. Good, they would protect her.

A fat man, loaded with luggage, came waddling up the aisle. Besides his bulging suitcases he was carrying an armload of blankets. Around his body hung various leather cases on straps. A Tyrolean hat perched rakishly on his head, belying his glowering face. He made a crash landing beside Janna, who was almost bounced out of her seat. The fat man took no notice of her or of Frau Mueller. He muttered something about the cold and began to wrap himself methodically in his blankets. He noticed a draft coming through the broken window beside Janna and pointed to it.

"Stuff up that hole," he commanded. "I've got delicate lungs." Janna had been taught to be obliging, so she picked up one of the newspapers, gritty with dirt, and plugged up the hole. A few slivers of glass broke off, but she finally got the paper to stick. She cut her finger and sucked it noisily. The fat man took no notice. He didn't even say "Thank you." He had swaddled himself so completely that he seemed to be in a cocoon, with only his nose sticking out. It was a fat, purplish nose and Janna pictured herself knitting a pink cozy for it. That made her laugh. With difficulty the fat man wrenched his face toward her and snarled, "Children shouldn't be seen or heard."

Janna thought that too much, after what she had just done for him. She sucked harder on her finger in protest.

It was indeed cold in the carriage. It looked as if the passengers were all smoking; their breath came in clouds. The soldiers, warmly dressed, were laughing and joking.

Frau Mueller produced a blanket for herself and a pillow. She did not offer to share them with Janna. While she was settling herself, her foot accidentally hit the fat man's. He barked immediately, "Woman, mind what you're doing!"

Just before the train started, a little man edged in and sat down in the only vacant seat, beside Frau Mueller and opposite the fat man. He was clasping a scuffed imitation-leather briefcase. His coat had a turned-up collar, which hid his mouth and chin, while his wide-brimmed hat shaded his forehead and eyes. All you could see was a slightly arched nose. The toes of his boots curled up, showing worn soles. He sat on the edge of his seat as if ready to jump up the next moment. He greeted Janna, the fat man, and Frau Mueller with timid nods. When the train pulled out of the station, he relaxed slightly and blew his nose.

The fat man kept staring rudely at him. At last he rasped, "Why aren't you wearing your star?" The little man sat up straight, his eyes widening. A hush came over the coach. Janna felt furious. Only Jews wore stars. "Don't mind him," she said to the little man. "He has been insulting all of us."

Now the fat man turned his attention to her again. "You are the most insufferable brat it has ever been my misfortune to meet," he growled. "I don't know what your mother is thinking of, letting you grow up with such objectionable manners!" He glared at Frau Mueller, who hastily disclaimed any relationship.

"She isn't my daughter, I am only looking after her for the trip."

"Then why don't you do it?" the fat man asked. "Shut her up." Frau Mueller sputtered as she took up her knitting.

Janna turned in disgust to the window and watched the fleeing landscape. The smoke of the engine streamed past like the tail of a runaway horse. Behind it rose and dipped the dappled beauty of the mountains. Her dear, dear Black Forest! How she hated to leave it! Tears came into her eyes as she remembered parting that morning with Hildegarde and the rest of the group. Even Kurt had come, briefly, on his bicycle, to take leave of her.

"Tough luck . . ." he had said. "I was looking forward to seeing more of you." He had put his hand on her shoulder for a moment. "Chin up," he had added, with his dazzling smile. "Don't forget us!"

Hildegarde had been most gracious. Janna had cried a bit as she told the leader how she'd miss being in the play. "Yes, it's a shame," Hildegarde admitted, handing her a package. "But never mind, you can be a Brunhilde in real life, that's even better." When Janna opened the package, she found a lovely book with colored illustrations and the text of the *Nibelungen* operas. She flung her arms around Hildegarde's neck and kissed her.

"I'm glad you like it," Hildegarde said. "It seemed such a shame for you to have to go just now. I thought it might help."

"Oh, it does! It does! I've never had such a beautiful book!" After that Greta had been shy about her own little gift, a homemade penwiper. But Janna kissed her too and thanked her just as much. Greta could not help it that her parents were not rich like Hildegarde's. The whole group had seen her to the bus stop. Erna had gone with Janna to Freiburg to meet Frau Mueller.

It seemed to Janna that she had been traveling for a long time already, but there was still an eight-hour journey ahead of her. Her body was being hurried forward while her mind lagged behind, clinging to her friends. When would she see them again?

Janna had insisted on wearing her Youth uniform, which was the nicest thing she had: a dark woolen skirt buttoned to a white blouse, and a black kerchief pulled through a real leather ring. Her coat covered it, but it made her feel more confident. They'd be starting rehearsals tomorrow; someone else would be Brunhilde, probably that stuck-up Ilse. Janna closed her eyes, feeling a stab of misery.

Wave upon wave of mountains passed as Janna brooded. She reminded herself that she was going home to the wonderful parents she had been telling everyone about. But as the train brought her nearer and nearer to them, misgivings crowded her mind. Did she remember them properly? It seemed so long since she had seen them. She

tried to think back, but the more she tried, the more unreal they became. As she thought about the old days in
Berlin, all she could remember were long periods when
her parents were on tour and she and Erna were left alone
in the gloomy flat with the heavy velvet draperies and the
large, round, gold-framed mirrors decorated with eagles.
With an effort, she remembered parties: the rooms lit up
and buzzing with visitors, servants hurrying back and
forth with trays—Janna dressed up and presented to nice-
smelling ladies who kissed her . . .

"She's not a bit like you, is she, Mechtild? Much more
like her father . . ." Laughter. . . . Sometimes concerts to
which she and Erna listened, sitting at the top of the
stairs . . .

On St. Nicholas Eve, the fifth of December, there was
always a special party for Janna. Then St. Nicholas, dressed
in purple robes, came to the flat. The family and their
guests awaited him in the living room, forming a semicir-
cle with Janna and Erna in front. St. Nicholas would ask
if she had been good, and to Janna's horror Erna would
betray Janna's most shameful secrets: that she had wet her
bed, told lies, and sucked her thumb. St. Nicholas then
beat her with a switch in which candies were hidden. The
harder he beat her, the more sugarplums fell out. It made
the grownups laugh very much, but it hurt—and once
Janna had refused to pick up the candies afterward and
had been carried to bed in disgrace.

Why did these silly incidents come into her mind?
Why couldn't she remember her parents helping her with
her homework or taking her for walks? Had she a bad
memory, or . . . or . . . were they not really a proper family?
She had always been with Erna. This was the first time
she had been away from her. Maybe that was making her

feel strange. She was older now, almost thirteen. Her parents would treat her more like an equal. They knew everything about her, she had written them so many letters. Reassured, she felt her eyelids close . . . she'd started *very* early that morning . . .

She woke up because Frau Mueller shook her.

"The *Rhine*," she said. "You must look at the *Rhine*." Janna saw a fairy-tale river flowing between high mountains dotted with castles. The Rhine! The abode of the Rhine maidens, who had owned the gold which the Nibelung dwarf stole to make his magic ring. There was a picture of them in her book. She took it out of her bag and leafed through it. Yes, there they were, pale and translucent, dancing on a wave, their arms lifted, their hair flowing. Beautiful.

The Rhine was an especially German river. Many tales and legends were connected with it. Janna remembered Herr Schultz, the geography teacher, telling the class, "Because the Rhine starts in Switzerland and ends in Holland, those countries really belong to us."

Janna felt hungry. She was glad when she saw people opening their lunch boxes. The fat man had wriggled out of his cocoon and was eating bread and sausage, washed down with beer. Most people had only meager provisions. Janna herself had two cheese sandwiches and an apple. She ate slowly to make them last. Frau Mueller had unpacked buns, cakes, hard-boiled eggs, and a flask of coffee. The little man beside her must be hungry, for his nostrils seemed to twitch as the delicious smells of Frau Mueller's meal wafted past him. But he sat motionless, his hands tightly clasped, his eyes cast down. He had no lunch, that was obvious. Looking at him, Janna could not enjoy hers. And there was Frau Mueller with oceans of food, gorging beside him. It made Janna mad. Closing her eyes, she *willed* Frau Mueller to share her food with the little man. But when she opened them, Frau Mueller was still placidly chewing, her jaws working, the long hair on her chin wiggling. Her throat moved up and down as she swallowed her coffee. How could she be so selfish? There was only one thing left for Janna to do.

"Here," she said, thrusting her second sandwich at the little man. "I have two." The little man came alive. He grabbed the sandwich. "Thank you," he said hoarsely. In a few seconds the sandwich was gone. Now Janna could finish her own meal.

The fat man had taken no notice of the transaction. He was too intent on spreading smelly cheese over crackers.

The train was now speeding through a settled part of the country. In Mainz, Janna saw that many houses were in ruins.

"What happened?" she cried. People left their seats to look.

"Don't you know?" asked Frau Mueller. "Don't you read the papers? That's the work of our enemies. You see what barbarians they are, bombing helpless women and children." It was an appalling sight. Houses gaped like rotten teeth. Here and there wisps of smoke still wandered over the ruins, like ghosts. There were pathetic remnants of furniture: a picture on a crumbling wall, patches of flowered wallpaper, a cradle hanging drunkenly from a rafter. There was a stench of burning.

"Why don't we stop them?" asked Janna. "Aren't we winning?"

"Of course we're winning," snapped Frau Mueller. "Gustav, my husband, says it is only a matter of months. If the

English had surrendered like the other countries, we'd all be better off. Now Hitler will destroy them, and America too. He has a secret weapon, you know."

"Pardon me," said the fat man disagreeably. "If you have such important information, you should keep your mouth shut."

"Everybody knows it," Frau Mueller answered defensively.

"Then there is even less need to mention it."

"It gives people courage," argued Frau Mueller.

"Only fools are encouraged by hearing of a weapon that is not being used," sneered the fat man.

"If it isn't finished yet . . ."

"Then it might come too late." And the fat man gave a ghoulish chuckle. Janna had been listening with growing annoyance. The fat man did not seem to care what happened to his country. He could not be a good German. Perhaps he was a spy, or . . . a smuggler! It wasn't really cold enough to make an Eskimo of yourself. Janna wondered whether the fat man was hiding something.

The little man was sitting as straight as ever, hugging his briefcase. He had picked up one of the newspapers and he ducked behind it every time the train stopped at a station. For a while the only sound in the carriage was the hum of the wheels and the snores of sleeping passengers. They had passed Koblenz. The afternoon sun slanted across the fields, painting long shadows. Janna leafed through her book, reading bits here and there. She began to nod over the pages. She did not know how long she had dozed when a cry from the passengers aroused her. The train was slowly chugging through a desert of rubble. No house stood upright. Only the Cologne Cathedral rose proudly above the ruins. There was a hush after the outcry. Cologne gone . . . the *whole* city!

"I heard there had been bombing," said Frau Mueller. "But I did not know it was this bad!" Janna clenched her fists. Hitler was right to fight the monsters who did such things.

When the train reached the bridge over the Rhine, a warning voice sounded from carriage to carriage: "Shut the windows, shut the windows." No one had been so foolish as to open one in Janna's carriage. It was bad enough to have the cold air whistling through the cracks.

"Why do they say that?" Janna asked. Frau Mueller pointed to the notice which informed passengers that they were to close their windows when crossing the Rhine. "In case of violation," it said, "the soldiers have orders to make use of their guns." Janna looked at the soldiers in the carriage, but none of them seemed interested in his gun.

"Why?" she asked.

The fat man turned on her. "Always asking questions," he scolded. "You're supposed to do as you're told without asking why. If you weren't such a little fool, you'd see that an enemy could throw a bomb through an open window and blow up the bridge."

"He'd blow up the train too, then, and himself," Janna pointed out.

"Never heard of Samson?" asked the fat man.

"No," said Janna. "Who is he?"

"Never mind," said the fat man. "Now shut up, I want my nap."

Janna kept her eyes on him. She did not trust him. He might be only pretending to sleep and suddenly jump up, pulling a bomb from under his wraps. But they reached

the other side of the Rhine without mishap. The landscape looked as if someone had ironed it. Gone were all
the hills or hillocks. The sky arched vast and endless. Little houses huddled under little trees, trying to escape the
threat of the black clouds that were massing on the horizon. Janna watched the clouds creeping nearer and nearer;
soon they would blot out the sun. Harsh voices in the next
coach warned the travelers that train control was on the
way. Everyone braced himself for the ordeal. Janna's papers were in order. As a Hitler Youth she had no fears, but
Frau Mueller was fidgeting. She had lost her ticket and,
made nervous by the obvious interest of the fat man, ransacked her possessions. She finally found it with gusty relief, disappointing the fat man.

Everywhere people were searching their inside pockets,
wallets, and handbags. As the officials entered, all chatter
stopped. They walked to the rear of the car and started
there. They looked at identification papers, work permits,
travel permits, tickets, and passports. They asked if anyone had cameras or other forbidden articles. No one reported any. The officials lingered for a while by some
ill-dressed, lean young men who said they were Dutch
labor draftees on a visit to their parents. After a lot of
questions the officials passed on. The little man was growing paler as they approached. While they were questioning the fat man, the little man began to tremble. His hand
shook as he held out his passport and identification papers.

"I'd take a good look at those, Officers," said the fat
man with a grin as he whisked his own credentials back
into the folds of his blankets. "I should imagine they are
forged."

"Take off your hat," the officials told the little man,

comparing his face with the passport photo. Janna suddenly saw what the fat man was up to. That's why he had hoped Frau Mueller had lost her ticket. He wanted attention diverted from himself. She pointed to the fat man.

"He is only saying that because he is a smuggler himself," she shouted. "He wasn't telling the truth when he said he had no cameras. He has several. I saw them before he put on those blankets!"

The officials flung the little man's papers back at him and pounced on the fat man, whose cheeks turned purple with rage.

"I am an important person," he blustered. "You fools, you don't know what you're doing. You're obstructing the affairs of the nation. You'll suffer for it!"

The officers were peeling him like an onion, and not too gently. They did not like being threatened or called fools. They were used to obsequious submission.

Janna had guessed right. The various leather cases contained expensive cameras and other photographic equipment.

"I'm a professional free-lance photographer. I've done work for Göring and I've a right to carry these," said the fat man, trying to control his temper.

"It doesn't say anything about that in your papers," the officers pointed out sternly. "All it says is that you are going to work for an art dealer in Amsterdam."

"Yes, I take photographs for reproductions. Is that so strange?" the fat man said. He was sweating.

"Oh, very neat," praised the officials. "Why did you not tell us that right away? Why didn't you declare the cameras?"

"Because I've mislaid my confounded permit," exploded the fat man. "That can happen to anyone, can't it? I just

couldn't find it . . . and the train wouldn't wait. I knew I'd
have trouble with you people, you vultures in uniform, always happy to peck at your betters over some trifle . . ."

"That's enough," said the officials. "You can explain all
that at the police station." Now the fat man really got
angry and became so abusive that the officers began to
think he must be an escaped lunatic. They put handcuffs
on him and took him off the train, trailing his blankets.

The little man, forgotten now, put down his newspaper
and leaned back limply, with closed eyes.

Janna felt elated. She had *done* it. She had captured a
smuggler! Maybe she could be Brunhilde in real life, as
Hildegarde had said. She must write and tell Hildegarde
about it. There were moments when flashes of fear pricked
her self-satisfaction: what would have happened if those
leather cases had held only shoe polish? Nor could she
forget the fat man's face as he snarled at her, "You obnoxious, meddlesome brat, I'll pay you back for this," before
he was dragged off. But she consoled herself with the
thought that he would be locked up and unable to carry
out his threat.

She watched the snowy fields, spread out like handker-
chiefs. The clouds had gobbled up the sky now and it was
beginning to snow. At a red-brick building the train stopped and went backward, as if reluctant to cross the border.
Then, with a spurt, it entered Dutch territory. Immediately the rhythm of the wheels changed from clack . . .
clack . . . clack . . . to clickety-clackety. They passed a
freight train with a long row of cattle cars. Janna had seen
similar ones before. She had seen the wet straw in them
and had smelled the stench of urine. She had seen cows
herded through the open doors. But the doors in these
cars were not only shut but padlocked, and at intervals

armed guards stood on the roofs. Out of the small, barred windows peered faces, human faces. Something froze in Janna as she saw the closed wagons rattle and swoosh past: swoosh, swoosh, swoosh. More and more of them, an endless procession. And people, yes, *people* in all of them! White faces with dark, staring eyes.

"There are *people* in there," she cried, and some of the horror she felt spilled over in her voice. "There are *people* in there! What's going to happen to them?"

"Hush," said Frau Mueller. "Hold your tongue, child. It's a cattle train," and she pulled down the shade so that Janna could not see any more. "You are imagining things."

"I am *not* imagining things. There *were* people in it . . ." Janna repeated. The coach was silent. Everyone seemed to have drawn a blind in front of his face and disappeared behind it. Only the little man lifted his head and looked at Janna. The suffering in his eyes made her own fill with tears. And so they looked at each other, Janna and the little man, and they seemed the only ones alive in the coach.

✠ THREE ✠

The Arrival

LATER THERE WERE delays. The train stopped at Amersfoort. All the passengers had to transfer to another train, and in the shuffle Janna lost sight of the little man.

It was dark when they arrived in Amsterdam. Janna's parents were waiting for her in the dimly lit Central Station. Frau Mueller delivered Janna to them and hurried off to her husband. Janna stood facing her parents. They seemed unreal until they spoke. Then their voices brought a flood of memories and Janna flung herself into their arms.

"Thank God, we have our daughter back," her father said. "Welcome to Amsterdam." As he kissed her, Janna smelled the familiar odor of make-up. Then it was her mother's turn. "Janna, darling," she sang, pressing her daughter to her fur coat. "Is it really *you*, at last?" Other people were pushing past them, jostling them, until Frau Oster's melodious German sentences rose above the hubbub. Then, suddenly, there was an empty space around them.

"It's been so *long*," Janna's mother wailed. "At last I could not bear it any more. I told the Baron that he'd better do something and he did. Wait till you see the house. It's *superb!*"

"The Baron's car is waiting outside," said Herr Oster,

picking up Janna's suitcase. "Is this all the luggage you have?"

"And this," said Janna, showing her small bag.

"But that's *nothing*," said her mother. "What can you have brought to wear? Did Erna use your clothes coupons for herself?" Janna flushed. Her attachment to Erna was more from habit than from genuine affection, but Erna had been good to her and she was part of Janna's life in the Black Forest.

"Oh no," she cried. "Erna wouldn't do that, she's very honest, but you could buy so little in the village and Erna was too tired to sew for me."

"Too lazy, you mean," corrected her father. "We paid her enough! Never mind, that deal is off now." He was hurrying after the crowd through a tunnel. Janna and her mother had to run to keep up with him.

"No, no," Janna panted. "Erna was not lazy . . . she had a lot . . . to . . . do . . . She took in washing and her mother was old . . . often ill . . ." But her father was not listening.

They reached the exit, where Janna handed her ticket to the collector. From the station they stepped into the murky confusion of a blacked-out city. It was snowing and raining at the same time. A drizzly fog absorbed what glimmers of light there were. Passengers were dispersing in all directions. No one lingered. People shrugged up their collars, unfolded ragged umbrellas, or mounted rattling bicycles with wooden tires. The only car in sight was the Baron's Mercedes, waiting for the Osters. The chauffeur, who opened the door for them, tried to ignore the rude whistles of some urchins.

Janna sank gratefully into the rich upholstery of the car. She was still shivering after her cold journey. Frau

Oster rubbed Janna's fingers between her soft, fragrant palms. "Poor lamb, you're frozen. Was it a terrible journey? I was so afraid you'd be bombed!"

The car began to crawl along the streets, its dimmed lights barely showing the way, making spooky ghosts of anyone they lit up. The windshield wiper creaked busily as wet snow kept slapping against the glass. Here and there the blue flashlight of a pedestrian wavered like a will-o'-the-wisp. There was a strong smell of dirty water.

"That's the canals," Janna's mother said in a low voice. "There are more here than in Venice. I hate them. You can hardly see them at night . . . especially in this weather. They have no guard rails. Many of our people have blundered into them."

"Been pushed in," said Herr Oster.

"Oh no, Otto!"

"When will you face the facts, Mechtild? The Dutch hate us. They are a dour, obstinate, cantankerous, inhospitable lot, and they hate our guts."

"Otto . . . mind the child."

"She may as well know what she's in for. I wasn't too keen on sending for her, remember? She was safer where she was." Frau Oster squealed as the car gave a sudden lurch.

"Otto, tell the chauffeur to be careful! Tell him to go slow. This is where the car drove into the canal last week and all the officers were drowned . . ."

"That was a bit farther on, and they were drunk," said Herr Oster. "It came out in the autopsy. You wouldn't have been so upset if they hadn't been friends of your baron."

Janna was peering into the gloom. She couldn't see anything. "There was a fat man in the train . . ." she began, wanting to tell her parents about her journey.

"Was there, dear?" said her mother. "What do you mean, *my* baron, Otto? He is yours too. What would we do without him?"

"And what will you do if he wants a return for his favors?" asked Herr Oster.

"I'll give him my autographed picture," said Mechtild lightly.

Otto burst into laughter. "You always were a devil, Mechtild!"

"And when the train control came . . ." Janna said for the third time.

"Yes, dear . . . Otto, shouldn't we turn left here?"

"He knows the way," Otto said.

"And when the train control came . . ." Janna repeated once more.

"I'm sure we should have turned left," said her mother.

"Mechtild, what are you worrying about? He knows these streets like the back of his hand by now."

"Not in this weather," said Frau Oster, shivering.

"They asked if anyone had a camera and he said he hadn't but . . ."

"There now! I told you!" The car had come to a sudden stop against a dark lamppost. The chauffeur was addressing an invisible pedestrian with an assortment of German curses. The pedestrian slunk off, but several snowballs thudded against the windows. The chauffeur backed carefully.

"The fat man tried to make the train officers suspect the little man. But I said he had cameras and then . . ." Janna went on doggedly. Her mother's eyes were straining into the darkness.

"Yes, darling . . . Otto . . . what is he doing now? Are you sure he knows the way? All these canals look alike."

"Calm down, Mechtild, we're here." The car stopped. Janna was helped out, feeling wet snowflakes in her face. They went down a few steps to a kind of basement door, which opened into a warm, dry, clean white-marble hall with a black-and-white tiled floor. A thin, frightened-looking maid took their coats, shaking them and hanging them in a closet. Janna followed her parents into the dining room, which was warmed by a coal stove. Vaguely she was aware of oak paneling, carved furniture, and a thick carpet, for her attention was caught by the supper spread on the dining table and lit by a hanging lamp. On the white tablecloth flowered dishes held a variety of food: pickled herring, slices of meat, homemade bread, and rich, yellow butter. While Janna was looking at the food, her parents were studying her.

"I thought she'd have grown tall and strong after more than two years in the country," Frau Oster said in a disappointed voice. "I think she has got a little taller, but so skinny! And her hair! What possessed Erna to let her scrape it away from her face like that, in tight braids? She used to have curls."

"I see you are a member of the Hitler Youth, Janna," said her father approvingly, noticing her uniform. Janna flashed him a smile.

"Heil Hitler!" she said, raising her arm as high as she could.

"Heil Hitler," answered her father, raising his. Janna looked at his slightly graying, curly black hair, his florid, handsome face and expressive brown eyes. He looked kind, but there was something stern about his lips and chin. Janna remembered being afraid of him as a small child. Her mother, beside him, looked frail and fluffy.

Mechtild never seemed to age. Her hair threw a golden mist around her elfin face with its elusive, silver eyes.

Meanwhile, those eyes were taking in Janna's uniform. "You'd have thought," she said slowly, "that a Strength Through Joy movement, as it's supposed to be called, would have come up with something more cheerful. You look like a magpie in mourning." Tears sprang into Janna's eyes.

"It's a *good* uniform," she said hotly. "Pure wool, no imitation, not even the leather ring. The other girls envied me. And when we marched it looked . . . it looked . . ."

"Magnificent," her father said, finishing the sentence for her. "Of course it did. Your mother doesn't understand." He frowned at his wife, who waved an expressive hand.

"All right, come and eat, dears." They sat down. Janna felt ravenous. Her parents let her stuff herself in peace while they talked about their current play.

"If it weren't for you, it would have flopped," Otto said. "Such a dreary interpretation of the saga. Anything for novelty, I suppose."

"You do your share," said his wife, "though I wish you were my lover and not my husband." She added milk and water to his cup. "That Siegmund is so empty-headed."

"Well, he had to be your twin, and I suppose he was the only actor blond enough," said Otto tolerantly.

"You do the lover ever so much better."

"I've had practice," Otto said, smiling. "He is only a stripling, but he does match your general appearance. Those old folktales should not be put into modern dress, it takes away their glamour. That's especially true of the *Nibelungen* saga . . ."

"The *Nibelungen* saga?" Janna's head shot up, her eyes

sparkled. "Are you playing in the Nibelungen saga? I am too . . . I was, I mean, if I hadn't come here. They gave me the part of Brunhilde and I'm not even a senior!" Her parents exchanged proud glances.

"Well, well," said her father, tweaking her ear. "You've inherited our curse . . . I guess you're doomed. You must act bits for us when we have time."

"Brunhilde, that was my first role," said her mother. "We must talk about it another day . . . but, if you've finished eating, we'd like you to tell us some things we have to know, since you're going to live with us." They started to ask her questions. Some of them puzzled Janna, for they could have got the answers out of her letters. She began to wonder whether they had received them. She had so much to tell them, but they kept wanting to hear stupid things like how often she'd been to the dentist, when she had been vaccinated last, and whether she had brought her school report.

"We'll have to see about schooling for you," her father said. "It's a bad situation at present. The teachers are uncooperative. And many schools are closed because of fuel shortages. I think the best thing would be to find you a tutor. Meanwhile, a little vacation won't do you any harm. You look as if you need it."

"Yes," said her mother eagerly. "We'll have to fatten you up! We have plenty of food, thanks to the Baron, though it's sometimes unusual food, whatever he manages to find. We enjoyed your letters, Janna. That Hildegarde you wrote about seems a nice girl. Was she in your class?" Janna stared at her. She had written over and over that Hildegarde was her group leader, so how could she be in Janna's class? She was much too old! Janna tried to explain this, but her mother said it was time for bed.

"Bed?" asked Janna. "But it isn't eight yet. At home I don't have to go till nine."

Her mother frowned. "This is your home now," she said. "And we make the rules here. You must be tired out after that long journey and I want to tuck you in before we have to leave for the theater."

The theater! Of course, Janna had forgotten. That was why she could not remember any family evenings, there hadn't been any. That was when her parents worked. Her lips trembled.

"Why did you let me come," she burst out, "if we're not going to be a proper family? If we're not going to be together, if you're going to be away all the time. There I had friends . . . I was going to be in the play . . ." Her mother shrank back, hurt.

Her father's voice came like a whiplash. "That's enough, Johanna. You do not talk like that to your mother, who was so anxious to have you and took such pains to get you here. Tell her you are sorry at once."

"I'm sorry, Mother." Janna's voice trembled. Her eyelids stung.

"It's all right, dear. You're overtired, I know."

"I'll carry her upstairs," said her father in a kinder tone. In his strong arms Janna was carried up the two flights to her room, as if she were still five years old. The room was pretty, with silvery wallpaper, a frilled dressing table, and bright pictures on the walls. But what Janna noticed first was an enormous, old-fashioned wardrobe.

"My dresses will look silly in that . . ." she murmured sleepily. Frau Oster found Janna's nightgown and toothbrush in her bag.

"You can unpack your suitcase tomorrow," she said, helping Janna undress. Janna sank into the soft mattress, so unlike the straw one she was used to. Her mother tucked the fluffy blankets around her.

"Sleep well, Jannelein, there are lots of surprises awaiting you tomorrow. We haven't had time to tell you everything. We're so happy to have you back," she said, kissing Janna and flicking out the light.

Janna lay staring into the darkness. She knew she should be happy. This was a lovely house and her parents had been very kind. Yet she felt homesick. Not for the Black Forest, though she missed the scent of pine trees coming through her attic window, nor for Erna, though it seemed queer not to hear her rattling about in the kitchen and scolding her old mother. . . . No, what made the tears come in the darkness was the loss of those perfect, devoted parents she had lived with the last two years, those parents who hung on her every word, who read and reread her letters, and spent the rest of the time talking about her, the parents to whom she had poured out her heart. They were gone. They had been chased away by the real ones, who had their own lives to live, their profession, and each other. They did not need Janna.

It made her feel as lonely as a pluck of sheep's wool on a barbed-wire fence. She groped for her uniform. Clasping it, she fell asleep.

✠ FOUR ✠

The House

JANNA DREAMED that she was Brunhilde, but Wotan had sent her away in disgrace. The fat man had told him stories about her and he was very angry. Janna tried to make her horse fly, but it wouldn't. Its feet seemed glued to the ground. She tugged at the reins but it wouldn't go up . . . and it must, it must. They had to get away, for behind them the town was in flames. Only the cathedral still stood. All the houses were burning and white faces looked out of the windows. Swoosh, swoosh, went the flames.

Janna whipped her horse, terrified.

Wotan looked down at her and shook the clouds. Big hailstones fell out and exploded . . . bang . . . bang . . . bang . . . all around her.

Janna woke up, but the noise remained with her . . . There was a chattering of guns outside, a growling of airplanes, explosions. She cowered under the blankets, her fingers in her ears. Had the enemy come? Were they doing to Amsterdam what they had done to Cologne? Was she going to die . . . this minute? But she did not know how to die . . . she was not old enough. It wasn't fair. Yet it had happened to people in Cologne, in Mainz. There must have been girls like her, who did not know how to die . . .

The noise stopped. The drone of the airplanes dwindled and Janna went back to sleep.

When she opened her eyes the next morning, she expected to hear the crow of Erna's rooster and the sound of Erna raking the stove. Instead, there were street noises, a dog barking, children's voices. She was in Amsterdam! Hastily she slipped out of bed and pushed aside the thick blackout curtains.

What she had guessed to be windows were really glass doors opening onto a balcony. Beyond she saw a row of back gardens, separated by fences. The sun was shining on a dazzling white vista of snowy roofs, snow-trimmed trees, and distant, snow-capped spires. But thaw was already marring this beauty: drops from the roofs were pitting the snow on the balcony.

In the adjoining garden children were playing. They were making a snowman and their little dog was scurrying off with the pipe they wanted to put in his mouth. When they retrieved it, he grabbed the hat instead. There was a great deal of running, chasing, calling out, and laughter. The dog was called Fokkie. Janna watched for some time. Then, heedless of the cold, she opened the glass doors and called, "Hello!"

She expected the children to wave to her and greet her. Instead, they gave her a startled glance, whispered together a moment, and vanished into the house, the dog at their heels. Only the snowman was left, sagging a little, his pipe crooked, his hat over one eye. Footprints were scattered around him like confetti.

Janna shivered and closed the doors. She pulled at the string which opened the draperies, and sunlight came flooding into the room. It was even prettier by daylight. The wardrobe looked even larger. A whole family could hide in it, Janna thought. It was decorated with prettily carved animals and flowers, and hugged the wall so closely it might have grown together with it.

The rest of the room was dainty enough: it had a desk with a small statue on it of a praying child, flanked by two candlesticks, a bookcase filled with picture books, delicate watercolor paintings on the walls, and beside the bed a little white rocking chair with a blue cushion. Janna's eyes filled with tears. She felt remorse. She had misjudged her parents. They must love her very much to have spent so much thought and effort to get a room ready for her. She noticed a doll sprawling on top of the bookcase, an old doll that had lost its hair. The color had been washed out of its cheeks, but it smiled confidently, knowing its value. Janna touched it gingerly. She had never played with dolls . . . where had her parents got it?

When Janna returned from the bathroom, she unpacked her suitcase. She hadn't realized that her dresses were so shabby. In this room they looked like leftovers from a rummage sale, but she had to wear one, for her uniform was all wrinkled. She opened the wardrobe to hang up the others and she got a pleasant shock. It was not empty, as she had expected; it was full of pretty girl's clothes. That must be her mother's doing. She must have been shopping in the Black Market. Her parents must have become rich!

With a glow of gratitude, Janna lifted down one of the dresses and tried it on. It fitted snugly. Janna put the other things on in turn and they were all the right size. How clever of her mother! They were of better material and cut than Janna had been used to, though not quite new. Secondhand, probably.

She looked in the oval mirror above the dressing table,

shaking loose her braids and brushing out her hair into a dark cloud. In the drawer she found a pink satin ribbon, just the shade of the dress she had decided to wear. She tied it around her head. She really did look pretty without her braids. Feeling quite glamorous, she went downstairs, slightly awed by the thickness of the carpets and the intricate design of the wrought-iron banisters. Searching for the dining room, she blundered into a large kitchen where a fat cook stood frying eggs at a stove. She was talking over her shoulder at the wispy maid Janna remembered from the day before. When Janna entered, she stopped and turned. Her mouth fell open, the frying pan sagged in her hand. Suddenly she pulled herself together, leveled eyebrows as dark and thick as crowbars at Janna, and rasped in a deep voice, "What are you doing here?" It sounded like German and Janna understood.

"Please," she asked, "where is the dining room?" The little maid hastily put down a boot she was cleaning and wiped her hands on her apron.

"I'll show you," she said in school German. She opened the kitchen door and pointed to the door just opposite, across the passage. She looked scared. Janna smiled reassuringly and the girl smiled back, a wavering smile of great sweetness.

As Janna entered the dining room, she saw her father and mother sitting at the table, which was surprisingly laid for six people. This room looked different too in the daylight. There were strong, bright pictures of sunflowers and corn fields on the paneled walls. Here too, French windows opened into the garden. The snow outside cast a bluish light into the room. A carved wall clock with a picture on it and long weights hanging down seemed to scrape its throat and then chimed nine times. On the table was a lavish breakfast of eggs, toast, hot milk, and steaming coffee.

Herr Oster had disappeared behind *Die Deutsche Zeitung in den Niederlanden,* the local German newspaper. Her mother, who was sipping coffee from a translucent porcelain cup, complained, "You never talk to me. I think it's rude to read at mealtimes."

Janna's father raised his eyes above the paper. "My dear Mechtild," he said, "every evening I am either your jealous husband or your besotted lover. Can't I have the mornings off?"

Mechtild dimpled. "It is rather hard on you," she conceded, pouring more coffee.

Janna ran to her mother. "Thank you for the lovely dresses," she cried, hugging her.

"Dresses?" asked her mother, who was looking lovely in a shimmering green negligée. "The one you have on is enchanting, much better than those widow's weeds of last night. But why thank me for it? Didn't Erna look after your clothes?"

"This is one of the ones you bought me," said Janna.

"But I did not buy you any clothes," her mother said, bewildered. "I was waiting to measure you. Where did you find them?"

"In the wardrobe," said Janna. "Beautiful ones."

"Heavens!" Mechtild was upset. "That good-for-nothing Corrie! I told her to clear away everything in the drawers and closets and store it in the attic. She is a lazy girl, and if I scold her, she'll say she didn't understand . . . though she knows German well enough. Take the dress off at once; it doesn't belong to us."

Janna's father peered over his paper. "What's the trouble, Mechtild?" he asked.

"She's wearing one of the dresses of . . . of the people . . . who lived here before."

"The van Arkels, you mean," said her husband. "What's the harm? Don't tell me that you swallow the house but choke at a dress? It suits Janna. Let her wear it." He dove behind his newspaper again. Janna saw that her mother was trembling. Was she angry or scared?

"What do you mean, swallow the house?" Frau Oster asked. "I only wanted a little place where I could have my daughter with me. Is that so bad?"

"I explained to you how it would be," her husband answered patiently. "I was against incurring the obligation."

"What obligation? It did not cost the Baron a thing."

"You don't know that, my dear. He may have had to do some bribing. But even if he didn't pay anything, we're still beholden to him."

"I only wanted something empty, something no one was using," Mechtild continued.

"And where would you find that, in overpopulated Holland?" her husband asked. "What in the world did you expect the Baron to do for you, perform a miracle? As it is, he almost did that. I'm enjoying this house very much. It's a lot better than living out of suitcases."

"Then why do you object to the Baron?"

"Because he is too fond of you, my dear."

"Nonsense," said Mechtild. "He sees a sister in me, someone to confide his troubles to. He has suffered a lot in the war; most of his family were killed, and he is never without pain from his shoulder wound. He is a sensitive person and I'm trying to help him."

Otto lowered his paper. "I don't doubt your intentions, my dear," he said. "I just don't share your faith in the Baron."

Janna was looking from one parent to the other. Their conversation was full of hidden meanings which she could not fathom, but one thing was clear: the house did not belong to her parents. It was a borrowed house.

"Did the furniture in my room also belong to the van Arkels?" she asked. She couldn't keep her disappointment out of her voice. The van Arkels must have a girl her age, and all the love and effort had been for her.

"Everything in the house belongs to them," said her mother. "We chose that room for you because it seemed just right." Janna stroked her dress. It felt soft, not scratchy, like her own dresses.

"I'll take it off, Mother, if you want me to."

"No, no," sighed her mother. "If your father says it's all right, you may wear it." She buttered some toast. "Here, eat your breakfast, my dear. Perhaps I am foolish. By the time the van Arkels get back their house, the girl may have outgrown her clothes."

Corrie, the little maid, came in with the mail and put it beside Herr Oster's plate. Herr Oster looked up at her. When she had gone, he said, "Do the servants get enough to eat?"

"Of course," said his wife. "What do you take me for?"

"Corrie looks thinner every day," he said, opening his mail.

Janna's parents began to read their letters. Janna took another slice of toast and spread it with fried egg. She was thinking about the Dutch girl who had had her room and must be exactly her size. What had she looked like and what had happened to her? Had she anything to wear now? Why had she left all her clothes and possessions behind, even her doll?

Herr Oster looked up from the letter he was reading.

"Mechtild, have you seen a Rembrandt anywhere?" he asked.

"A Rembrandt!" His wife jerked to attention, her eyes widening. "Do they have a *Rembrandt* here? A genuine one? I know they're collectors—these are real Van Goghs in the dining room and there are good Impressionists in the long room—but a *Rembrandt!* No, I haven't seen it. I would have been sure to tell you if I had."

"I have a letter here from Seyss-Inquart, inquiring about it. Apparently Hitler is interested in it. He wants it for his new museum in Linz."

"We can't give it to him, it doesn't belong to us . . ." protested his wife, sounding frightened.

"It has nothing to do with us," said Otto. "This house belongs to the Reich now. War spoils, my dear. All we are asked to do is to take care of the picture and hand it over to the men who will be sent to collect it."

"I hate that," said his wife, covering her face with her hands.

"You'd hate it still more if you lost it and had to pay for it," said her husband. "It must be worth well over a million marks."

Frau Oster lowered her hands and looked at Otto in alarm. "What kind of picture is it?" she asked.

"It's a small picture of a church interior . . . the Presentation or Circumcision or something. Probably lots of shadows with a glittering gold spot in the middle . . . You've seen Rembrandts before. Do look for it. We should put it safely away."

"If it hasn't already been stolen," said Mechtild.

"It would be hard to get rid of," her husband assured her. "No ordinary thief would touch it."

At this moment the door opened and a pale-eyed,

stocky boy of about nine swaggered into the room, followed by a bullnecked, tough-looking gentleman with a close-cropped head and eyes like oysters. Behind him tripped and twittered a small wrenlike woman.

"Good morning, Herr Oster, *gnädige Frau*," they said, bowing and clicking their heels at Janna's parents and ignoring Janna. The boy paid no attention to anybody and went straight to his plate.

"Why aren't there currant buns?" he whined. "I want currant buns."

"Janna," Frau Oster said, "these are Herr and Frau Frosch and their son, Heinz. They have the suite on the fourth floor and share their meals with us."

"How do you do," said Janna politely, shaking hands with the Frosch couple. When she came to Heinz, he put his hands behind his back and stuck out his tongue. Janna restrained an impulse to do the same. It was beneath her dignity.

"Please forgive him," chirped his mother. "He is so shy!" Shy Heinz made a rude noise.

"Well," said Frau Oster, "I'd better go look for that picture. Excuse me." And with a graceful bow to the Frosches, she made one of her superb exits.

Janna ran after her, spoiling the effect. "Let me help you!" she cried.

As they mounted the stairs to the second floor, Janna asked, "Who are they, Mother? I didn't know there were going to be other people in the house."

"Hush!" said her mother, frowning. "Not so loud. The Baron could not get us a house to ourselves. There's a shortage, you know. The Frosches are friends of Seyss-Inquart and were already installed when we came. They have the whole fourth floor. Herr Frosch is secretary to

Herr Brigadeführer Rauter, the chief of security in Amsterdam. Don't offend them, please, Janna. They could make things unpleasant for us."

"They are already making it unpleasant for us," said Janna resentfully. "What a pimple that Heinz is!"

"Don't make snap judgments, Janna. You should be glad of another child in the house."

"He is much too young for me."

"He is the age your brother would have been," sighed her mother, remembering a small coffin.

Janna quickly asked, "Who is Seyss-Inquart?"

"He is the present ruler of Holland. Didn't you know? Hitler appointed him. He is an Austrian and helped us when we annexed his country."

"And the Baron, who is he?"

"The Baron?" A warm light came into her mother's eyes. "He is General Dietrich von Schönheim, a great friend of ours, an officer in the Wehrmacht who has seen many campaigns. He was wounded in Russia and is now stationed here because he is still recuperating. You'll meet him soon, he often visits us. We owe him a lot."

They had arrived at the second floor, and Frau Oster was inspecting the pictures in the passage.

"There is another front door here," said Janna, pointing at the heavy oak door. Its fanlight was making a halo of her mother's hair.

"Yes, isn't it interesting? We had a visit from Mynheer van Tonningen, the head of the Netherlands Bank, the other day and he told us about these canal houses. Most of them have two front doors: one on street level and one on the second floor."

"How do you get in from the street then?" asked Janna.

"I forgot you arrived at night! Otherwise you would have seen the stone steps leading up to the door."

Frau Oster finished examining the mottled prints in the hall, while Janna opened the door nearest the front door and peeked into a library, where the walls were so covered with books there was no room for pictures. She followed her mother into a neighboring anteroom, furnished in French style with elegant gilt chairs and sofas. It was warmed by a Franklin stove and got its light from a window opening into a shaft and from glass doors leading into another room. Janna noticed an interesting dollhouse in the corner and would have gone to look at it, but her mother restrained her.

"That's not a toy, it's an antique," she said nervously. The paintings in this room were mostly Amsterdam street scenes by an artist called Breitner.

"Mother," said Janna, "if the Frosches were here first, why do they have the fourth floor? Why did they not take the one we have?"

"The Baron arranged it all," her mother said curtly. "The Frosches are quite comfortable. . . . There is an extra living room on the fourth floor, which I think belonged to the . . . to a nursemaid . . . and there's a boy's room, just suited for Heinz. It's a funny thing . . . the fourth floor seems larger than the third . . ." She stood musing for a moment. Then she shook herself and mounted the few steps leading to the glass doors and opened them. Janna followed her into a long hall. It was the most beautiful room Janna had ever seen. It stretched at right angles to the other rooms and seemed to extend beyond the front width of the house.

"That's another interesting thing," Janna's mother explained. "These canal houses were built in the seventeenth century when simple merchants often became richer than the old, established Dutch families. So the burghers passed a law that social position, not money, should determine the amount of canal frontage you were allowed to have. Very important people could have a door in the middle and two or three windows on each side. The less important you were, the fewer windows you were allowed. The merchant who built this house had a low social position but a lot of money and a large family. He was only allowed one window, so he built two houses side by side, each with a door and a window. Then he cheated. At the back he used the width of both houses, which resulted in this beautiful room. He also had a double garden. The next-door house, which he sold, has only the front rooms. With five stories, that is still plenty."

Janna's mother began to look at the pictures, but Janna still gazed at the room. Such space! If only they could have had it for their Youth meetings! The light from three tall windows shone between floor-length golden draperies on a gleaming parquet floor which was covered here and there with Persian scatter rugs. Little inlaid tables supported tall Chinese vases. It was easy to see that the Dutch had ships traveling to all corners of the world! A row of lyre-backed chairs stood against the wall opposite the windows. The room was so large one hardly noticed the grand piano in the far corner. On the short side nearest her, Janna saw a marble fireplace with carvings. Above it hung a huge gold-framed mirror. The ceiling was painted with gods and goddesses floating on clouds. Several chandeliers, winking with crystal, hung down from it like huge tears. The wall opposite the fireplace was half covered by an enormous painting. The other walls held smaller ones.

Janna started to look at them. They reminded her of other pictures she had seen in museums: ladies drying themselves or on couches, tables covered with spilled food, landscapes with cows and windmills.

"Those were probably bought quite cheaply, when the painters were young," Janna's mother said appreciatively. "They are all famous Dutch Impressionists now. This one is a Post-Impressionist, Charley Toorop. Her father was an artist too." Mechtild pointed to what Janna thought an ugly picture of some huge faces, painted in broad strokes and looking as if carved out of wood.

"I don't like it," she said.

"It's powerful," said her mother. "How do you like this one?" She was standing in front of a shimmering gray picture of an old beggar, sitting under the drooping coats of a secondhand-clothes shop, staring dreamily into the distance. Something in his face reminded Janna of the little man in the train.

"It's the sort of subject Rembrandt might have chosen," said Frau Oster. "Only handled quite differently. It's painted by a Jew: Jozef Israels."

"Do Jews paint?" asked Janna, surprised.

"They paint, they compose music, they act, they write . . ." her mother said gently. "They are a very gifted people."

Janna flushed. "That's not true," she said. "Whatever they do is only imitated from the Aryans; they are parasites of Aryan culture . . ."

"Who told you that?"

"I learned it at school. It's in *Mein Kampf*," said Janna. Her mother was silent. "That's right, isn't it?" insisted Janna, who did not like the expression on her mother's face.

"I can't believe anyone said that about the Jews," her

mother said slowly. "Whatever they may have done politically, the world is full of their creations. We owe them our Bible, and they have influenced all our modern thinking: Bergson, Karl Marx, Albert Einstein, Freud . . . to name only a few . . ."

"But it's bad, Mother," said Janna earnestly. "It's un-German."

Her mother sighed. "How like your father you are."

Janna wondered whether her mother meant it as a compliment. Her eyes had been straying toward the large picture at the end of the room. It represented a family gathered around a table, exactly in the way that Janna felt families should. They were all looking at the antics of a baby lifted in his mother's arms. A bearded father had lowered the book he was reading, two adolescent boys were glancing up from their homework, and a girl of Janna's age held out a doll. The baby, painted in quick, fresh strokes, kicked its legs and reached for it. The lamplight created a luminous circle, uniting all the figures. It slanted across the mother's face, which shone with gentle pride. Tendrils of her hair curled delicately golden against the shadows of the girl's blue velvet dress. The boys' faces were strongly lit, showing square jaws and smooth cheekbones. Their blue eyes twinkled. The father, half in shadow, looked as if his mind were still busy with what he had been reading. Something about his high forehead and firm lips seemed to promise that he was not one to pass by when others were in need. The kind of father you could run and tell your troubles to, thought Janna. But she was most interested in the girl, who was very pretty, with dark hair and eyes like her father. The others were all blond. Janna's mother noticed her interest.

"Do you admire that picture?" she asked. "It's by a

young Dutch artist and only recently painted. I like it because the girl resembles you."

"Does she?" Janna blushed with pleasure. She studied the picture again. Surely she wasn't as pretty as that? She knew she wasn't. Yet there was something familiar about the picture. Janna looked closer. It was the doll! There was no mistaking that smug expression, though here the doll still had some hair straggling from the top of its head. And the velvet dress . . . hadn't she seen its counterpart in the wardrobe upstairs?

"Mother!" she exclaimed. "That doll . . . I've got it in my room. Mother, this is a picture of the van Arkels . . . don't you see? That's the girl whose dress I'm wearing! Now we know what they look like . . . isn't that marvelous!" She turned around. Her mother had grown pale. She had put her hand to her head.

"We've searched enough for today," she muttered and hurried out of the room. Janna followed her slowly. She found her mother lying on her bed upstairs.

"What's the matter, Mother?" she asked, alarmed.

"I've got one of my headaches. Get me some aspirin, dear," she said, scarcely moving her lips. "They're in the drawer of my dressing table."

"Do you mean this bottle?" asked Janna. "It's empty."

"Oh, I'd forgotten, I'm out of it. And in half an hour I'm due at rehearsal. What shall I do?" her mother moaned.

"I'll go and get you some," said Janna.

"Alone? Do you dare? That would be wonderful, darling. It's quite close. You'll find money in my handbag over there on the chair. Take a gulden. When you go out, follow the canal to the left till you come to a bridge. There's a cross street there with shops. The druggist is on the corner. Please hurry, and thanks! You're an angel."

Janna was glad of the opportunity to put on the lovely blue coat trimmed with white fur which she had seen in the wardrobe. It had a little cap to match. She let herself out by the top front door so that she could try the steps. They were slippery with melting snow; she had to hold on to the iron railing. Reaching the cobbled street, she looked around curiously, inhaling the peculiar canal smell. Though the snow was mostly gone from the street, the stepped gables of the houses opposite were still trimmed in white. The water of the canal murkily reflected the houses and trees opposite. Little wisps of straw and leaves bobbed among fragments of ice on its dark surface. Janna heard the clatter of wooden shoes behind her. She looked around. Some children started to wave at her, then stopped . . . and ran. The click-clack of their shoes echoed from the houses.

"Nella—Nella van Arkel . . ." shrieked a voice. "Have you come back? Did the Muffs give you back your house?" Janna turned around. The girl who had called to her stood still, stopping in her tracks when she saw Janna's face. She gave an exclamation of disgust and gave Janna a hostile look. Then she jerked around and ran back to her house, which was next to Janna's. She was one of the children Janna had seen playing in the garden that morning. Though she had spoken in Dutch, Janna understood. The girl had mistaken her for the van Arkel girl, whose name was Nella.

When Janna arrived at the bridge, it was not hard to find the druggist. There was little traffic; only Germans seemed to own cars. One passed, filled with singing Wehrmacht soldiers.

There were people in the druggist's shop, which had a counter crowded with glass jars and a brass weighing scale. The customers stopped talking as Janna entered. They all stared at her, then averted their eyes. An old lady had just bought something and was snapping her bag shut. She gave a start of surprise when she saw Janna and began to smile. Then her face froze and her eyes narrowed. There was a hush in the shop as the lady stood staring at Janna, her cheeks slowly flushing. Then her lips tightened, her eyes sparkled, and before Janna knew what was happening, the old lady had darted at her and given her a resounding smack in the face. With a strangled exclamation she then turned and hurried out of the shop.

Janna stood dumbfounded. Her cheek tingled. She could not believe what had happened. There was a general sigh as the other people in the shop let go of their breath. Somewhere a clock chimed.

The lady behind the counter bent forward and addressed Janna in German. "What can I do for the Fräulein?" Then she added, "That old lady . . . she thought she saw a friend's child; she was disappointed . . . Please forgive her."

Janna asked for aspirin. Everybody began to talk again.

When Janna walked home with her purchase, she grew more and more angry. That lady would not have dared slap her if she'd been a grownup. People thought you could do anything to a child. It was unfair! This was a beastly city, a cold, horrid, nasty city. Her father was right. The Dutch were awful.

When she had given her mother the medicine and the change, she went to her room and took off Nella's clothes. Returning them to the wardrobe, she vowed never to wear them again.

✠ FIVE ✠

A Fountain in the Garden

JANNA HAD FOUND some notepaper in the desk in her room and was writing to Hildegarde. There was so much she wanted to say, but all she managed to get down was:

> *Dear Hildegarde,*
> *How are you all? It was so sad to leave you. The book is lovely. I've finished it but I'm starting all over again. It is horrid here. The house is beautiful but the Dutch people are unfriendly. The German child who lives in the house is only nine. I am homesick for the Black Forest. There are no mountains here and people act as if they thought Germans were bad. How is the play going? Who is acting Brunhilde, Ilse or Marianne? I wish I were there.*
>
> *Your loving Janna*

She licked the envelope shut and looked for a stamp. When she did not find any inside the desk, she opened the drawers below and found some of Nella's schoolbooks. She spent some time comparing Nella's marks with her own. The Dutch children were ahead, but they probably didn't have to work on farms every afternoon. Nella was better at drawing, but she didn't have as good marks for composition. You could see that Nella had been fond of drawing. All her copybooks were illustrated with sketches. Funny little figures danced between her sums, and garlands of flowers surrounded her grammar. Dutch teachers must be more lenient than German ones. Then Janna got a shock. On a loose piece of paper she found a caricature of Hitler. He was unmistakable with his small mustache and dark cowlick. He was trampling with big boots over a lot of small houses with Dutch gables. From his hands dropped bombs, and a balloon out of his mouth said in Gothic letters the German words, "I want peace."

Janna sat still as a stone. She had begun to think of Nella as a friend, but to make fun of *Hitler* was sacrilege.

"What have you got there?" asked Heinz's voice near her elbow. Janna almost dropped the drawing. She quickly pushed it back into the drawer.

"Nothing," she said. Then, angrily, "What are you doing in my room?"

"I want you to come and play with me," said Heinz. "There's a recreation room and a big garden with a swing and a summerhouse. Wait till I show you."

"All right," said Janna. At least Heinz was German, if he had nothing else to his credit. "But next time, knock on the door," she added.

Heinz began to talk excitedly, pointing out things as if they belonged to him, a trait that irritated Janna.

"My father says to be careful of those statues in the hall. They're valuable. Most everything in this house is valuable. When I'm grown up, I'm not going to have a single valuable thing in my house. Don't go into the kitchen, the maids are mean. Corrie shoved a broom into my face. My mother says if she does it again my father will fire her."

"And what did you do?" asked Janna.

"Oh, I can't remember," said Heinz. "I probably left my soldiers lying around. She hates my soldiers because they are our Wehrmacht and SS. She threw some out the other day. I found them in the trash can. Look, that's the recreation room, it's got a real billiard table and lots of games. But I want to show you the garden first."

"Let's get our coats then," said Janna, fetching her school coat out of the hall closet.

When they entered the garden, Janna was glad she had come. It was a beautiful place, surrounded by an ivy-covered fence. There were old apple trees in the back. One held a swing on an outstretched limb. Heinz ran to it. Janna's attention was caught by a pretty little fountain standing among what later would probably be flowerbeds. It was made of marble with a round, wide basin. In the middle three mermaids danced, their tails touching, their arms swinging open like flower petals. Water must have gushed between them in the summer, falling over dainty heads and shoulders. Now they were covered with snow.

Poor things, thought Janna, climbing on the brim of the basin and starting to brush away the snow. It was fun to see the lovely little faces appear, laughing up at her as if thanking her. She scooped some snow out of a hollow and saw something glitter. She picked it up and gazed at it. It was a little ring.

Janna tried it on. It fit. Perhaps it was Nella's. Perhaps she'd been playing in the fountain and lost it . . . Janna had always wanted a ring . . .

She looked up at the mermaids, who smiled down at her. It's their present, thought Janna. I'm going to keep it. She felt a little guilty. Her mother had said . . . but that was *inside* the house. How could anyone be sure this ring belonged to Nella?

"What are you doing there, Janna? Come on . . ."

Heinz cried imperiously. He was sitting on the swing. "Come and push me!" But Janna was admiring her ring and did not push very hard.

"Just like a girl," said Heinz scornfully, jumping off and running to the summerhouse. It was overgrown with ivy; an unpleasant, dank place with drifts of snow in the corners and on the metal chairs. Heinz cleaned a chair for her and gallantly offered it, but when she sat down, he jerked it away so that she landed on the cold, wet ground.

"Horrible boy!" she cried, slapping the snow from her skirt. "If you behave like that I won't stay," and she marched off.

"Please come back," Heinz called after her. "I promise I won't play tricks any more." Janna wavered. She did not like Heinz, but there was nobody else.

"If you come back I'll show you a secret," said Heinz.

"All right," said Janna, retracing her steps. "What secret?"

Heinz walked to the fence which separated the van Arkel property from the one next door where Janna had seen the children playing. He pulled back strands of ivy and revealed a clever hideaway where an old chair wobbled on a bit of carpet, which was sodden with melting snow.

"Look through the peephole," he said. There was a large knothole in the wood of the fence. When you sat on the chair, you could see through it with one eye. Janna noticed that the snowman was melting. The hat sagged, the carrot had fallen off. There were no children in the garden.

"I don't see anything," she said.

"Of course not. They always go in when I come out. But when I sit here a long time and keep quiet, they think

I'm gone and then I can spy on them," said Heinz with satisfaction.

"And what's the fun of that?"

"Fun? It isn't *fun*," said Heinz indignantly. "It's work. I'm helping our war. Don't you know we're fighting a war?"

"We're fighting the Russians and the English and the Americans," said Janna, "not the Dutch. They're part of Germany now."

"That's what you think. We're fighting them all the time. You should hear my father! This country's supposed to be called Westland now, not the Netherlands, and the Dutch are supposed to obey Hitler; but they don't *want* to belong to us. They still want their old queen."

"How do you know?"

"By the things they do. They don't give to our Winter-help. They pretend to, but the collection box is always full of buttons and pebbles and bits of glass. They're supposed to give up their bicycles, but they only give us the old ones and they keep the new ones hidden somewhere. They print secret newspapers with pictures of the queen and the princesses, and they listen to Radio Orange from London, and then they do what the queen tells them. If I hear the people next door doing that, I'll tell my father and they'll all be put into prison."

"How horrid," said Janna.

"Why? The Dutch are our enemies; they're dangerous, don't you know? It's not safe here for Germans. My father won't let me go out alone on the street, I might be pushed into a canal. Don't you know how the Dutch hate us?"

"Maybe we would hate the Dutch," said Janna slowly, "if they came into *our* country and gave it a different name and told us what to do . . ."

"What a silly thing to say," said Heinz scornfully.

"They're not strong enough. This is much too small a country."

Janna was looking at the back of the house, all covered over with ivy. She remembered what her mother had told her.

"Who lives in the garden on the other side?" she said.

"Only grownups," said Heinz. "They don't even have a dog. They never go outside."

"And who lives in the house next door in front, the one without a garden?"

"Two old ladies," said Heinz. "Haven't you seen them? They're always sitting in their window and looking into the little mirrors on each side. I bet they spy on us. My father says when people get that old they should be put to sleep." A shiver went down Janna's back as she remembered Aunt Hedwig. She turned and almost ran into the house. It was no use trying to be friends with Heinz, she thought. When she passed the kitchen, a lovely smell made her peep inside. There was no one there, but a rich soup was bubbling on the stove and nine pink meatballs sat on a plate waiting to be fried. Janna withdrew and went upstairs. Nine meatballs for eight people. They might be expecting company.

As she arrived at the second floor, she saw that Corrie was admitting someone at the front door. It was a German officer in uniform. Corrie offered to take his coat, but the officer said he had only come to deliver a note and would leave right away.

"The *gnädige Frau* isn't in," said Corrie in her best German. "Only Frau Frosch and Fraulein Janna."

"Ah, Fraülein Janna! Tell her I'd like to meet her," the officer said in an agreeable cultured voice. Corrie showed him into the anteroom.

Janna hadn't waited. The glimpse she had caught of the officer, who seemed to have a very high rank, had been exciting. She ran to her room and changed quickly into Nella's blue velvet dress. It was only a few hours since she had vowed never to wear Nella's clothes again, but then she had not known that a handsome officer was going to call. She washed her face and hands and brushed her hair till it was glossy. By the time Corrie found her, she was ready.

The officer was standing over the Franklin stove, warming his hands. He had opened his greatcoat and laid his cap and gloves on the table. He was tall, with a long, mobile face, a high forehead, and deep-set, rather melancholy eyes. His dark-blond hair was swept back smoothly. He turned to Janna, and when his eyes met hers, mysterious and probing, she felt herself blush.

"So this is the daughter?" he said pleasantly. "We've waited for you a long time, your mother and I." He smiled as if he approved of her, but it did not lighten the shadow in his eyes.

Janna frowned. What right had he to wait for her, and why had he not mentioned her father? Summoning all her dignity, she said, "I am Johanna Oster. Who are you?"

The officer responded immediately. He stood erect, clicked his heels, and bowed. "I beg your pardon," he said. "Let me introduce myself. My name is Dietrich von Schönheim."

"The Baron," said Janna, looking up at him wonderingly.

"Yes," said the officer. "The Baron." Janna again felt his gaze on her. She wanted to shake it off. Motioning to a chair, she sat down herself.

"Do you like living in Amsterdam?" she asked politely,

folding her hands in her lap. The Baron had taken the chair. He looked at her and burst out laughing.

"How like your mother you are!" he exclaimed.

"Everyone says I'm like my father," said Janna stiffly.

"In looks, yes," agreed the Baron. "But in manner . . . you're the image of her."

"Do you know my mother well?" Janna asked coldly.

"We are dear friends," the Baron answered. "We're like brother and sister." A quick glance convinced Janna that she had better look away. The Baron's face was too flatteringly attentive. She stared down at her hands and noticed for the first time that her fingers were lacing and unlacing, just the way her mother's did when she was agitated. It was a disconcerting discovery. She put her hands at her sides and cleared her throat.

"Can I offer you something?" she asked. "Are you thirsty?"

The Baron laughed again. He stretched out his hands and captured one of Janna's between them. They were large and warm. "Can't we be friends?" he pleaded.

Janna's heart longed to say yes, but something made her answer sternly, "I don't know you well enough."

The Baron withdrew his hands. "Of course you don't," he said. Then he went on lightly, "Would you like to be an actress when you grow up?"

"Oh yes," she said eagerly. "I was going to be Brunhilde in a play, only then I had to leave."

"So you know the story of the *Nibelungen?*" the Baron asked thoughtfully. He had stood up and was looking down on her. Janna glimpsed an array of decorations on his uniform.

"Your parents are acting in a modern version of the story of Sieglinde," he went on. "Would you like to see it?"

Janna jumped from her chair. "I'd love to . . . could I?" she asked.

"I'll take you," promised the Baron, picking up his gloves and cap. "Now I have to go. But remember, we have a date!" He kissed Janna's hand, the one with the ring. Janna watched him go and stared after him, her feelings in a muddle.

There were meatballs for lunch that day but no visitor.

✠ SIX ✠

The Play

JANNA HAD NEVER had any jewelry, she certainly had never owned anything that was real gold. She wondered why people talked about the gold of wheat or of sunflowers. People were always using the word "gold" when they meant yellow. Gold wasn't a color, it was a shine. She thought all this while studying the ring. The fact that it didn't belong to her, that it must be part of the van Arkel possessions, nagged at the back of her mind, but she wasn't paying attention to it. She was getting very fond of the little ring. It somehow made her feel grownup, less of a schoolgirl.

The Baron was as good as his word. One morning Janna was sitting at breakfast with her parents, after the Frosches had left, when a written invitation arrived for her to see the play *Sieglinde*. Her mother, noticing the crest on the envelope, was going to open it when she saw it was addressed to Fraülein Johanna Oster. Janna flushed with pleasure, opened it, and showed the invitation to her mother.

"I forgot," said Mechtild. "You did meet the Baron, didn't you? He told me. Isn't that kind of him!"

"Do you think the play is suitable for a child?" asked her husband.

"I know it already," Janna blurted out. "It's about Siegmund and Sieglinde. They were twins but they were separated as babies, and later when they were grownup they

65

met and fell in love. Sieglinde was married already, so they ran away, but her husband killed Siegmund, and later Sieglinde died too, though Brunhilde tried to save her."

"You see, Otto," said her mother. "It's no use trying to shield Janna from the facts of the story. She knows them already. It's only fair that she should see her parents act." She looked at her daughter and said suddenly, "Where did you get that ring, Janna?"

"I . . . I found it . . . " Janna stammered.

"In the house? I told you . . . everything is . . ."

"Outside," said Janna quickly.

"Let me see . . . is it valuable? Otto, have a look . . ."

"I can't tell," said Otto, turning the little ring between his blunt fingers. "It could be gold, but I see no hall-mark. . . . It might be brass. Does it make your finger green, Janna?"

"No," said Janna.

"Then it may be gold-plated. For goodness' sake, Mech-tild, don't make a fuss about a trinket. Let the child keep it." Janna breathed a sigh of relief.

The Baron did things in style. He fetched her in his Mercedes. Janna wore the velvet dress and the pretty coat and cap. She could not disgrace the Baron by going in her school clothes.

"You look very nice," he praised, and she blushed. His eyes seemed to probe into her most secret thoughts. The chauffeur opened the door of the car and they soon sat side by side and were driven through the dark streets. There was no mist this time. Moonlight silvered the edges of the buildings and shone milkily into the canals. Janna looked at the Baron. His face was shadowy, but as he smiled at her she could see the gleam of his teeth.

"So you know the whole story of the Ring," he said.

Janna nodded. "We had to learn it at school. It's Hitler's favorite story."

"So I believe," said the Baron dryly. "Do you understand the meaning of it?"

"I think I do," said Janna. "They explained it to us." She thought for a moment. She did not want to make a bad impression. "It's about greed," she said. "Greed for gold, like the democracies have. The dwarfs start it by making the ring, and even Wotan gets greedy and plays tricks to get it. Siegfried is the hero and he gives the ring away because he is too noble to be greedy, and Brunhilde only wants it because it's Siegfried's pledge of love, but the curse slays them all the same . . . though even in death they are greater than the greedy dwarfs who triumph over them."

"Very interesting," murmured the Baron. "Have you ever seen the operas?"

"Oh no, Erna could not afford it, and before, in Berlin, I was too young."

"That's a pity. The music says so much more than the words. I think the main idea of the story is that there is a curse on stolen power. There is a legitimate power which goes with responsibility and discipline. To want absolute power is to court disaster, for it is only an illusion. In the *Nibelungen* the gods who grasp at it go up in flames. Yet at the end the music of the opera tells us that after their destruction a new order will arise where power will come only through love. This is shown in *Parsifal.* There the self-sacrifice of the knights overcomes the evil machinations of the sorcerer. It's the last of the Ring series, though it is not generally included. It was also Wagner's last work."

"I did not know there was another one," said Janna, immensely flattered at being addressed as an equal.

"Someday, if we have a chance, we'll go to see *Parsifal*," the Baron promised. "In the play I'm taking you to, Siegmund and Sieglinde are ordinary people in modern dress. Siegmund is drafted and dies in battle. Sieglinde dies in childbirth. Brunhilde doesn't come into it. It's a dreary play, but your mother makes it great."

The car stopped suddenly. There were beams of flashlights and shadowy men in uniform.

"What's the matter, Ludwig?" the Baron asked.

"The SS are arresting somebody, Herr General . . ." answered the chauffeur.

"I'll have a look." The Baron left the car and Janna followed. She didn't want to miss this. The SS were holding a lanky, skinny lad who was convulsively clutching a paper bag. He gaped like a fish; his Adam's apple bobbed up and down.

"I don't understand . . ." he quavered. His voice ended in a squeak.

"You're the right age, you should have reported for labor. You'll have to come with us," the SS officer told him.

"No, no, I'm only sixteen and my mother is ill, she has nobody else . . ." the boy said desperately. "I only went out to get her medicine . . ."

"What's this?" asked the Baron, shouldering aside the SS officers, who stood to attention at once when their flashlights revealed the Baron's high rank.

"What do you think we run in Germany, a kindergarten?" the Baron asked. "Even if this boy were the right age, what sort of labor could he do to justify the cost of his transportation? Let him go back to his mother, for heaven's sake!"

"We have orders," said the SS men.

"I take the responsibility," the Baron answered firmly. The lad, finding himself free, scurried off like a rabbit, and the Baron returned to his car, after showing Janna in first.

"Sadistic idiots," he muttered between his teeth. He seemed very angry. Janna was impressed. The Baron, she thought, had legitimate power.

They stopped in front of the dark theater and entered the building along with a lot of other people who were all speaking German. The Baron was very popular with the ladies. Many approached him, started to talk to him. He was polite, exchanged pleasantries, but never made Janna feel he had forgotten her. His hand was at her back, gently pushing her toward her seat. He bought a program for her. It had a photograph on it of her father and mother. Janna gazed around, enchanted. She had never seen so many beautifully dressed people.

The play was strange. Janna hardly recognized the story in all the ordinary everyday chatter and the plain clothes. Perhaps, if it had kept to its romantic setting, she would not have found it so disturbing to watch her parents on the stage. They made it all so real! Her father was Sieglinde's husband, Hunding, and he was perfectly horrid. Janna tried to remember that it was only a play, but her father was too good an actor, she kept forgetting. In this play Siegmund and Sieglinde did not know they were twins till it was too late. Janna's mother was beautiful. Her voice and gestures compelled you to look at her. You hardly noticed the pale blond actor who played Siegmund.

There were moments when Janna sat on the edge of her seat and held her breath. She wasn't the only one; the audience was visibly moved by the plight of the ill-starred lovers. The sleeping tablets had been put into Hunding's drink and the twins had had their talk and were sneaking

out of the house. The first act was over. The curtain fell to
thunderous applause. The lights went on and Janna glanced
at her escort. He sat in a dream, his arms folded, his eyes
staring unseeing into the distance, his lips firmly closed.

"Did you not like it either?" she asked. She had to repeat her question before he shook himself awake and
looked at her.

"Didn't you like it?" he asked. His voice was a little
hoarse. "It's a poor play, but the acting . . ."

"It's seeing my father and mother like that . . . as if it
were *real* . . ." stammered Janna. "It . . . it frightened
me . . . Father was so horrid!" She found instantaneous
understanding.

"Come backstage," the Baron said. "Then you'll see it
wasn't real." She followed him through narrow passages
where people greeted the Baron as if he were a familiar
figure, to the dressing room, where her father and mother
were preparing themselves for the next act. Her father
frowned at first but relaxed when he saw Janna.

"She got frightened," explained the Baron. "You acted
too well, Otto."

Otto looked pleased. "I'm still your old papa," he said,
grinning. "But remember, I've got to make people believe
that your mother has a reason to go running off with that
pale apology of a Siegmund." It made Janna laugh.

The Baron had been saying something to Janna's mother
that was making her blush. Bells rang, and the Baron and
Janna went back to their seats.

The rest of the play was less harrowing to Janna because it seemed less real. All the same, her mother looked
so frail and deserted and died so beautifully that Janna
found the tears streaming down her cheeks when the
lights went on again.

The Baron wiped them off with his handkerchief. "I can see you're not used to plays," he said, which was unfair, for his own eyes shone suspiciously.

The curtain went up and down many times while people clapped. Janna's mother got a bouquet of orchids. "She gets them every night," someone whispered behind Janna. "I wonder who sends them . . ."

People were moving toward the exits.

"It's no use going backstage," the Baron told Janna as he propelled her along with his hand. "There'll be a mob there, wanting autographs. Silly custom," he added. "We'll wait in the car for them."

The chauffeur opened the door. It was cold in the car and the Baron wrapped a rug around Janna. He had scarcely settled the folds when the drone of planes overhead disturbed the quiet and antiaircraft guns began to spit fire. Searchlights crisscrossed the sky; there was a deafening burst of explosives. Janna disappeared under the rug, trembling, but she felt the Baron's steady hand on her shoulder as his voice said, "Don't worry, they're after definite targets in Germany—this is not a dangerous area."

Janna's head emerged again. "But Cologne then, and Mainz?" she quavered.

"Those were enemy towns to them," the Baron said. "They are trying to spare Dutch civilians."

"Oh." Janna sat straight again. The noise did not last long, the airplanes went on, the sky became dark again.

"How can you be a soldier?" Janna asked with a shudder.

The Baron fumbled for a cigarette and lit it. "There is a need for soldiers as well as policemen, as long as all men are not of good will," he said. "But I agree that it is often unpleasant. I had no choice. It was all my brothers and I were fit for. We were raised in a castle in Bavaria, we were noblemen, and it was understood that noblemen don't learn useful crafts. All they are supposed to do is fight. We could ride horses when we were five, and our bodies were trained and drilled till they were perfect. We learned to obey and not to flinch at pain. We were also taught history and literature and music . . . oh, we were happy enough. Above all, we were taught *'noblesse oblige,'* the duty of being kind to the helpless. My father was a devout Catholic. He died of a broken heart."

"Why?" asked Janna.

"Because my three brothers were killed in battle . . . but most of all because he disagreed with Hitler about why and how a war should be fought. Never mind, we won't go into that now. You're coughing. Does my cigarette bother you? Sorry." The Baron opened the window and threw it out.

"Will my parents come soon?" asked Janna.

"As soon as they've got rid of the autograph hunters."

"If you weren't here, how would they get home?" asked Janna. She was looking out of the window.

"On the tram, or they'd walk," said the Baron. "It isn't far."

"Heinz says the streets aren't safe for Germans," Janna remarked.

The Baron gave a short laugh. "A lot safer than they are for the Dutch," he said. "We are the only ones who are armed. Curious thing, this fear of the conqueror for the conquered."

"There they are," said Janna, catching sight of her parents.

Not much was said when they drove home. As they reached the house, the Baron took his leave. "Thank you for a lovely evening," said Janna, stretching out her hand. He bent over and kissed it, just as he had done to her mother.

"Are we friends now?" he asked, his eyes dark in his face. Janna withdrew her hand.

"Maybe," she said. She really did like him.

The Baron turned to her mother. He laughed. "You all over, Mechtild," he said, and jumped into the car.

SEVEN

A Tea Party

JANNA SAT IN front of the mirror, admiring her ring. When she moved her hand, it flashed. She had compared it with the ring in her *Nibelungen* book and they were alike, plain gold rings. The *Nibelungen* ring was magic: perhaps this one was too, perhaps it would bring her luck. She breathed on her ring and rubbed it. When Aladdin rubbed his lamp, a genie came out, but a genie could not come out of a ring.

She was feeling lonely. Her parents were away so often. Every night they were at the theater and they had rehearsals during the day. Even when she was home Mechtild seldom had time for Janna, what with her dressmakers and hairdressers. Janna missed her Youth meetings. She had no friends, for you could not count Heinz. And the people in the house were all so strange. Frau Frosch seemed to live in a world of her own, from which she emerged occasionally to utter absurdities. Herr Frosch was like a dark cloud with a grumble. He seemed to have a secret magic, a black magic, Janna thought. She avoided him.

Mina, the cook, was like the Norns in her book, always uttering prophecies. She'd appear when you least expected her. Sometimes she disappeared into thin air. Once Janna saw her go into the long room. She followed from a distance, curious to know what Mina wanted there. But when she entered the room, there was no trace of Mina.

Janna searched everywhere, behind the drapes and the Chinese screen, even under the piano. There was no other door and the windows were too far above the ground. Janna finally gave up, half convinced that she had only imagined seeing Mina go in there. As for making friends with her, you might as well try to make friends with a crocodile.

Corrie was much more approachable. She laughed at Janna's attempts to speak Dutch and corrected her pronunciation. She didn't mind chattering in her own language, giving Janna a chance to learn it. Janna noticed its similarity to Low German, which she used to speak with her Westphalian grandmother. But Corrie was always tired. Janna wondered whether she was ill. One day, at dinner, Corrie came in with a heavy tureen of soup. She staggered all of a sudden, dropped the tureen, clasped her head, and sagged to the floor. Herr Oster carried her to the sofa in the corner. Frau Oster chafed her wrists. Janna ran to fetch Mina, while Herr Frosch lamented over the soup. Mina brought ammonia and a rag. Corrie was lying back, white and still. Janna feared she was dead. Mina held the drenched rag under Corrie's nose. Her eyelids fluttered and opened.

"What happened?" she asked weakly.

"You fainted," said Mina.

"She doesn't weigh more than a ten-year-old," said Otto. "Does she eat enough?"

"Do you, Corrie?" asked Mina. "You've been eating your meals while I was out of the kitchen. Have you been starving yourself?"

Corrie seemed frightened, her round blue eyes opened wide. "I only took what you gave me . . . nothing else . . ." she quavered. "They're all depending on me to bring them something . . ."

"She's been taking her meals home to her family," Mina told Frau Oster. "She has her parents and five younger sisters."

"For goodness' sake," exclaimed Frau Oster, appalled. "Why didn't she take some extra food and eat her own?"

"She'd consider that stealing," said Mina primly.

"Well, I give her permission," said Frau Oster. "And you too, Mina, if you have starving relatives somewhere. The idea! Poor Corrie . . . is her father out of work?"

"No, he has a good job, *gnädige Frau*," said Mina tolerantly. "But money does not mean anything; there just isn't enough food to go around." Frau Oster blushed. Meanwhile, Janna had been wondering whether to test her ring. Rubbing it a little, she wished Corrie to get better.

But Herr Oster, who had fetched a glass of wine and made Corrie drink it, took all the credit when she revived.

"When are we having dinner?" complained Herr Frosch. Mina and Janna cleared away the mess and then Mina brought in fresh soup.

From that day on, Mina packed a basket of food for Corrie to take home every evening. It was a pleasure to see her fill out and regain color in her cheeks. Soon the house echoed with her singing as she scrubbed the floors.

> *"My father is a jolly man,*
> *He thinks the world of me.*
> *He only works for the fun of it,*
> *And I'm the same as he."*

"What kind of a song is that?" asked Janna.

"It's a soldier's song," said Corrie.

"Our soldiers sing of bravery and victory," said Janna.

"I know," said Corrie. "I've heard them. I'm glad ours don't. War is nothing to boast about."

Janna had got interested in Corrie's family and encouraged her to talk about them.

"They're so happy with the food I bring home," Corrie said. "Of course, they aren't selfish about it, they share with the neighbors. Only I'm worried carrying that basket. There are so many people who'd think nothing of doing you in for a basket of food. The Mussert boys are the worst, those nasty Dutch traitors. . . . They'd kill you for the fun of it. They're lording it over us now, and they've stolen our old prince's flag—orange, white, and blue—so we can't use it any more. They're allowed to parade it around, while we can't hang out our national flag without being clapped into prison. What's worse, they've stolen our old rallying cry, '*Hou zee*,' which means 'Stick to the sea.' It's used instead of 'Hurrah,' but they've made a traitor word of it, the scoundrels"—suddenly Corrie clapped her hand to her mouth—"There I go again!" she cried. "It's my month to speak kindly and look what I've been saying."

"What do you mean, your month to speak kindly?" asked Janna.

"Well, you see," said Corrie, embarrassed, "this priest has started the League without a Name; anyone can belong to it. Once a bunch of Mussert men came to our meeting to start trouble. They sat in the back with their belts and big boots. But Father preached so beautifully on love of your neighbor that even the Mussert men cried. Father says we must reform ourselves before we can improve the world. Every month he sends out a leaflet with a special task for us. Last month we weren't allowed to speak or listen to scandal. This month it's kind words. You don't know how wicked you are till you try to be good."

"I don't think you're wicked," said Janna. She had been impressed with Corrie's self-sacrifice and honesty.

"I don't mean to be, and that's for sure," said Corrie. "It just comes natural."

The van Arkel family had captured Janna's fancy. At night, before she went to sleep, she imagined she was Nella's twin sister and they had all sorts of adventures. Nella was always getting into trouble and then Janna had to help her out. That was easy, because she had the ring. When she rubbed it, her wishes came true, and that way she could extricate Nella from all sorts of hopeless situations. Afterward Nella's parents thanked her with tears in their eyes.

She often stood in front of the big picture, studying it. She had invented names for the boys. It irritated her that whoever did the cleaning, probably Corrie, often left the picture hanging crooked. She had to keep straightening it.

She explored the rest of the house. The recreation room was Heinz's domain. There he massed his tin soldiers on the billiard table and held battles with cannons and paper airplanes, when he wasn't sitting in his spy hole or shooting birds with his popgun. He was always trying to get Janna to play backgammon or checkers with him, but he was such a bad loser that Janna thought it no fun.

She liked to play with the dollhouse in the anteroom. Its front was like that of a canal house with a sawtoothed gable. Inside, the rooms were full of old-fashioned furniture: canopied beds, a tiny spinning wheel, a coal range, a milk churner, warming pans, etc. China dolls in period costumes leaned stiffly against the chairs.

Janna also liked rummaging in the table drawers, discovering lace gloves, a magnifying glass, ballet slippers, pencils, and leathered fans. Janna's mother would stop her when she noticed it.

"Janna, remember, nothing is ours . . ." She said it all the time, whether Janna was winding up an old music box or leafing through photograph albums. "Take care, don't touch, leave it alone . . ." It got to be tiresome. Mina was worse. Janna could not peek into a room, open a closet, or investigate a cubbyhole without Mina suddenly appearing like a spider in a web, saying, "Take care, Little Miss Snoop, that your nose doesn't get caught in a door!"

Janna was glad when her parents found a teacher for her. He was a Dutch law student who needed extra money. "We tried to find a German tutor for you," her father explained. "But they're scarce. This Dutchman is all right. He is excused from labor in Germany because of his poor health. His friends call him Erasmus, after the Dutch philosopher of the sixteenth century. They say he is brilliant. Heinz's father wants him to teach Heinz too, so you won't be alone."

The library was arranged suitably with tables and chairs. When Hugo van Hoorn entered the room that first morning, Janna felt embarrassed. He was short and one shoulder was higher than the other. He had a pronounced hump on his back. He looked frail.

"He is a hunchback," whispered Heinz.

But when Hugo sat down and began to talk, Janna forgot his handicap. His face came alive and proved quite attractive. His brown eyes, under his domed forehead, smiled at her behind flickering glasses. They shone with intelligence and understanding. Janna's pity and concern soon changed into admiration. She realized that she had never had a better teacher.

But that first day was awkward because of Heinz. He

showed no respect, answered Hugo's questions rudely, and imitated the teacher's posture and gestures behind his back. Janna did not want to look, but Heinz knew how to draw her attention and she had to laugh, whether she wanted to or not. After a little of this, Hugo turned around and beckoned Heinz to face him.

"Let me enjoy it too," he said quietly. It wasn't funny, with Hugo looking on, but Hugo smiled serenely and said, "Very good, young man. Now let's see if you can do as well in arithmetic."

Heinz soon found out that he did not meet Hugo's standards for his age. That irritated him; he began to play tricks, disappearing under the table and tickling Janna's legs. He shook the table when Janna had to write and let a beetle dipped in ink crawl all over her books.

Janna complained to her parents. "With him there I'll never learn anything," she said. So Heinz was withdrawn from the lessons. His mother undertook his education and could be heard every morning running through the house calling, "Heinz, Heinzchen, time for your lessons!" while the wretched boy hid somewhere. Janna thought him a spoiled brat. She slept under his bedroom and could hear his tantrums almost every night. She wondered how his parents put up with it.

She got to love her lessons with Hugo. Under his gentle direction many mysteries which had baffled her in mathematics were explained. Ancient history came alive. German literature acquired new glamour. She read poets she had never heard of: Heine and Rilke. At her request, Hugo taught her Dutch too.

Janna was much happier now, with work to do and interesting things to think about. Herr Frosch was the only fly in her ointment. She did not like him. He talked rudely to his wife, was barely polite to Janna's mother, and shouted at Corrie. The only one he treated with some respect was Janna's father. The two men often agreed on political issues. But Mechtild wasn't finished complaining about Herr Frosch.

"Otto, it's ridiculous. He does what he likes without telling me. Either I run this household or I don't. Let his wife do it. Maybe she can manage him."

"Frau Frosch?" Otto chuckled. "We'd be in the soup. You'll just have to put up with him."

"But he's impossible! He brought a party in for billiards the other day and upset Mina's entire schedule. Besides, he brings in such gruesome characters and the place is in a mess afterward. Can't you tell him this is our home too and that he has to let me know when he invites people? Some of them aren't fit for Janna to meet."

"My dear, he is in the secret police. You don't want to get into trouble with the SD."

That always silenced her mother. She seemed to be afraid of Herr Frosch, for she never said anything to his face.

The winter had fled and spring came tiptoeing through the garden, waking a snowdrop here, a crocus there. Soon the place was a riot of color enlivened by a whole orchestra of birdsong. The birds, at least, were happy. Janna asked for a little plot of land, where she sowed radishes and cress. She picked some of the flowers and made wreaths out of them for the mermaids, whom she called her Rhine maidens.

One afternoon the Baron was coming to tea. Otto had an engagement and would not be there, but Mechtild invited Janna to help hand around the cups. It was a lovely day. The March sun was pouring through the windows of the long room, where Janna's mother sat behind the tea table. She was pouring tea from a silver teapot into fragile cups. Her wide sleeves fell away from her slender, shapely arms as she did so. Behind her, on the white marble of the mantelpiece, skillfully carved cupids sported among garlands of grapes. The Baron sat opposite her, talking earnestly.

"You've no idea what we're up against," Janna heard him say. "We do the fighting and bear the losses, but most of the recruits and equipment go to Hitler's favorites, the SS and the air force. None of our formations are complete and we aren't allowed to disband some and bring the remaining up to strength, for that would be bad propaganda. We need not have lost three hundred thousand men at Stalingrad; we wanted to withdraw when we saw it was hopeless, but Hitler ordered us to stay: 'A true Aryan does not turn his back.' It was a massacre . . . all those fine young men!"

"Can't you *do* something about it?" asked Mechtild. "Talk to someone?" The Baron laughed bitterly.

"To whom? Hitler is not only commander-in-chief of all the armed forces, he is also the supreme ruler of the civilians. He is the 'sole judge of what is good for the German people without being bound by legal regulations.' Besides, all officers of the Wehrmacht had to take a personal oath of unconditional obedience to Hitler. We have marvelous soldiers—it is owing to them that things aren't worse—but if this goes on . . ."

"Oh dear," said Mechtild.

"Meanwhile, officers are withdrawn from the Russian front to guard against an invasion here," the Baron added. "Including me."

"It's a rest for you . . . your poor shoulder," said Mechtild soothingly.

"My shoulder can go to blazes. I eat my heart out here, knowing that my fellow officers are getting hell out there."

Mechtild looked up and saw Janna standing in the doorway. "Janna, I didn't see you. Come in," she said. "Have you been listening to Dietrich's wild talk? Don't pay attention to it, he is a great patriot, I assure you."

The Baron got up to greet Janna. "Have you recovered from our night out?" he asked.

"It was very nice," said Janna lamely. She felt uncomfortable with the Baron. What had he said about Hitler?

The Baron sat down and turned to Frau Oster again. "We could have had Russia in our hands," he growled. "In the Caucasus we disbanded the communal farms and established self-government. We had the people all fighting on our side, but Hitler stopped it. No equality for Slavs."

Quite right, thought Janna. The Slavs were inferior. She scowled as she handed the plate of cakes to the Baron, but he did not look at her.

"It's those infernal racial policies that are cooking our goose," he remarked morosely.

There were voices in the anteroom. Frau Oster frowned. The glass doors opened and in stepped Herr Frosch, followed by two natty SS officers. Herr Frosch bowed to Mechtild and introduced his friends: Herr Sturmbannführer Schmidt and Herr Obersturmbannführer Wolff. They had wanted so much to meet the famous Mechtild Oster that he had taken the liberty to bring them. Janna's mother was not a trained actress for nothing. She smiled graciously and asked the gentlemen to sit down. Janna brought extra chairs. The Baron's face froze. He rose and sauntered to the window, his back to the visitors.

"Janna, fetch more cups," Frau Oster said. When Janna returned with a tray holding extra cups and saucers and a second plate of Mina's delicious cakes, she saw that Herr Sturmbannführer Schmidt and Herr Obersturmbannführer Wolff were talking animatedly to her mother while Herr Frosch was quietly consuming the cakes. The Baron still had his back turned to them.

"Forgive me," Herr Obersturmbannführer was saying to Mechtild with boyish enthusiasm, his face flushing into his shining blond hair. "I've seen you as Sieglinde five times and I've seen you every night in *Doll's House* and I've wept, positively *wept*, every time. The beauty of the Aryan wife, her love, her courage . . . how can you bear such suffering every night?" Mechtild's lips twitched a little as she answered, "A good supper helps. Do have some tea, Herr Sturmbannführer; wouldn't you like a cake, Herr Obersturmbannführer?"

Herr Schmidt was too busy gazing at her. "This is the greatest day of my life . . ." he said dramatically. "You don't know what a fan I am of yours . . . I used to pin up your picture in my room. And here I am . . . face to face . . ."

Herr Frosch had cleaned up one plate of cakes and was starting on the other. The Baron turned around and silently surveyed the SS officers. There was such contempt in his eyes that Janna felt shocked. They were a bit uncouth, she allowed, but they probably had not had the Baron's advantages. She urged a cake on Herr Wolff before Herr Frosch had eaten them all. The Baron must have repented of his churlishness, for he sat down, hand-

ing his cup to Mechtild for more tea. Herr Frosch followed his example.

"Genuine tea," he praised, smacking his lips. Herr
Schmidt discovered that his own tea was cooling and
hastily drank it, too hastily, for the spoon fell from the
saucer to the floor. In diving for it, Herr Schmidt spilled
tea on Mechtild's pretty shoe. Straightening up, he apologized profusely and took a cake to cover his confusion. He
promptly choked on it. The Baron looked at his wrist-
watch.

Herr Wolff was blushing at the awkwardness of his
companion and rose from his chair. "We'd better not take
up more of the *gnädige Frau's* time," he said, clicking his
heels. With a sigh Herr Frosch abandoned the last cake.
"You're right, we've got work to do," he agreed. They
bowed themselves out of the room. Janna ran after them
to show them to the front door. She heard the Baron say,
"There goes the master race," and her mother answering,
"I did not know you were such a snob, Dietrich."

When Janna returned, the Baron was talking again.
". . . against all rules of decent warfare: shooting and tor-
turing prisoners, murdering old people, babies . . . no
mercy. We've tried to save whom we could, I threatened to
shoot it out once with the SS if they did not release the
civilians to us, but we are not always there. The cruelties
have been unthinkable."

"Perhaps Hitler doesn't know . . ." began Mechtild
timidly. The Baron laughed harshly.

"His orders, Mechtild, don't fool yourself. Inferior races,
you see."

"Can't someone stop the SS?"

"We did stop them sometimes, as I said, but we have

no jurisdiction over them. They are outside anyone's control—and they have sown a hatred of us in the Russians which our children may have to pay for."

Janna tiptoed off. She did not want to hear more. The Baron's words had upset her badly. She did not want to believe them, but neither could she believe the Baron to be a liar and a traitor, not with all those medals! Was Hitler then not the benevolent ruler she had supposed him to be? And Herr Schmidt and Herr Wolff . . . were they really cruel? They had such clean, open faces!

Janna wandered about the garden, clenching and twisting her hands, fiddling with her ring. She passed Heinz's secret place and wondered if he was there. She peeped inside but the hideaway was empty. She sat on the chair and looked through the knothole. It was funny how much of the garden you could see with one eye. As usual, it was deserted. She wondered if the neighbors guessed that Heinz was spying on them! There was a rustling noise as Janna saw the little dog come running into the garden. He had a newspaper in his mouth. He was always picking up things. Amused, Janna watched him worrying the paper. The wind flapped it open and Janna could see the letterhead: *Vry Nederland.* That meant *The Free Netherlands.* Startled, she looked again. But . . . that was one of the forbidden papers, a paper printed by the Dutch Resistance! Herr Frosch often said they should make an example of people caught reading these papers and shoot them. One of the children had followed the dog. It was the girl of her own age. She did not call "Fokkie, Fokkie" out loud as usual. She whispered it, with frightened gestures. The dog came to her, wagging his tail. He'd dropped the paper; she had to go and fetch it. After they had gone into the house, Janna sat for a long time on the chair thinking.

Why had she looked? Heinz and his horrible spy hole! She wished she hadn't seen it! Now she did not know whether to tell or not. Herr Frosch did say the people should be shot. Was it really so bad for the Dutch to have their own newspaper? She'd ask her father about it. Meanwhile, she'd keep her mouth shut.

She left the spy hole and went inside. Her father and mother were talking in the hall. The Baron must have left. Her father was holding the evening edition of the German paper, looking grave.

"I'm afraid this will mean reprisals," he said. "We can't let such insubordination pass, we have to keep things under control."

"What's the matter?" asked Janna.

"Nothing, dear," said her mother, putting a hand on her father's arm. "Nothing. Go tell Mina to take away the tea things." Janna trudged discontentedly down the stairs. When were her parents going to treat her like an equal? Probably never, she thought bitterly.

Mina and Corrie were arguing in the kitchen. Janna's Dutch was good enough now so that she could follow their conversation.

"I don't know what you want with a foreign church," Mina was saying.

"It isn't a foreign church . . ." Corrie answered hotly. "It's as patriotic as any. Didn't they clap our priest in prison for speaking his mind?"

"Yes, they do stand up to the Germans, I'll allow that," Mina conceded graciously.

"And you a Lutheran . . ." Corrie continued. "Your church was started by a German!"

"There you're wrong," Mina answered with dignity. "I'm now Dutch Reformed." They stopped talking when they saw Janna, who hastily delivered her message under the threat of Mina's eyebrows.

At dinnertime Janna learned what had bothered her parents. Herr Frosch did not seem to think it unfit for her ears.

"I see you read about it," he said, pointing with his fork at the paper by Otto's plate. "Those Dutch renegades burned the registry at Plantage Avenue. They forced their way in, dressed as police, and set it on fire." There was a look of satisfaction on Herr Frosch's face. He'd always *said* the Dutch were bad, and now he was proved right.

"What is a registry?" asked Janna.

"A public registry is where people keep the data of births and deaths. We won't be able to separate the Jews from the Aryans now," her father explained.

Herr Frosch laughed. "That's all taken care of. Holland is free of Jews now except for the last lot in Amsterdam, and they'll be going soon. No, it's labor we need and we have to know who is the right age to call up."

"Did we capture the people who did it? Were they tortured?" asked Heinz with glittering eyes. Janna's parents looked at him with distaste, but his mother bent over him soothingly.

"No, Heinz darling, don't worry. No one was tortured, they all got away." Heinz looked disappointed and stretched out his hand for a cake.

"Eat your vegetables first," said his mother.

"I hate kale." And Heinz spat out a mouthful, which fell like green slime on the white tablecloth.

"Really . . ." said Frau Oster in an outraged voice, rising from her seat. Herr Oster beckoned her to sit down again.

"Now, Heinz, see what you've done," wailed his mother, making things worse with her napkin. Herr Frosch stared fixedly at his son. A vein in his temple had begun to throb. His eyes were like stones.

"Go to your room and wait for me," he said in an ice-cold voice. Heinz grew pale with fright and ran. Janna, looking at Herr Frosch, suddenly felt scared too.

✠ EIGHT ✠

The Birthday

JANNA LOOKED THROUGH the windows of her room at the neighboring children, who were playing in their garden. Several times she had made efforts to befriend them without result. Yet they were at her mercy. If she told they'd been reading an underground Dutch newspaper, terrible things would happen to them. She wondered whether she was a traitor not to tell. She tried to find out from her father.

"What is an underground newspaper?" she asked him.

"Huh, what do you know about that?" Her father looked at her suspiciously.

"Herr Frosch talks about it," Janna said truthfully.

"Herr Frosch talks about everything," her father said irritably. "His mouth is so big, someday he'll swallow himself."

Janna thought that very funny. When she had stopped laughing she said, "Yes, Papa, but tell me now, why is it so bad for the Dutch to have an underground paper?"

"Well," said her father, "it is written by people who oppose our government. They write up everything we do or say in a bad light and they report what they hear over Radio Orange, which is enemy propaganda. You can see how that could interfere with our discipline."

"Will it make us lose the war?" asked Janna. Her father looked at her.

90

"Whom have you been listening to?" he asked. "We're not going to lose the war. Our armies are too powerful."

"But the Baron says . . ."

"The Baron!" said her father angrily. "I'm not a bit surprised to hear he is behind this. Those Junkers all feel superior to the ordinary man. They can't stand that they are considered no better than anyone else now. Don't talk to me about the Baron." And her father dove behind his newspaper again.

Janna felt her father was unfair to the Baron and had been jumping to conclusions, for she had not told him what the Baron had said. If he was so sure they were going to win, she thought, there was no need to bother him with a little transgression of the neighbors.

Heinz had been hanging around, wanting her to play checkers with him. He was becoming a nuisance. Janna felt sure he was spying on her, as well as on the neighbors. She was forced to lock her door now and walk with the key around her neck. When she forgot, she would find her neat drawers disturbed, dirty footprints on the rug, and sometimes the windows banging when she knew she had shut them. She believed he even invaded her room at night. Once she had woken and felt sure she heard someone else breathing in her room. She stayed quite still; she wasn't going to give Heinz the satisfaction of having scared her.

Now Heinz proved to her that he had been snooping. As she again said she did not want to play checkers, he threatened, "You'd better or I'll have you put in prison." They were standing in the upper hallway opposite one of the "valuable" statues.

"Nonsense," said Janna. "I'm a Hitler Youth. You're not, you can't do anything to me." That was an unkind cut.

Heinz wanted nothing so much as to be a Hitler Youth, but he hadn't reached the right age yet.

"It isn't nonsense," Heinz protested. "I've got something of yours that's real bad."

"That's ridiculous," said Janna. "I've never done anything that bad."

"Yes, you have; yes, you have," jeered Heinz, pulling the caricature of Hitler out of his pocket. Janna realized at once how hard it would be to prove she hadn't done it. She had been sitting at the desk when Heinz had surprised her and he had seen her shoving it into the drawer. The lettering and the words were German. Who would believe it had been drawn by a Dutch girl? She chased after Heinz, trying to grab it, but he was too quick for her. He was waving it in front of her to tease her, and just as she thought she had it, he was off again. He finally locked himself in his room and laughed at her through the transom. The following days she had to play a lot of checkers under threat of the sketch, which annoyed her. She watched for an opportunity to slip into his room and search for it. She found it one morning while he was in his spy hole. She had never been in his room before. It was a large room, larger than hers. It had been furnished by the van Arkels: there was a bookcase full of adventure stories and a lovely model of a sailing ship. But Heinz had superimposed his own treasures. The walls were full of photographs and newspaper clippings of the war and of Youth rallies and marching Jung Volk, and of Hitler making speeches and kissing babies. Above Heinz's bed hung an enormous blood-red flag with a black swastika. On the opposite wall hung a framed text.

"Almighty God," it said. "We don't need Your help, we

can take care of ourselves, but please refrain from helping our enemies. Adolf Hitler."

Janna rummaged in Heinz's drawers and closets and searched through the things on the table beside his bed. She could not find the sketch. She kept peering through the window to make sure Heinz was not emerging from his hideaway. She grew more and more desperate, wondering where to look next, as she played nervously with her fingers, sliding her ring up and down. It slipped and fell off, rolling over the floor. Janna crawled after it. It had landed under the bed, and as she groped for it among clumps of dust, her hand touched a piece of paper. She pulled it out along with the ring . . . yes! It was the missing sketch! She tore it at once into little pieces and put them into her pocket to throw away later. She slipped her ring on again, but she looked at it with awe. Had it wanted to help her? Could there be power in the ring? Was it not just her imagination?

The hunt for the Rembrandt was still going on and Janna was getting bored with it. She did not understand why Hitler wanted it. He ought to be concentrating on winning the war, not looking for pictures. Still, she enjoyed accompanying her mother to the attic, which was a regular storehouse of discarded objects, all suggesting happy days in the van Arkel family.

"Oh, look, Mother, they must have had grand parties . . . all those Chinese lanterns . . ." and "Oh Mama, the little cradle . . . do you think all the children slept in it?" But her mother never answered these questions. Janna was rocking on an old rocking horse one day while her mother searched in trunks and closets.

"Why did the van Arkels leave?" she asked. "If they wanted to move to another house, they would have taken their things with them, wouldn't they?" Her mother rubbed her forehead. "Don't bother me," she said. "I don't know. I think the army requisitioned the house."

"You mean, the family was put out so we could live in their house and use all their things?" Janna asked incredulously.

"I hope not . . ." said her mother, sounding miserable.

"Did the Baron do it?"

"Oh no, no," her mother said, too quickly. "Not Dietrich. He is much too kind. He'd never do a thing like that . . ." But Janna wasn't convinced. The Baron was a soldier. He had to kill people. He probably didn't mind taking away their things, that was much less bad than killing them. She had heard of armies plundering. Why should the Baron be different?

"You're not wearing the van Arkel clothes any more," said Mechtild, changing the subject.

"People recognize them," said Janna.

"You're right. It's much better not to wear them. We aren't thieves. I've written down everything we break or use up so we can replace it later."

"Later? You don't think we're going to win the war, do you?" asked Janna, looking sharply at her mother, who flushed and bit her lip.

"You and your father . . ." she said angrily. "You think only of what men do to you. What does it matter whether we win or lose? Is that going to help us when we die and God asks us what we did with the van Arkel possessions? Have you ever thought of that?" Janna hadn't, and it embarrassed her to have her mother talk in that way. Hildegarde or Kurt would have laughed at her; they thought it superstitious to believe in God . . .

Mechtild saw Janna's embarrassment and again changed the subject. "You need some clothes of your own," she said. "I can't have you looking like a dust mop. Next week you'll be thirteen. I'll take the day off and we'll go shopping."

Janna had not celebrated her birthday since she was nine. Erna had not approved of such a waste of time and money. So on the morning of her thirteenth birthday she woke with a feeling of excitement. She wondered whether her mother would remember. She did not expect presents, when they were going to buy clothes, but she hoped for something festive: perhaps pancakes!

When she came down and entered the dining room, she saw that her chair had been decorated with little bunches of violets. At her plate lay a pile of presents. From her mother she got a gold locket and chain. It held a blond curl on one side, from her mother, and a lock of her father's dark hair on the other side. She also got a large signed photograph of the two of them. The Frosches gave her a handkerchief embroidered with swastikas. She had kept the biggest parcel for the last. It was from Heinz. She unwrapped it, layer by layer. At last it ended in a small box. When she opened it, a horrid big spider crawled out, glad to be released from its captivity. Janna gave a yell and dropped the box. The spider scurried over the table, over Mechtild's plate, and over the cheese. Janna's father captured it, opened the window, and released it.

Heinz had been watching all this with satisfaction, until his father boxed his ears. "That'll teach you not to spoil my breakfast," he growled.

"Why didn't you kill it, Otto?" Mechtild asked, shivering.

"A useful insect, the spider," said Otto, unfolding his napkin. "In its place, of course."

"A spider is not an insect," said Herr Frosch pompously. "It has eight legs."

"What would you call it then?" asked Otto. "An octoped?" Herr Frosch mumbled something, he had taken too big a bite of his peanut bun to be intelligible. The Baron had sent a big bag of peanuts, a rare luxury, and they had them three times a day: as a spread, in bread, stirred into curries, or sprinkled over desserts.

Janna was to go shopping with her mother after breakfast. As she put on her old coat, she noticed it was getting too small for her. She could hardly button it. Too much good food. As they were opening the upper hall door, they came face to face with the Baron, who was carrying a bouquet of tulips. Janna and her mother took off their coats again and Corrie was sent for a bottle of sherry and glasses. Janna went to get a vase for the tulips. When she returned, the Baron held out a beautifully wrapped parcel to her, tied with gold ribbon.

"I remembered it was your birthday today," he said, smiling at her.

Janna undid the ribbon and found a dark-red velvet box. Opening it, she saw it was lined with white satin and held a shimmering string of cultured pearls. She stood staring at it, unable to believe it was really hers. Out of the corner of her eye she saw her mother, flushed and trembling, stretch out her hands to the Baron.

"Dietrich, how kind! I do thank you . . ." The Baron took her hands.

"My dear," he muttered.

The velvet box fell out of Janna's hands, the pearls slid along the floor. When Janna had retrieved them and stood up again, her face flushed, the Baron and her mother were talking normally, sipping sherry.

Frau Oster was saying, "I think Herr Frosch suspects me of having done away with the Rembrandt picture."

The Baron frowned. "I wish I hadn't had to land you with those people," he said. "But I could not get out of it. This was the best I could do."

"Yes, yes," Mechtild said hurriedly. "I understand."

When the Baron had left, Janna gave the pearls to her mother. "They're too beautiful," she said. "I don't want to wear them."

Her mother stared at her. Then she said, "Maybe you're right. They are a bit old for you. The locket is better."

"Yes, and that was for *me*," said Janna. "But the Baron gave me the pearls because he wanted to please *you*."

"Don't be a goose," said her mother, blushing.

Janna and her mother finally reached Kalverstraat, that special shoppers' paradise where even before the war no cars were allowed. On the way they passed a round pillar covered with posters and announcements. It caught Janna's eye because there were big pictures on it of her father and mother with an advertisement for their play *My Sister and I*. Under it was an announcement of the Hallensport Festival of the Hitler Youth in the Apollo Hall. Beside it a notice said: "Jews in Holland are not allowed to reside anywhere except in Amsterdam." She remembered the expression on Herr Frosch's face when he said, "The last lot will go soon."

What was happening to these people?

Then she read: "Obligatory application for labor. All men between eighteen and thirty-five years of age who live in occupied Holland's territory and do not have special dispensation must present themselves at their local labor office." Followed by the notice: "The higher SS and police leaders announce that the following have been condemned to death." Several women who were reading the notice wept. There was a long list of names.

Janna's mother was studying something on the other side of the pillar and Janna joined her. It seemed to attract attention; quite a number of people were reading it.

"On the twenty-seventh day of March, 1943," it said, "unknown ruffians wearing the uniforms of Amsterdam police, after attacking the guards, broke into the public registry at Plantage Avenue, Amsterdam, and set fire to the place with incendiary material. Any information that can lead to the discovery of the criminals should be given to the German and Dutch police. To discover the perpetrators, the higher SS and police commands have offered a ten-thousand-gulden award. SS Sturmbannführer Lages."

"Those boys must be far away, if the Germans are offering so much money," came the quivering voice of an elderly gentleman who was gazing at the announcement.

"What do you mean, so much money?" snapped a skinny old lady who was wearing one black and one brown shoe, tied with string. She blew her nose in a piece of newspaper. "I would not betray someone for less than a pound of prewar coffee."

"Or a loaf of prewar bread," agreed another woman. "They take our good food and give us their dirty money."

Frau Oster hurriedly pulled Janna away. They crossed

the Mint square, where barges carrying a colorful array of spring flowers lay moored in the canal. Entering Kalverstraat, they sauntered past shops which were anything but tempting. Everywhere were signs of dilapidation: peeling paint, torn window shades, windowpanes cracked and mended with tape. Frau Mueller had been right: the merchandise looked shoddy, skimpily cut, of artificial material. Yet shabbily dressed people stood in line to buy it, clutching their coupons. Janna noticed that there were very few young men about, apart from those in uniform.

"I suppose they've all gone to work in Germany," said her mother. They left Kalverstraat and crossed the Dam, which Frau Oster said got its name from the dam erected to protect the first settlers from the sea. Now it was a big square in front of the palace paved with large cobbles called "children's heads" in Holland.

Janna did not much care for the gray, square, unromantic palace, which bore no resemblance to the turreted castles of Germany. Her mother said it was a good Renaissance building, designed as a town hall. It became a palace much later. It was filled with French furniture left there by Louis Napoleon, who had once occupied the same position Seyss-Inquart held now.

A group of children stood looking at a Punch and Judy show. There were bursts of laughter, and more and more grownups came to join the children.

"I believe this is a regular institution," said Janna's mother. "It's a tradition to have this show here. Let's look at it."

Punch, who was called Jan Klaassen in Holland, was trying on a lot of hats, but none seemed to fit. They were all too large.

"I'm trying to get a V," he said, holding up his hand with his fingers in the V position, "but all I'm getting is six and a quarter [*zes en'n kwart*]."

There were howls of laughter and it wasn't hard to figure that *zes en'n kwart* sounded like Seyss-Inquart.

"I don't think we should listen to this, dear," said Janna's mother, trying to pull her away. "It's political."

"It's funny, Mother," said Janna. "Just another minute . . ."

Jan Klaassen was now standing absolutely still, with his arm up in the Hitler salute. The audience waited, not knowing what to make of it.

"That's how high my doggie jumps when he greets me in the evening . . ." said Jan Klaassen, which raised a storm of delight. Katryn, Jan Klaassen's wife, now joined him. She was reading a newspaper.

"Dear, dear," she muttered. "Those English and Americans, they're so stupid. They never hit munition plants, or railways, or harbors. All they ever do with their bombs is kill cows. I hear Hitler is going to put up a statue to the Unknown Cow." More laughter. Coins began to tinkle on the pavement. Now a gaunt character appeared, clad in a white nightshirt with a sleeping cap on his head. He represented Death and was affectionately called Pierlala. In the traditional show he was always after the landlord and ended up stuffing him into a coffin, but this time Pierlala had no coffin.

"There's a shortage," he explained. "The Germans took them all. They need them at the Russian front." There was thunderous applause. A policeman approached to inspect the noise.

Jan Klaassen hastily asked, "For whom?"

"For the Russians, of course," said Pierlala unctuously. "You know the Germans have come to save us from the Russians, don't you? They are *taking* measures to save us from what the Russians would take. They are thieves, those Russians!" When the policeman had strolled out of earshot, Pierlala said quickly, "Every night Hitler thanks God for the Russians. If they did not exist, he'd have to invent them."

The laughter was uproarious and Janna's mother shivered.

"Come on," she said to Janna, "this is disgraceful. You should not listen to it. They are making fun of us." Janna left reluctantly. She dearly wanted to know what Jan Klaassen would say next.

"Don't say anything about this at home," warned her mother. "We don't want more trouble than there is already."

"No, I won't tell," said Janna. Then, with a rush, "Mother, I noticed something about the neighbors . . ."

"Don't tell me," her mother said quickly. "I don't want to know."

They went to a large department store called the Beehive and there, after a lot of waiting in line, Frau Oster bought Janna a navy-blue coat and hat, and a red dress. Frau Oster had to pay a lot of coupons, which came out of her own clothes allowance, so Janna was grateful.

"May I keep them on?" she begged, admiring herself in the mirror.

"You'd better," said her mother. "I don't want to see you in those rags any more." She gave Janna's old clothes to the saleslady, who was very happy to get them.

"They will fit Anneke, my little girl," she said, tears in

her eyes. "I was just wondering how I was going to dress her, she has grown out of *everything*. You don't know what you have done for me." It made Janna a little ashamed.

When they left the Beehive, her mother said wistfully, "I'd like to take you to a restaurant for coffee as my mother used to do on my birthdays, but unless we paid the black-market price, all we'd get is colored water. What we could do, since we have no parcels to carry, is to take a walk through the old city and visit the house where Rembrandt lived. I'd like you to see it; it's typical of his period and full of his etchings."

"I'd like that," said Janna.

It was a lovely spring day. The old city, with its narrow streets and humped bridges, looked its best. Elm and linden trees leaned over the canals with their lazily undulating water, and the dark brick houses, topped by scalloped gables, leaned too. Frau Oster explained that this was done on purpose.

"Their doors and passages are so narrow that the burghers have to hoist their furniture through the windows. Do you see the lengths of beam sticking out at the top of the gables, with hooks on them? People haul up their furniture by slinging a rope around the hook, and because the house leans forward, the furniture swings clear."

A loud singing interrupted their conversation. Boots came ringing and clacking over the cobbles. A company of uniformed men passed, slouching, not quite in step. They were not Wehrmacht soldiers nor were they police. They wore three-cornered insignia on their sleeves with the letters N.S.B. The man in front carried a banner with horizontal stripes of orange, white, and baby blue.

"Who are they?" asked Janna.

"Those are members of the Dutch National Socialist Bund," said Frau Oster. "A person called Anton Mussert is their leader." So those were the Mussert boys Corrie had been complaining about.

"Who is Mussert?"

"He was made head of the Netherlands by Hitler last December."

"I thought Seyss-Inquart was head here," said Janna.

"Of course. Mussert only got a courtesy title, to reward him for helping us. He has no power at all, except over his own men. The Dutch hate him and his crowd more than they hate us. There is no doubt that they help us to control the Dutch civilians with a minimum of our own forces."

"You don't like them?"

"Does anyone like traitors? Besides, they are no good. Many volunteered to go to Russia, but we had to send them back again. Look at the way they march!"

Even after the Mussert men were out of sight, the street still seemed to ring with the sound of their boots.

A pale April sun smiled faintly down, reflected in the canals. Light-green sprouting leaves shone tenderly against the deep magenta of the old houses, with their shutters and stoops and small-paned windows. A few seagulls wheeled screeching over the water and up into the sky again. A long barge was churning mud out of a canal with metal cups which whirred around on a belt, scooping the mud into the barge and going back empty into the water again. Janna and her mother watched for a while, but the stench chased them away.

A few hopeful youngsters were fishing from a bridge, their eyes intent on their lines, little pails standing ready for their catch. A woman shook out a mat from an open window, making the dust fly. She called a greeting to the bargeman, who shouted back. An errand boy rattled past on a dilapidated bicycle which looked as if it were held together by strings. As they sauntered on, Janna and Frau Oster came to an archway where a charitable organization was distributing soup. A long line of people stood waiting patiently, holding empty bowls in their hands. Janna saw pale, thin faces, etched with suffering, hollow eyes, skinny legs. She smelled cabbage, and peering into a pot she saw thin, watery soup. Some people in the line complained it wasn't worth waiting for, it didn't fill you for long.

"Even a little is better than nothing," mumbled a toothless old man.

As they went on, Janna was thinking. "Why is there such a shortage of food here?" she asked. "Have they no farms?"

"They are helping to feed our army now," her mother said in a low voice. "We requisition their food."

"But . . . isn't that stealing?" asked Janna.

"We've had shortages for a long time ourselves, it's natural to think of our own people first," said her mother.

Janna stared at her. "If I were Dutch, I'd hate us!" she said. Her mother was silent.

They had come to a street which was roped off. An SS soldier, heavily armed, refused to let them pass.

"We only want to see the house where Rembrandt lived," pleaded Frau Oster.

"Impossible. Against orders," said the guard.

"But I was here only last month . . ."

"It is forbidden," said the guard. Frau Oster looked worried as she and Janna retraced their steps.

"Those are the Jewish quarters," she said in a trembling voice. "What are they doing to those unfortunate people?" Her footsteps dragged. Suddenly a scream pierced the air. It came from the dark alleys behind them—a scream of such wild despair, such pain, that Janna and Frau Oster stood as if glued to the ground. It was followed by another and again another, corkscrewing into the skies. Janna twisted her hands together . . . she could not bear it. . . . There were some shots, then silence.

Janna's mother seemed to be sagging. She was deathly pale.

"I've got my headache again," she moaned. "And I forgot to bring aspirin."

"Let's go to the nearest tram stop," Janna suggested. Her legs were trembling and she was feeling sick herself. "Lean on me." She supported her mother and they walked slowly across a bridge. When they were away from the Jewish quarters, Mechtild began to feel better.

As they waited for a tram, Janna marveled at the strange transportation in Amsterdam. There were bicycle taxis for one passenger, old motorcars pulled by cadaverous horses, carts of all shapes and sizes. A fine, aristocratic lady, dressed in silk and holding a parasol, sat in a velvet armchair on top of a handcart. She was being pushed by a chauffeur in gold-braided livery.

"That's what I call keeping up appearances," said Janna's mother, smiling. The sight seemed to revive her.

The first tram that passed was a special. It was decorated with garlands of tulips and daffodils. Inside sat a bride and bridegroom in all their finery. The other seats were filled with waiting guests. Someone was playing an accordion. It seemed a merry party.

"How clever," said Frau Oster, looking herself again. "I suppose they can't rent a car so they're doing it this way. I've noticed," she added, "that the Dutch are not the staid people I always believed them to be. They seem to take a childish pleasure in festivities, rather like the Italians."

Another tram arrived. Janna and her mother got in. Everyone seemed to be looking at a portly businessman smoking a cigar. He seemed to enjoy this, and leaned back, dramatically puffing out rings of smoke, which drifted like the ghosts of pretzels through the carriage. The man sitting opposite breathed in the scent with an ecstatic face and closed eyes. He leaned over to the smoker.

"That looks like a nice cigar," he said. "I wouldn't mind paying fifty gulden for one of them. Have you any to spare?"

"Do you mean it?" asked the smoker.

"I do."

"Then I can give you ten."

"Done." The owner of the cigar handed over a box of ten and the other gentleman gave him a wad of banknotes. The people in the tram looked on with various expressions of envy, disapproval, and amusement.

The tram stopped and Janna and her mother got out. They had not dared to say a word in the tram for fear of betraying their nationality. Now they walked home silently, each wrapped in her own thoughts. As they rounded a corner and entered the Keizer's canal, the street where they lived, they saw a woman wheeling a pram. Her clothes were threadbare but clean; her face, with its skin tightly drawn over delicate bones, had a certain beauty. There was a proud, defiant lilt to her walk, something queenly. The baby in the rickety pram resembled a shriveled monkey with liquid brown eyes. He was dwarfed by an enormous yellow star. The woman wore one too.

"Those are Jews . . ." Janna said it wonderingly. They weren't in the least like the pictures she had seen of Jews.

"Yes," said Frau Oster nervously. "They should not be here, they're not allowed out of their ghetto . . ."

Janna's thoughts were in a muddle. She remembered the teaching at school: "Jews are dangerous, they deserve all they're getting . . ." How could a little baby not a month old deserve anything . . . or be dangerous?

There was an echoing noise as two SS officers on motorcycles stank up the air. They looked like black beetles under the fresh green of the trees. When they saw the young woman, they uttered coarse German curses. A fanatical fury distorted their faces. They shouted at her to stop. Leaving their motorcycles, they grabbed her by the arm and shook her. They pointed to the inner city and told her to go where she belonged. They said the next time they'd shoot, and kill the baby first. One of the officers struck the woman in the face. The other pulled her hair. She never said a word, but quietly went where they told her. The men kicked her and made her run. The poor baby bounced up and down and began to wail, a thin sliver of sound slicing the air. The woman was holding a handkerchief to her face. It was red with blood.

Janna clung to her mother in terror. Frau Oster was trembling. The SS officers caught sight of her. They straightened their caps and their faces and for the first time Janna recognized them. They were Obersturmbannführer Wolff and Sturmbannführer Schmidt.

"Mechtild!" they cried, cordially approaching Janna's mother. "We saw you in *My Sister and I* last night. You were superb . . ." They kissed Frau Oster's fingertips. They had been transformed in a twinkling from brutes into gallants.

Janna felt a sense of shock, a numbing of sensation. As her mother conversed glibly with the officers, charming and gracious, Janna felt as if something had cracked under her feet . . . as if the firm ground no longer supported her. And her mother . . . her mother was a stranger.

✠ NINE ✠

Lessons

JANNA WAITED impatiently for Hugo. There were things she had to ask him. No one else would give her a real answer. She knew there was injustice somewhere. The Dutch were not being treated fairly, and as for the Jews. . . . She gave a little shudder.

Little things she had observed, little drops and trickles, were flowing together and making a stream on which she was floating she knew not where.

What was the matter with grownups, who had all the power? Why did they not do something? Why did they draw blinds and chatter with monsters? Rebelliously she thought that all children ought to get together and disown the grownups. But would that help? Had the Children's Crusade accomplished anything?

Perhaps Corrie was right. You had to start on yourself, with your own conscience. But what if you didn't *know* enough? Which brought her back to Hugo. So she waited for him, peering out of the library window, shooing off Heinz, who wanted to play checkers again.

As Hugo entered the library, it struck her how frail he looked, almost as if his body were incapable of carrying the weight of his thoughts. He sank into his leather chair with a sigh of relief, took off his glasses and rubbed them, his mild brown eyes contemplating the room.

"Yesterday," Janna began with a rush, "yesterday I was

109

out with my mother and I . . . we . . . saw starving people and we couldn't get into the Rembrandt house because the guard wouldn't let us. I heard awful screams and later I . . . we . . . saw a woman and a little baby wearing stars and the SS officers hit her and kicked her and were *awful* to her and she hadn't done anything except walk. They said they would *shoot* her, even the baby!" Hugo looked at her questioningly. He did not seem surprised or shocked. "Well?" he asked quietly.

"Well, it isn't what I learned. . . . At school they said Hitler was helping the poor democracies who had become so weak they could not stand up to Russia. They said Jews were dangerous people who were being sent to some other place where they could do no harm. But how can babies be dangerous? And that woman, she didn't look dangerous either. They said all Aryans wanted to belong to Germany, and it isn't true, they don't. I don't blame them, for it seems to me . . . it seems to me . . ." She hung her head, played with her fingers. "We've only come . . . to rob them . . ." she whispered.

Hugo sat very still. Janna looked up with tears in her eyes. "You've explained so much to me, can't you explain this?"

Hugo gave a deep sigh. "I promised your parents I would not discuss politics," he said.

"I would not tell on you," Janna answered indignantly. He was her last hope. She trusted his honesty more than that of anyone else she knew.

"I know that," said Hugo gently. "It is not fear that is keeping me back. It just so happens that I value my word."

"How will I ever learn the truth then?" asked Janna despondently.

"The way other people learn it," said Hugo. "Do you

think newspaper reporters find it easy to learn the truth? They may have to interrogate many liars, sift the facts, and draw their own conclusions. Or judges . . . think of their difficulties; yet a human life may depend on what they decide. Then take scientists, how many years of patient observation it takes them to find out the tiniest truth about our universe. You want to be spoon-fed. You've just learned that you may not have the true idea of what is going on and you want to spend no thought and effort on it yourself. That's a bad attitude. There's a library full of information right here . . . with enough books in German for you to do some research. Besides, your Dutch is getting good. You have brains, use them." He took off his glasses and polished them again.

Janna looked at him indignantly. "You talk as if there was *time*," she said. "But there's injustice going on *right now* and I don't want to be unjust. I want to *know*." She looked fiercely at Hugo. He smiled.

"What do you want to know?" he asked.

"Are Aryans the master race?"

"I believe I can answer that," said Hugo. "It's an anthropological question. There's no such thing as an Aryan race, except in legends. There's an Aryan language spoken by Hindus and other Indo-Iranian people. It's also loosely used to designate Indo-European people, but it's unscientific to call it a *race*. There are few pure races and it would be bad if there were. I don't know whether you've heard of inbreeding?"

"Yes, the farmers used to talk about it," said Janna.

"It happens to old families, especially royal ones who won't marry commoners. The bad genes multiply and are not counteracted by good ones. The more varied our ancestry, the more vigorous we tend to be."

"Were the Jews inbred, is that why they're inferior?" asked Janna.

"The Jews are not inferior," said Hugo. "A greater percentage of Jews reach prominence than of any other people. They were civilized when we still walked in bearskins and gnawed bones. We have only just begun to enact the humane laws the Jews have obeyed for centuries."

"But . . . but they killed Jesus, didn't they?" asked Janna.

"Have you never read the Bible?" Hugo asked gently. "The Romans killed Jesus. The Jews never crucified anybody; such a cruel death was not on their books. They condemned Jesus, after a trial, because they did not understand his closeness to God. They thought it blasphemous when he said, 'I and my Father are one.' But they lived in an occupied country like Holland. They had to deliver Jesus to the Roman authorities, who could have released Jesus had they so wished. We do not blame the present-day Italians for his death, do we? Don't forget, all the first Christians were Jews. We Gentiles have been grafted on the root of Judaism, and in his letters to the Romans, St. Paul tells us not to boast of that, for the root bears the branches, not the other way around. These are mysteries, not to be talked of lightly. The Jews have a very special relationship with God. As St. Paul says again, 'God hath not cast away His people which He foreknew.' They bear testimony to God's holiness, where we are inclined to be a little too familiar. I think they have a mission just as much as the Christians—and how you Germans dare point a finger at them when you condemn millions to death without a trial . . ." Hugo bit his lip. "I beg your pardon. I had no right to say that."

"I don't mind," said Janna. "I want the truth."

"And you think you can get the truth from me?" asked Hugo. "You might as well ask a chicken the truth about the fox."

"It might be truer than the fox's own story," said Janna.

Hugo laughed. "You may be right at that," he admitted.

"But why do people dislike the Jews then?" asked Janna.

Hugo reflected for a moment. "It's part of the mystery," he said. "They have always been kept apart, a chosen people, and perhaps that dislike was necessary to keep them from melting with the crowd. But there is another reason. They are a minority in all countries, and minorities are often resented and persecuted. As soon as we ill-use people, our conscience troubles us and we have to justify our mistreatment by believing they deserve it. I'm sure you've heard the Germans say that the Dutch are bad."

"Yes," said Janna, struck. "I have. How do you know?"

"For the same reason," said Hugo. Janna felt confused. So much of what she had been taught was being overturned.

"What else do you want to know?" asked Hugo.

"About the last war," said Janna in a rush. "Did we really win it and did the Jews in Berlin stab us in the back by signing the Treaty of Versailles?"

"That's a political question," said Hugo.

"No, it's in our history and race-science books," protested Janna.

Hugo smiled. "You're a minx," he said. "The Allies and Germany had got into a stalemate on the battlefields after three years of ghastly bloodshed in the trenches. When fresh, enthusiastic, well-equipped American soldiers arrived, the exhausted Germans were soon beaten. There was a peace conference among the Allied heads of state to which Germany was not invited. It accepted the resulting treaty under protest, as there was nothing else for it to do." Hugo got up and fetched an encyclopedia, which he opened at the words: *Versailles, treaty of . . .* "You could have found that out for yourself. It's all in here, see?"

Janna kicked the leg of the table in a burst of temper. "Why did they lie to us at school?" she asked. "It isn't fair!"

"Careful!" warned Hugo. "Don't make sweeping accusations. The teachers may very well have believed what they told you. It is much easier to believe lies than the truth."

"Why?" asked Janna.

"Because lies are manufactured to satisfy the emotions. A mother would rather believe her pretty girl lazy than accept the fact that she's a dumb cluck. Germans would rather believe they were stabbed in the back than that they lost a fair fight. And anyone would rather blame someone else for his misfortunes. The truth is hard. Don't fool with it unless you realize that."

Here there was an interruption. Corrie came in, smiling broadly and bearing a tray with coffee and sandwiches for Hugo. He was a great favorite in the kitchen. Janna noticed the eagerness with which Hugo tackled the food. Was he starving too?

After the lesson, when Hugo was gone, Janna darted to the bookshelves to search for a German Bible. She found a Dutch one, but the words were too hard for her. She knew her mother had a little German Bible beside her bed, but Janna was shy about asking for it. She finally found an old German Bible bound in scuffed leather on the rare-book shelf. She peeped at it with trepidation, feeling wicked. It was a forbidden book for Hitler Youth.

The language awed and gripped her, so that she began to read in earnest. Right away she stumbled on a difficulty: God's treatment of Cain. Cain slew Abel brutally, for no reason. Janna wanted God to slay Cain in return. Instead, He held a long conversation with Cain and merely banished him, which was the least He could do, thought Janna, since Adam and Eve probably did not want him around any more. Cain even had the effrontery to point out to God that others might kill him, presumably his brothers, for who else was there? And God put a sign on Cain to warn people not to kill him. Why did He do that, with Abel's blood crying to heaven?

Janna did not talk to her parents about her conversation with Hugo. Ever since the outing on her birthday, there had been a barrier. She avoided her parents. They were always busy anyway. The Baron came often and took them to cocktail parties to meet important people. Janna was left to brood by herself.

Herr Frosch brought friends in more and more often. Janna's mother complained about it. She said there was no one to keep an eye on Janna at night. She told Janna to stay away from the parties. But Janna was lonely. One evening she felt especially depressed. She had a headache and wandered desolately through the house. It was Mina's night off; she always went to visit a relative. There was no one Janna could talk to, no one to cheer her up. There were sounds of laughter and merriment coming from the long room and she drifted toward it. At that moment she felt that even Herr Frosch was better than nothing. She peeped around the glass doors. What she saw reminded her of those Dutch pictures where everyone is laughing and drinking and spilling food. The beautiful room was in a mess. Herr Frosch was plying his friends with drink.

Gaily dressed ladies, showing fat legs, were being kissed and teased. One of the SS officers was boasting of his day's work.

"You should have seen the last batch we got out of that Jewish men's home . . . with their silly beards and skull-caps! 'Hop like frogs,' I said, and, *zum Teufel,* they did . . . If they didn't, I helped them with the butt of my gun. 'Bark like dogs' . . . sure enough, they did. . . . They have no pride, those Jews." He spat on the parquet floor. The others all laughed noisily and emptied their glasses. One of the SS men noticed Janna standing in the doorway and beckoned to her.

"Come in, come in," he shouted. "We can use a pretty girl . . ." He was grinding out the stub of his cigarette with his heel. Janna never could understand afterward why she obeyed him . . . had he hypnotized her? She felt as if she were dreaming, as if an outside force were pulling her into the room. The officers all welcomed her, calling her darling and sweetheart. Someone handed her a glass with a drink in it that made her throat sting, but it did revive her a little. Then one of the SS men grabbed her and pulled her onto his lap. The dream had turned into a nightmare. Janna struggled feverishly, but the SS man held on. The others all laughed.

Janna panicked. "For God's sake, let me go . . ." she shouted.

"God?" the soldier sneered. "God doesn't exist, or we would not be here."

Holding her tight, he pressed wet lips against her mouth. His breath smelled awful. Then Janna bit his lip hard. He cursed and pushed her off his knees.

"Vixen," he growled, and kicked her. His lip bled. The

others only laughed. Herr Frosch, who had been mixing drinks, came hurrying toward them.

"Herr Oberführer," he cried. "That's the daughter of the house, a friend of the general!" There was an immediate hush, but Janna had fled already. She was sick in the bathroom and spent a lot of time rinsing out her mouth.

The next day Janna had a fever. Her mother fetched a doctor who prescribed lots of liquid and bed rest. For the first time, Janna realized how much her parents loved her. Mechtild let an understudy take over while she stayed at Janna's bedside. Otto came in with amusing stories about the theater. Mina cooked her favorite dishes. Even Heinz brought her daffodils he had picked in the garden. Her mother took them but sent Heinz away.

"The doctor says she must be kept quiet," she explained.

Janna had never been so cherished. Her mother read to her from famous plays, which her beautiful voice brought to life. They held discussions afterward. Janna confessed that she'd like to become an actress, and after that her mother let her read parts in plays and corrected her expression. Janna began to feel guilty about her former critical attitude and her secrets weighed on her.

"Mother," she said, when they were having an especially intimate talk, "it isn't right, is it, to maltreat the Jews? Whether we like them or not, it isn't right?"

"No," whispered her mother. "It isn't right."

"But you didn't say so . . . you were kind to those SS officers . . ."

"I wondered when you'd come out with that," said her mother. "I knew what you were thinking then, but what could I have done for that poor woman? I could only have made trouble for us. Anyone who takes the part of the Jews is treated like a Jew. I'm a coward, I admit it." Janna began to cry. "I'm bad too, I was disobedient," she said. And she told her mother what had happened at Herr Frosch's party. Her mother was very upset.

"I can't stop Herr Frosch from bringing those people in," she said. "It's his house too. But don't . . . don't ever join them again, and lock your door at night."

Janna nodded. She never wanted to come within arm's length of an SS man again. Then she told her mother, "That officer said there was no God because, if there was, he himself would not exist." She expected her mother to react indignantly to this impious remark; instead she looked thoughtful.

"Did he really say that?" she mused. Janna nodded. "Poor boy," said her mother.

"Why do you call him poor?" asked Janna resentfully.

"Because he would not say that if he did not think himself very bad," her mother answered. "He thinks God, if He existed, would already have struck him dead."

"God did not strike Cain dead," said Janna. "Why didn't He? Cain murdered his brother, but God only banished him."

"Do you think death would have been the greater punishment?" her mother asked.

"Yes," said Janna.

"That's because you are young. When you are older, you'll learn that death can be a friend. It would have been the easy way out for Cain, though he did not realize that when he pleaded with God to spare him. Perhaps he had to learn what life was like without Abel." Janna flung her arms around her mother's neck.

"I love you," she whispered. Her mother kissed her back.

"I'm glad we're friends again," she said. Janna looked at her, surprised.

"Did you know?" she asked.

"Did you think a mother wouldn't know?"

Janna was getting better. The doctor said she could get up the next day. Corrie usually brought up Janna's tray of food. On the last evening Corrie brought up her dinner, and after she had eaten it, her mother came up with another tray.

"A second dinner?" asked Janna. "I've already had mine."

Her mother looked surprised. "But this tray was standing in the kitchen, ready to be brought up. I saw it when I went to tell Mina something. She wasn't there and I thought I'd save Corrie the trouble."

"Maybe Heinz is ill too," suggested Janna.

"Heinz is in excellent health," said her mother. "He managed to get most of the pudding."

"Perhaps Mina forgot that Corrie had already brought me a tray."

"That's possible. Corrie may have made you one on her own, without Mina knowing about it. Could you tackle another one?"

"I'll try," said Janna. Her mother smiled. Janna's appetite had come back!

When her mother had left, Janna accidentally shifted her plate a little and discovered a paper package. It contained a razor blade. A *razor blade!* Now what in the world would that be doing on Janna's tray? Razor blades were precious. Herr Frosch was constantly complaining of their scarcity and threatening to grow a beard. Janna's father was better off with his old-fashioned knife.

Was it another prank of Heinz's? But what a senseless one! Janna put the blade on the table beside her bed and promptly forgot about it. When she remembered it the next morning, the razor blade was gone.

✠ TEN ✠

Sef

THE FIRST MORNING Janna was up, there was a surprise waiting for her at the breakfast table. Heinz told her about it even before she saw it lying by her plate.

"There's a letter for you," he said enviously. "May I have the stamp?"

Janna did not want to read it with everyone looking on, so she put it in her pocket. It was probably an answer from Hildegarde.

Then she listened, alarmed, to what Herr Frosch was reading from the morning paper. The owner of the Punch and Judy show on the Dam had been arrested.

"No . . ." she cried, "oh no . . ."

Herr Frosch frowned at her. "It's a good thing," he said. "I hear his talk was very subversive. There is too much rebellion in this city. Herr Rauter thinks it's the fault of the Dutch Army we allowed to demobilize. It's working underground now."

"How can it work underground?" Frau Frosch asked dreamily. "The ground is too soft. They build their houses on wooden piles, which they hammer into the mud. I've seen them."

Her husband looked at her coldly. "Women should not talk," he said. "They only show their ignorance. Underground is just a manner of speaking. It means hidden. Please make me another piece of toast, Jodoca, you let this

121

one burn. Those people think they are heroic but they are merely foolish. Hand me the sausages, *gnädige Frau,* please. They are done just as they should be, crisp and not greasy. How fortunate we are in having such a good cook. Herr Rauter is always complaining of his servants." Herr Frosch wiped his mouth. "As I was saying, what can a handful of Dutchmen do against our Wehrmacht? The whole idea of resistance is a product of weak democracies. Look what Gandhi is getting from the British by fasting! Ridiculous. We'd just let him die. You must be ruthless. Stop kicking the table, Heinz, you annoy me."

After breakfast Janna went upstairs to read her letter. When she entered her room, she felt a draft and saw that her glass doors were open. She thought she had shut them. She put her letter on the bed and stepped out on the balcony. She heard a rustling in the ivy. Could a prowler climb up that way? Looking closely, she saw spikes sticking out of the wall, between the ivy, forming a ladder. In a twinkling she was over the balcony railing, climbing down. It was scary. Her feet had to feel for the spikes while she hung on to the ivy strands, which sometimes broke loose. When she landed in the garden, she saw no one. Only the neighbors' tomcat blinked at her from a clump of daffodils. Not wanting to climb up again, Janna went into the house and up the stairs. She found the door of her room open and Heinz sprawled on the bed, reading her letter. He had opened it so clumsily that the envelope was badly torn. Its stamp was missing. He did not look in the least ashamed on seeing her but greeted her with a jeer: "Janna's got a boy friend, Janna's got a boy friend!" Janna flew into a rage. She attacked Heinz, dragged him off the bed, shook him, regardless of his kicking feet, pulled his hair, scratched his face, and yelled "Horrible sneak!" She pushed him out of the room, locked the door, and leaned against it, suddenly weak and spent. She could hear Heinz trudging upstairs, wailing for his mother.

Almost crying, Janna picked up the crumpled letter and smoothed it out. Now she understood what Heinz had meant. It wasn't from Hildegarde at all, it was from Kurt.

Dear Janna [it said],

Hildegarde tells me that you are homesick for the Black Forest. I can well imagine it. A flat country must be very dull. Do you go for hikes there at all? We miss you. The rehearsals for the play went badly. Ilse is making such a hash of Brunhilde, I have trouble not laughing, which doesn't help my acting. Anyway, I may not get to play Siegfried after all. I've volunteered to go to Russia, they've lowered the age limit.

Don't worry about the Dutch. They'll come around when we've beaten the English and Americans and they have no one else to look to. They'll soon realize the aims and ideals of our Third Reich. They are good, Nordic people.

Please don't forget me, and write . . .

Affectionately,
Your friend Kurt

P.S. *I'll be going to a training camp soon.*

Janna sat with the letter in her lap. She found it hard to sort out her emotions. For a moment she had been transported to the old, safe world of the Black Forest. But it seemed very far away now. How happy she would have been with this letter even a few weeks ago! Now it was too

late. Poor Kurt, going into the hell of Russia . . . she remembered what the Baron had said about it. Giving his
life for . . . for a parcel of lies? Germany hadn't a chance of
winning there, according to the Baron.

She was not allowed to brood for long. Heinz was
banging on the door.

"Let me in, I've got to tell you something!"

"I don't want to hear it," said Janna.

"You must, Mother says so."

With a sigh, Janna got up and unlocked the door. She
felt ashamed when she saw his swollen, scratched face.

"Mother says I did wrong. I'm sorry," he mumbled
quickly. Then he went on, "But you're horrid too, you
won't play with me!"

"I've been ill," said Janna.

"I could have played checkers with you; why didn't you
ask for me? Your mother would have let me in if you'd
asked for me." He sounded aggrieved. He looked babyish
with his swollen face. Janna pitied him.

"I'll play with you now," she said, feeling she had
something to make up for.

"Do you mean it? I've nothing to do. Mother has no
time for my lessons." Hugo wasn't coming either. Janna's
mother felt she wasn't well enough for studying yet. Janna
missed him. It seemed ages since her last lesson.

"But you must behave yourself," said Janna. "I don't
want to be ordered about."

"All right, we'll be equals," Heinz said magnanimously.
Since he was willing to forgo his masculine superiority,
Janna quietly pocketed her extra years.

"Do you want to play in the garden?" she asked.

"No, it's going to rain. Let's play hide-and-go-seek in
the house . . . one hides and the other one seeks. When

the hider is found, we race to the nearest banister and whoever gets there first wins."

It proved an amusing game. It was a lovely house to hide in. Janna was touched by Heinz's pleasure. He seemed starved for a little fun. She thought it must be a lonely life for a little boy who hated books. She let him win several times. The third time Heinz hid in the kneehole of the library desk. When Janna spotted him, he ran to the banister, but in his haste he bumped against one of the valuable statues. It fell with a crash onto the tiles. Its head broke off and rolled a little farther. Janna and Heinz contemplated the disaster in silent dismay. Janna thought of her mother's distress that one of the sacred van Arkel possessions should have been broken. Heinz's cheeks had paled till they were almost the color of the statue. They both awaited the inevitable arrival of the angry grownups, summoned by the noise, and braced themselves against reproaches, but no one came.

Heinz raised the statue and replaced the head. It fit nicely, you could hardly see the crack.

"I can glue it," he said hopefully. "My mother has strong glue. No one must know. You won't tell?" He looked anxiously at Janna.

"Not if you don't want me to," said Janna. "I'm not a tattletale. But why are you afraid? Your parents wouldn't punish you for an accident, would they?"

"My father would," said Heinz. "Look." He pulled up his sweater and showed his back full of scars from vicious beatings. Janna recoiled.

"Does he do that often?" she asked, remembering the screams she had thought were the tantrums of a spoiled boy.

"Pretty often," said Heinz.

"Why does your mother let him?"

"She is more scared of him than I am," said Heinz. "I think he beats her too. I *hate* my father." He looked and sounded so ugly, it scared Janna.

"Why don't you behave better, if your father is so strict?" she asked.

"He can't cow *me*," Heinz growled. "The more he beats me, the worse I'll be. I'll show him!" Janna wondered at him. She would have been careful not to annoy so cruel a father. It was brave of Heinz. Maybe there was something fine in Heinz after all.

"Let's go on with the game," said Heinz. Janna proposed continuing it on the third floor, where there were no statues to break. It was her turn and the best hiding place she could think of was her own wardrobe. She hid behind Nella's dresses and leaned against the back panel. She wasn't comfortable and pushed and shoved a little. A small hard knob pressed into her shoulder blades. She groped for it with her fingers, twisting it accidentally. There was a *click*, the back panel swung away—and Janna felt herself falling into space.

For a moment she lay stunned. She had fallen smack onto a hard surface. She opened her eyes in a greenish twilight and found a face bent over her—a pale, angry face—while a voice whispered in Dutch, "What are you doing here? How did you get here?"

She felt too dizzy and scared to answer. Her throat felt dry. Strong hands pulled her upright and shoved her against the wall, pinning her arms. The boy's face looked desperate. His straight red-blond hair was badly cut, his skin looked waxen.

"How did you find this room?" he asked, shaking her till her head banged against the wall.

"I . . . I was playing hide-and-seek," said Janna hoarsely, in her best Dutch, looking at the boy with terrified eyes.

"I could kill you," the boy went on, "except that people would go looking for you and find me anyway. But I warn you, if you ever breathe a word to anyone that you've seen me, I'll kill you. . . . Whatever they do to me, I'll kill you first!" Janna did not doubt it, he looked and sounded so ferocious.

"I won't tell," she whispered.

"How do I know I can trust you?" the boy asked. "How do I know you won't run tattling to your mammy and pappy the minute I let you go?"

That was exactly what Janna had been planning to do and she didn't see how he could prevent it, for, as he had said himself, if she disappeared, her family would tear down the house to find her. Who was he, anyway?

"Why should I keep your secret?" she asked, taking courage. "I don't know you. You're not one of the van Arkels, for you're not in their picture and you don't look like them."

Notwithstanding her bad accent, the boy seemed to understand her, for he said, "I'm a friend of theirs. I've their permission to live here, which is more than you can say, I bet. I work for them."

"What work?" Janna asked. He pointed behind him, at the table. For the first time Janna was at leisure to take in her surroundings. They were in a small, hidden room. She could not see a door; it must have been closed after she fell through. There was a fold-up cot with blankets and a pillow, an empty fireplace, and a closet. In the middle stood a table and chair, all very close together in the cramped space. The window was completely covered with ivy. A shaded gooseneck lamp shone on the table, which was covered with a variety of papers. The boy must have been working there when she had come tumbling into his sanctuary. She guessed he was about Kurt's age.

Janna took a closer look at the papers. The boy did not stop her. Janna saw identification papers and food-distribution cards. The boy had been copying the official stamp on them with the help of stencils, various inks, small brushes, and a penknife. She also saw a new razor blade among his tools.

"So you're falsifying papers," said Janna. "You belong to the Dutch Resistance." She looked at him curiously. What would Herr Frosch say!

The boy shrugged his shoulders. "You could call it that. I'm just helping the van Arkels rescue innocent people from certain death. They need these identification papers and food cards to keep alive. If you betray me, all these people will either starve or be forced to give themselves up to be sent to the gas chambers of a concentration camp."

"Gas chambers?" Janna looked at the boy with horror. "You mean . . . they are killed?"

The boy looked sternly at her. "Do you think," he said, "that Germany is sending Jews to a nice vacation in a spa, or to pretty villages with geraniums in the windows? That's what we were told at first, though in Holland we never believed it. We got the Jewish children that were chased over the Dutch border by frantic parents and left wandering through the woods of eastern Holland with no place to go. Mrs. van Arkel and other women collected them in their cars and found homes for them. Do you think those parents thought they were being sent to pretty villages? But even in Holland we did not know the worst till last year, through Radio Orange."

"It may just be enemy propaganda . . ." began Janna.

The boy shook his head.

"Not a hope. There is proof . . . much proof. Escapees smuggled photographs . . ." His lips quivered.

Janna felt shocked. Death for all those people in the cattle cars!

"And these papers are helping some to escape?" she asked.

The boy looked at her curiously. "You care, don't you?" he said in a warmer tone. "Funny, I didn't think any Muff cared." Janna blinked and he explained: "That's what we call the Germans, because in the old days German officers wore muffs to keep their hands warm."

"Oh," said Janna. She had never heard of that. Hitler would not have allowed it. His officers had to be tough.

"Show me what you do," she said.

"As you see, I copy stamps. It's tricky work. I would not have the patience if I did not know that each stamp saves a life."

Janna was impressed. She nodded. "I promise to keep your secret," she said. The boy gave a sigh of relief.

A trapdoor in the floor slowly opened and Mina's head stuck out. Her expression of surprise was ludicrous. Her eyebrows did not know which way to go.

"Janna!" she gasped. "What are *you* doing here?"

"I found the place," said Janna calmly, beginning to enjoy herself. "I should report this boy and you too . . . but I won't," she ended hastily, as Mina made a motion to throw the tray which she was carrying at her head. There was food on it, and a lot of mysteries were cleared up at once.

"You'd better not, Miss Snoop." Mina heaved herself out of the trap hole. "For if you breathe a word of this to anyone, I'll come when you are sleeping and slit your throat with my carving knife. That's a promise." She talked in a low voice, but it sounded all the more fierce.

"I won't, I won't," Janna whispered back.

"That's understood then." Mina put the tray on the table. "How did you find this place?" Janna explained again and Mina examined the blank wall. Only a very faint crack showed the outline of a door. She felt the spring catch.

"You must not have shut it properly," she told the boy. "I warned you it was dangerous. He *will* sneak out at night, to get air on your balcony," she told Janna.

So that was the breathing Janna had heard, and not Heinz at all!

"Have you been hiding here long?" she asked the boy.

"Almost two years now, isn't it, Mina?" Mina nodded, an expression of pity on her face which Janna thought misplaced. You don't pity heroes.

"I am Johanna Oster," she said, holding out her hand. "Who are you?"

"I am Sef van Gelder." They shook hands formally, as if they hadn't been glaring at each other a few moments ago. Mina's eyebrows registered approval.

"You'd better go now," she told Janna. "Lunch is ready and they'll be wondering where you are. Now, don't you go in and out of here, that's too dangerous. Remember!" And she made a movement with her finger across her throat.

"You don't have to threaten me," said Janna proudly. "I gave my word already before you popped up, didn't I, Sef?"

"You did," Sef confirmed.

"Because of his work, because he is saving lives," Janna explained.

Mina nodded at Sef. "She means it, it's all right," she said. With this unexpected compliment, she showed Janna how to work the catch of the door, which was one with a panel in Janna's wardrobe.

When Janna hurried down to lunch, Heinz intercepted her. "Where were you?" he asked. "I looked everywhere, even in your wardrobe, but you weren't there. If you went into the garden, it was no fair. You *said* the third floor . . ."

"I'm not going to tell you where I was," said Janna. "I want to use the place again next time."

"You cheated," said Heinz, glowering at her. "I bet you went to the attic or someplace like that!" and he stuck out his tongue at her.

Janna wondered why she had wasted sympathy on him that morning.

✠ ELEVEN ✠

The Accident

JANNA WORRIED about her secret. She kept noticing things that should have given it away: the amount of milk Mina took in, for instance . . . though Corrie's basket could account for that. Then there were extra sheets hanging on the line, and Mina's disappearances. But Janna soon found that people don't see what they don't look for. A stowaway in the house was too fantastic for anyone to suspect.

Now Janna had another worry. Her conscience began to bother her, especially when her parents were nice to her. Was it right to keep such a serious matter hidden from them? She'd always been very open with them. The ring didn't count; that was her own private make-believe. You didn't tell your parents when you didn't walk on the lines in the street, or had a bet with yourself to touch every third tree with your finger.

The trouble was, would Sef's secret be safe with them? On no account must the Frosches hear of it. That would be the end of Sef, and probably of Mina too, and the van Arkels.

One morning, when the Frosches had breakfasted early, Janna was with her parents alone at the table. Sitting there so intimately, her guilt pressed on her till she decided to confide in them.

"Papa," she began.

"Yes, dear," her father answered absently, his mind on his paper.

"Papa, there's something I must tell you . . ."

"Fire away then," said her father without looking up. "A little more coffee please, Mechtild . . ." and he gave a shove to his cup in Mechtild's direction.

"I was playing hide-and-seek with Heinz," began Janna.

"That was nice of you," said her mother. "I feel sorry for that boy. He has atrocious manners, but he lives an unnatural life with no boy of his own age to play with. I don't like the way his father treats him either . . ."

Otto gave an exclamation. "Listen to this," he said. "They found a Dutch Resistance worker who was making fake passports for Jews. He'll be shot, of course . . . but he's the father of eight children. How can anyone be so irresponsible and foolish as to risk his life for some Jews! What's going to happen to his family now?"

"But if he saved the Jews' lives?" asked Janna.

"Nonsense," said her father. "That's melodrama and propaganda. No harm is coming to the Jews. They are merely removed to a safe locality where they can live their own lives without harming anyone. They'll be made comfortable. We're Germans, not barbarians."

Janna looked at her mother, who was staring at her plate. She remembered the cattle cars, the scream in the Jewish quarter, the baby with the star. . . . What had Hugo said about lies? . . .

"Well, what was it you wanted to tell me?" asked her father.

"Oh, it's not really important," said Janna. "Just something about Heinz." Her father went back to his paper.

Janna could not help thinking a lot about Sef. He was so good-looking, rather like Siegfried in her book. Sef was a hero too, risking his life to help other people. Yet he was in Janna's power. One word from her. . . . It was a thrilling thought.

Every night there was a clatter of antiaircraft guns. Janna was used to it now, she usually slept through it, but one night the noise was so loud and accompanied by explosions that she woke up and left her bed to look. It was like a fireworks display. She was standing in her bathrobe by the window, watching the battle in the sky, when a voice behind her said, "Pretty sight, isn't it?" Sef was standing beside her. His enthusiasm was not for the spectacle, she felt, but for the enemy action.

"Sef!" she whispered, alarmed. "My parents might come in here, to see if I'm all right."

"I locked the door," said Sef calmly. Then, with concern, "Oh, look, they got a British plane . . . poor fellows . . ." as an airplane hurtled from the sky, a flaming missile.

"How can I keep your secret if you act like this?" Janna scolded. "Heinz might hear us talking. He sleeps right overhead. He already thinks the house is haunted because he has heard noises."

"With this racket?" asked Sef as Janna shrank under a deafening volley of antiaircraft fire. They watched a bomb explode in a sunset of sparks, throwing a red glow over the houses. Fire engines screamed.

"Can't you understand?" Sef coaxed. "I've been cooped up for two years and I haven't talked to anyone but Mina for months. Mina is all right, she's a darling, but she's pretty old. In a way I'm glad you found me, it makes a diversion."

Janna felt a thrill. She began to realize the possibilities of having a real friend in the house, someone to talk to instead of Heinz.

"You've been in my room before, haven't you?" she asked.

"Yes," said Sef. "I climbed down from your balcony into the garden and stretched my legs. . . . There, that was a big hit . . ." as a fountain of fire sprayed upward.

"I could have woken up," said Janna. "I did wake once, only I thought it was Heinz playing a trick."

"You learn to take risks," said Sef coolly, "when you live with death at your elbows all the time. If you didn't, you'd soon stop breathing for fear it would betray you. But the necessity of it makes me angry. How does anyone dare to lord it over other people's lives like that?"

Janna thought Sef was referring to the war and said, "Hitler is trying to save Europe. It is now in the same danger it was when the Teutonic Knights stopped the hordes of Genghis Khan at Liegnitz."

Sef burst into laughter. "Don't you learn history in Germany, little Muff?" he asked.

"Yes, we have history," Janna answered stiffly.

"Then you ought to know that if the Teutonic Knights stopped the hordes of Genghis Khan it must have been with their dead bodies. They were soundly beaten at Liegnitz, their leaders killed, their armies wiped out, to the relief of the Poles, who were being cruelly oppressed by them." Janna bit her lip. Was there no end to the lies she had been told?

"Is that really true?" she asked.

"Look it up in an encyclopedia if you don't believe me," said Sef.

The bombers had drifted off; the sky was black and empty again.

"The show is over," sighed Sef. "I'm going back to my prison." He disappeared into the wardrobe and Janna went back to sleep.

The next day the papers were full of the bombing of the Carlton Hotel and the descent of the burning plane behind it. There were several dead and wounded. At breakfast Herr Frosch held forth on the wickedness of the British and his conviction that Dutch traitors had had a hand in it. How otherwise could the English have known that the Luftgau Command was in that hotel? He began to enumerate the reprehensible and dangerous doings of the Resistance forces and the necessity of punishing them. Every time he looked in Janna's direction, she blushed.

Janna had enjoyed Sef's midnight visit, but when, later, at a safe moment, she rapped at the wardrobe panel and obeyed Sef's signal to come in, she found Mina lecturing him about it.

"Young gentlemen don't invade ladies' bedrooms at night," she decreed. " 'Hear counsel and receive instruction that thou mayest be wise in thy latter end!' " Sef's eyes met Janna's and they laughed. With a thrill Janna realized that they were in league against Mina's narrow ideas of propriety. Janna looked around Sef's "prison." The first time she hadn't taken it all in. She noticed that the ceiling was made of thick wooden beams. She realized suddenly that Heinz's room must be above it . . . the part that made it larger than hers. Of course!

She realized that the clothes in the wardrobe muffled all sounds coming from the secret room. Perhaps that's why the dresses had not been brought to the attic! The wall behind the cot adjoined the home of the old ladies, and the next wall was taken up by the closet and the fireplace, which probably shared the chimney of the house with the uninteresting garden. So there were three families who might have heard unusual sounds, though Sef had of course been careful. Now they'd have to watch out, but it was hard to whisper all the time. She looked at Sef, who was squatting on the ground, all bony arms and legs. Mina had spread herself out on the bed and Janna straddled the chair. Their lowered voices gave an intimate quality to their conversation.

There were books and papers all over the little room: piled in corners or stacked on shelves. All Dutch, of course.

"Sef is a great reader," Mina told Janna. She talked Dutch to Janna now, a great compliment to Janna's progress in the language. "He never likes the books I bring him, so maybe you'd better help him." A smile lit Sef's eyes and took the sulkiness from his face. He really did look like Siegfried, Janna thought.

"Nella used to do that for me," he said. "Janna reminds me of Nella, don't you think, Mina?"

"She isn't half as pretty," said Mina loyally, "Not that you're bad-looking, Janna," she added kindly.

But Janna had the feeling that Mina resented her. It was partly fear of the danger; Janna knowing about Sef doubled the risks. But there was something else. Mina was so watchful and suspicious. Janna wondered what was worrying her. Mina insisted that Janna and Sef should see each other only with Mina's approval and supervision. Janna thought she must be jealous, wanting to keep Sef all to herself. She tried to plead with Mina.

"I'll be careful, honest. He's right next door to me. . . . Why can't I hop in when it's safe and talk to him? It would be fun . . ." But Mina's mouth and eyebrows were unrelenting.

"A prudent man foreseeth evil and hideth himself, but the simple pass on and are punished," she quoted, which meant she was upset. The more she worried, the more she recited Scripture. Janna would have disobeyed her, but Sef would not allow that.

"Mina has done everything for me. She has saved my life," he said. "When the van Arkels were thrown out with only an hour to get together their belongings, they could not do anything about me. Mina stayed to look after me. It was very brave of her."

Janna accepted the fact that Sef's work was secret, but she wondered at his dependence on Mina. She felt frustrated. Sef was not the only one who had been lonely. Janna too had missed congenial companionship. Now Mina stood in the way of her finding it. She remembered her ring. Only half believing, she rubbed it, wished that Mina would stop interfering. Immediately afterward she felt guilty, she did not know why.

Janna always went up to do her room after breakfast. Corrie had more work than she could manage and Janna did not really like someone else putting things away so that she had to search for them afterward. Besides, Mina did not want Corrie to know about Sef.

"You mean, you never told her?" exclaimed Janna.

"It's too dangerous," said Mina. "Goodness knows whom she meets when she goes home every night. It's especially dangerous this time," she added, her eyebrows quirked, "for it is her month to tell the truth!"

Janna was straightening her bed when a noise made her look up. The wardrobe door was ajar and she heard Sef whisper, "Janna, come, something terrible has happened!" Janna dropped the blankets and crawled into the wardrobe, remembering to shut the doors behind her.

Once in the secret room she was grabbed by Sef, who

panted, "Mina was bringing up my breakfast and she fell down the ladder. I don't know what to do! Please come!"

Janna climbed down the ladder after Sef. Mina was lying at the bottom. The tray she had been carrying lay on the ground amid broken crockery and cracked eggs.

"Oh Janna, it's *you*," sighed Mina gratefully. "Please put some sense into that boy. I think I fractured my leg, but it isn't the end of the world."

Janna felt a shock of dismay and remorse. The ring! Her wish! This was *her* fault! But she hadn't wanted that, she hadn't meant for Mina to be harmed. She knelt down. Mina's ankle was badly swollen. It hurt at a touch. Janna looked around. They were in a room she had not seen before, slightly larger than the one upstairs. It was empty except for some gymnastic apparatus hanging from the ceiling and some chairs stacked against one wall. A bathroom was visible through an open door. An ivy-covered window let in the same greenish light as in Sef's room, and another empty fireplace let in some fresh air.

"What shall we do?" asked Janna. "Is this another secret room?"

Sef nodded. "If they find her here, they'll discover everything."

"Don't stand there talking," groaned Mina. "I'm in terrible pain. You've got to get me out of here. I have to have my accident someplace else." She closed her eyes, looking so pale that Janna was afraid she'd faint, like Corrie.

"The two of us could lift you into the long room," said Sef. "But there's nothing there to fall from, except the piano . . ."

"Don't be an idiot," said Mina. "Janna can fetch a ladder.

I had an itch to dust the ceiling. . . . Come, get a move on."

"How do we get into the long room?" asked Janna, bewildered.

"This way," said Sef. He pointed to another door. Janna opened it cautiously and stood facing a piece of canvas. It was the back of a picture. There was a hole in one of the corners. Janna stooped and looked through it. She saw the long room with the fireplace and mirror facing her at the other end. She was behind the van Arkel picture!

The long room was empty and Sef nudged her. "Go on," he said. "Get the ladder, quick!" Janna pushed the picture away from her and slipped down a foot or so into the long room. The picture slid back behind her. Janna ran to the kitchen, where Heinz was pouring himself a glass of milk.

"Where have you been, Janna?" he asked. "Hugo is waiting for you."

"You'd better go to your own lessons," Janna answered severely. "Your mother says she'll tell your father if you don't come."

It was an invention, but it served its purpose. Wiping his mouth, Heinz ran up the stairs. Janna fetched the ladder and carried it up, making as little noise as possible. She had an excuse ready if someone caught her at it; she'd say she'd seen a spider web high up in her room. But she managed to get to the long room unobserved. She had grabbed a dustcloth from the kitchen rack and she dropped it beside the ladder. Slipping behind the picture, she joined the others. Mina looked bad. Perspiration stood in pearls on her forehead.

"You took *ages*," Sef said reproachfully. He was tenderly stroking Mina's hair.

Mina smiled at Janna. "It only seemed long to us," she said. "Get me out of here now and try not to hurt me too much . . ."

Janna made sure no one was about. She and Sef lifted Mina awkwardly, upset by her stifled groans. They carried her to the door, where Janna held the picture away while Sef lowered Mina as gently as possible to the floor of the long room. Then Sef retreated behind the picture. Janna straightened it. She noticed that poor Mina's underlip showed how hard she had bitten it to keep from screaming. Now Janna threw down the ladder as hard as she could. Mina gave a blood-curdling shriek. (She said afterward that it was a relief after holding it in for so long.) Janna ran into the hall crying, "Mina's had an accident . . . Mina's had an accident!"

The Osters had not yet left. They came running. Corrie hurried down from upstairs, still carrying a broom, followed by Frau Frosch and Heinz. Herr Frosch was on the point of leaving for work and arrived in coat and hat. Hugo wandered in from the library, holding a book.

Herr Frosch showed great solicitude, scolding Frau Oster for letting Mina do such dangerous work as dusting a ceiling.

"We could get an orderly to do that sort of thing," he said pompously. "It's inexcusable to give such a task to a *cook*." Mechtild, bewildered, scarcely knew what he was talking about. She was all concern for Mina. She immediately rang the Baron, while Herr Frosch rang Herr Rauter. Within a short time, two motorcars stood ready to convey Mina to the hospital.

When Mina had left, Janna went to her lessons. The accident weighed on her. She could not help thinking it was her fault. She had not directly wished for it, of course, but perhaps it was the only way Mina could be kept from interfering.

"Do you believe in magic?" she asked Hugo. He was looking very tired, she noticed.

"The questions you ask," he said, smiling a little. "So much depends on what you mean by magic. I don't believe in arbitrary suspension of the laws of nature, but I think there are laws we have not discovered yet, hidden powers of the mind which we have hardly tapped. Much that is called magic may be caused quite naturally."

"For instance, the magic ring of the *Nibelungen,* do you believe in that?"

"Magic in legends is often symbolic," said Hugo. "Wagner made the ring's magic generate inordinate love of power. He meant to show that this only leads to doom and destruction; but Wagner, though he called himself a Christian, was a German too, and according to Heine, who was one himself, all Germans have a suppressed longing for violence. Heine warned that one day the thin layer of Germany's civilization would crack and that Germany's tribal hordes would then erupt like lava, to the horror and destruction of Europe. Wagner unconsciously, I think, gloried in the holocaust at the end of his operas. That's what gives them their compelling quality and their attraction for people like Hitler. There's a primitive satisfaction in destruction and bloodshed for its own sake."

It wasn't at all what Janna had wanted to hear. "I only meant . . . is there *ordinary* magic?" she said desperately, "Could you wish somebody just . . . to go away a little, and then she has an accident?"

Hugo looked at her thoughtfully. "Unfortunately, I do think it possible," he said, "but only if the wishing person has a powerful purpose and occult powers. These exist, I know, but shouldn't be meddled with."

When her lessons were over, Janna hurried to her bedroom, where she finished making her bed. Then she tapped on the panel door.

"Come in," Sef said. "What kept you? I was worried sick." His hair was ruffled and there was a strained look on his face. Janna realized that she had been thoughtless. She had left Sef in suspense. She told him that there had been a message from the hospital that Mina's leg had been set and that she was resting comfortably.

Sef groaned and ran his fingers through his hair. "Oh, what shall I do?"

"I'll look after you," said Janna.

"That's not the only thing. I've finished my cards and they should go off as soon as possible. People are waiting for them. Mina always looked after it for me."

"Can I help?" asked Janna.

Sef smiled. "No, little Muff," he said. "Good as you've been, we can't trust you with the secrets of our organization." Janna blushed. She hadn't thought of that. She'd be an underground worker herself then.

"I suppose you did not clean up the mess downstairs," she said.

"No, should I have?" Sef was taken back.

"We'd better do it; someone might miss the tray. I'll have to take the blame for the broken crockery, I suppose."

"I hardly think I can," said Sef wryly.

They found the mess just as they'd left it, except that the eggs had congealed into rubbery disks. Janna got a broom and gently swept the broken shards together on a piece of newspaper while Sef did exercises on the gymnastic apparatus.

"The van Arkels gave me that," he said, doing a somersault on the rings. "They thought my muscles might get weak otherwise." Janna leaned on her broom.

"Was this their gymnasium?" she asked. "Why was it hidden?"

"It used to be a Roman Catholic chapel," said Sef. "When this house was built, we had just freed ourselves from Catholic Spain and we'd outlawed all Catholic religious ceremonies. Priests had to disguise themselves as window cleaners or chimney sweeps and sneak into warehouses to say Mass among packing cases. Rich Catholics built hidden chapels in their homes and this was one of them. I'm sleeping in what was called a priest's hole. Look!" He went to the end of the room and pushed against the wall. Miraculously it receded and a tiny little altar of brown varnished wood swung toward them and clicked into place. It was a totally undistinguished little altar, but Janna stared at it with widening eyes. For there, hanging over it in a heavy, ornate frame, hung the most beautiful little picture she had ever seen. It glowed in warm tints of brown and copper, representing the inside of a church. A priest in glittering vestments bent over a baby, held by its mother, the husband slightly lost in the shadows. All the light, all the golden glow, hung about the baby. . . . Janna gave a stifled cry . . . *the Rembrandt!*

✠ TWELVE ✠

Janna Helps Out

"WHAT'S THE MATTER?" asked Sef. He had pulled out one of the chairs and was sitting astride it. He looked at Janna through strands of russet hair. Behind him the whitewashed wall was full of cracks and scribbles. The greenish light made everything a bit spooky.

"I think that's the painting my mother has been searching for," she said.

"It's a Rembrandt," Sef told her. "It's the most valuable thing the van Arkels own. It's been in the family for generations."

"Hitler wants it," said Janna. "My parents will be punished if they don't hand it over. They're suspected of stealing it, as if they were thieves!" Sef rocked his chair with his long legs. There was an odd expression on his face.

"What else do you call it," he drawled, "when someone enters a country uninvited and without warning, after having signed a non-aggression pact, and then kicks its citizens out of their homes without giving them an opportunity to collect their possessions? Have you another name for it?"

"That's not my parents' fault," Janna spat back. "They had nothing to do with it. They only wanted somewhere to live where they could have me. I'd been away for over two years. It was the army that did it."

"That does not prevent your parents from enjoying the spoils, does it?"

"They have no other place to go," said Janna, near tears. "And they don't want the picture. My mother said at first not to give it. But Hitler needs it for his museum and so . . ."

"So he must have it. He must always have what he fancies, whether it's right or wrong," Sef said softly. "Whether it's countries, or art, or a million helpless souls, he must have it served for his breakfast, mustn't he?"

Janna blushed and stamped her foot. "You don't understand," she cried. "He is our *ruler*."

Sef laid his hand warningly across her mouth. "Hush, this place isn't as soundproof as upstairs," he whispered. Then he went on, "More shame that he is your ruler. Can't you see he is an ogre?"

Janna stood with downcast eyes. "I must have that picture," she insisted. "I don't want my parents put in prison. I'm going to tell my mother about it."

"So?" said Sef. "And will you tell her where you found it, so you can serve Mina, the van Arkels, and me to your ogre?"

"Oh dear," sighed Janna. "I wish Mina were here. She'd know what to do."

"Why not wait till she comes back?" asked Sef. "There isn't that much of a hurry, is there?" He pressed a corner of the altar and it pivoted around silently, with its precious load, leaving a blank wall.

"Come on upstairs," said Sef. In his own little room he began sorting out his finished work. Janna watched him. She noticed how deftly and surely his long fingers handled the documents.

"You're clever," she said. "I can't see which are your stamps and which are the originals."

"I wish it were true," sighed Sef. "A microscope would show the difference at once, but it won't come to that unless the Germans become suspicious."

"How did you get into this?" asked Janna, suddenly worried. It seemed frightfully dangerous work.

Sef straightened and stretched himself. His hands almost touched the ceiling. "I was studying to become a sculptor," he said. "Every Saturday afternoon I went to this famous Amsterdam sculptor for lessons. When the racial persecutions began in '41, he started on these forgeries. His pupils were the first ones to help him. I'm only one in an assembly line. I do these particular stamps, but there are many others. One for each district. There are also signatures to be forged and a watermark which has to be simulated. That's very delicate work . . . a girl does it."

"How do you get the models?"

"Oh, we have patriots in the offices who smuggle them out."

"I thought you said you worked for the van Arkels?"

"Well, they're in it too."

"Can't the Jews get food without these papers?" asked Janna, shivering a little. She realized that it would matter very much to her if something happened to Sef.

"How could they? Everything is rationed. The shops have barely enough to honor the coupons. The only other way is the Black Market and few Jews are rich enough for that."

"How many people are there in hiding?" asked Janna.

"Over two hundred thousand, I should imagine," said Sef. "They are not all Jews. We have students hiding because they did not sign the oath of loyalty and others to escape the labor draft. Then there are our illegal workers, our Kuckel gangs, who do the sabotage. They're on the run all the time. The only place to hide here is in other people's houses. We have no forests or mountains."

"And you have to feed them all?"

"Our group? No, of course not. We take care of a limited number. There are other groups doing the same thing, all over the country." Sef went on sorting and wrapping the documents.

"What happens if Hitler wins the war?" asked Janna.

"Don't worry about that," said Sef. "It won't happen."

"But *if*," persisted Janna.

"Then," said Sef, looking at her with wide-open hazel eyes, "then all our work is for nothing. We'll all be killed and the killing will go on for a long time, because your ogre lives on blood."

"But he said . . ." faltered Janna.

"I'll tell you what he said," interrupted Sef. "He said that lies were the greatest weapon of a ruler, and the bigger the lie, the more readily it is believed."

"So . . . so . . ." began Janna again.

"So you can believe on his own authority that everything he said has been a lie." Janna felt uneasy. This was a little too radical for her.

"I . . . I think I'd better go . . ." she said. "Mina being away, they may need my help."

"Yes, little Muff," said Sef. "You'd better go and think over what I've told you."

Janna took the tray with the shards and the mess wrapped in newspaper with her, as well as the broom. She disposed of them tidily in the kitchen. To the surprised Corrie she explained that she and Heinz had wanted to have a party but she had accidentally dropped the tray. Corrie accepted her explanation placidly. Janna liked her but sometimes suspected that she wasn't very bright.

Lunch was a sketchy affair of biscuits and weak tea. Herr Frosch grumbled his way through, going on and on about the hazards of cooks dusting ceilings. Everyone longed for a hot meal, but there was no one to cook it. The household was in utter confusion. Corrie, so quick and capable under Mina's direction, now rushed around like a headless chicken, starting on one thing and leaving it for another. Mounds of dust lay on the floor beside an abandoned broom, silverware was left soaking in the sink while wrinkled clothing languished beside a cooling iron. Frau Oster, who had an exceptionally difficult part to rehearse, felt distracted. She hadn't been able to find a substitute for Mina. The hospital had advised her that Mina would have to stay there for a while. The prospect of eating out of cans loomed threateningly.

"Oh dear," said Janna's mother. "I wish there was someone in the house who could cook. Frau Frosch is useless. When I asked her if she could boil an egg, she wanted to know whether you used water or milk!"

"I can cook," said Janna. She might have dropped a bombshell, her mother looked so surprised.

"Didn't you read my letters?" asked Janna. "I told you Frau Kopp often made me cook her meals. As long as it's not complicated and I don't have to kill chickens . . ." she stipulated.

"Kill chickens!" Her mother shuddered. "You don't mean to tell me they made you kill chickens?"

"Mother, I wrote you. We had all sorts of things to do for those farmers: clear out manure, currycomb horses, feed pigs . . ."

"Heavens!" cried her mother. "And did Erna allow that?"

"Erna had nothing to do with it. It was the law. We were obliged to help on the land. Didn't you know that?"

"You said something . . . but I thought it was for rural children . . ." Her mother's voice trailed off as she realized that she had not thought about it at all. "Well, it's a good thing you learned to cook," she said, cheering up, "because I don't know the difference between a turnip and a potato. I'll leave the kitchen to you then. I've got to go." With a relieved smile she left.

And so, quite casually, Janna was made free in Mina's kingdom. She could poke about there to her heart's content and she found all sorts of interesting things . . . a little cellar where coal and potatoes and cabbages were kept and where Mina had hidden a perfectly good bicycle! She also found an unused stove in a corner of the kitchen which she had not noticed before. She realized that these were the only places in the house she and her mother hadn't ransacked for the painting. They hadn't dared to!

She also noticed that the supplies in the house were rather unbalanced. Corrie explained that it all depended on what the Baron had been able to get hold of. There was a larder full of Russian caviar, there were cartons full of pickles, boxes full of oyster crackers, and some vegetables in cans. On the other hand, though there was a sack of flour, there was no bread, and Janna didn't know how to make any. They were out of butter and milk, and the only fresh vegetable was cabbage.

Janna finally opened a can of mushrooms and made soup with them. She boiled some potatoes and made a salad out of cabbage leaves. Then she used some leftover porridge and made fried cakes with it.

"Why doesn't the Baron send us more sensible food?" she asked peevishly. "Who wants caviar?"

"You could serve it on oyster crackers," suggested Corrie. "You should not complain, you're well off. Many people are eating bulbs."

"Tulip bulbs?" asked Janna. "Can you eat those?"

"At certain times of the year," said Corrie. "At other times they're poisonous. You don't know how lucky you are."

A little ashamed, Janna went on preparing the dinner. It wasn't too bad, though Herr Frosch looked gloomy. He made his whole meal out of caviar.

Corrie stayed late to help with the dishes. Afterward Janna was faced with carrying up Sef's dinner. How to do that without being detected? Her admiration for Mina increased.

After Corrie had left, she looked about for a way to disguise the tray. She found a deep clothes basket in which it fitted. She draped newly ironed garments over the basket and cautiously mounted the stairs. Mina had always gone through the long room but Janna preferred to use her wardrobe. She did not think she could manage the ladder.

Her mother saw her and said, "Now really, Janna, you don't have to do that. . . . Let Corrie carry up the ironing."

"Yes, Mother," said Janna, hastily disappearing into her room and wondering how Mina had done it.

It was disappointing after all the trouble not to find Sef in his room. Perhaps he was in the chapel. She descended the ladder and looked around, she even peeped into the toilet, but he wasn't there. Where could he be? She climbed the ladder again. No, he wasn't hiding for a joke. She did not see him in his closet or under his bedclothes. Then she noticed that the table looked bare. The finished work was gone. Sef had left! He had risked going into the streets to deliver it. She remembered the skinny boy the SS had tried to arrest, thinking he was of age. Would they not think it far more of tall, stalwart Sef, with his manly voice? And if they arrested him, they would find the forged papers . . . Janna groaned. She sat on Sef's bed and buried her face in her hands. It was all her fault. Why, oh why had she made that stupid wish? She paced up and down the little room, her hands squeezed together, knowing there was no one she could go to for advice. She was left alone with the whole responsibility of Sef, with the secret . . . and she was afraid to use the ring again. At last she crawled into bed. As she turned down her blankets, she found a note on her pillow.

"Gone out—back soon," it said. It was risky, foolish, unnecessary . . . but it warmed her heart. With the note in her hand she fell asleep.

✠ THIRTEEN ✠

Troubles

WHEN JANNA OPENED her eyes the next morning, she knew something extraordinary had happened. Then she saw Sef's piece of paper and it all came back to her. She destroyed the paper (Heinz must not find it) and went to the wardrobe, half hoping Sef had come back in the night. She'd left the window open. But the room was just as it had been the day before. The bed had not been slept in. She knew it was no use looking in the chapel . . . he hadn't come back. Meanwhile, the household depended on her for its food. She dressed hurriedly and ran downstairs to the kitchen. Heinz was already banging about there and Janna began to understand Mina's dislike of children in the kitchen.

"When are you going to make breakfast?" whined Heinz. "I'm hungry!"

"It's not that late," said Janna, looking at the kitchen clock. "Leave me to it, will you?"

"No, I've just as much right to be here as you," said Heinz. "I'll help you." Luckily Corrie came in with an empty tray.

"Oh no, you don't," she said with deep feeling. "You march right out of here. Men don't belong in a kitchen," The word "men" mollified Heinz and he departed.

"Thanks, Corrie," said Janna.

"That boy," grumbled Corrie. "If I have to tell the truth, I'm glad there are only girls in our family. A brother like that would have driven me mad."

Janna made coffee and fresh porridge. She piled more caviar on oyster biscuits. Herr Frosh ate the caviar but refused the porridge, and then grumbled at the monotony of his diet.

As Janna was washing up afterward, she could not get Sef out of her mind.

"Corrie, when a boy looks the right age and is walking the streets, do the police always pick him up?"

"Mostly," said Corrie. "Of course, if he doesn't meet an official, he might get away with it. But it's a risk hardly anyone would dare take. When they are caught they are punished, you see. They're supposed to give themselves up."

"What if they are carrying something forbidden, like forged papers?"

"Oh my goodness," cried Corrie. "They'd be finished then!" Corrie was talking quite naturally to Janna. Sometimes Janna thought she forgot that Janna was German.

A sick feeling spread upward from Janna's stomach. She almost lost her breakfast. When Hugo arrived that day, he seemed to echo her mood. He looked more ill and spent than usual. Janna told him to sit down, she'd get him some coffee and something to eat, but he stopped her.

"I couldn't swallow a bite," he said, sinking into his chair and covering his face with his hands. "My best friend and his wife were arrested in the night, with their little daughters. Police banging on the door . . . they had hardly time to put on their coats. I heard it all from the neighbors."

"Oh dear," said Janna, thinking of Sef. "Why were they taken?"

"For the crime of being Jewish, for breathing when they're not supposed to exist. I offered to hide them long ago. I begged them to share my flat. Rachel was willing—she was thinking of the babies—but Saul would not hear of it. He did not want to endanger me. 'As if that matters,' I said. 'What's my life worth? I, a hunchback, with no prospect of a normal life . . . why can't I risk it for you? I'd be glad to.' But he would not listen. I think he had a religious reason. He seemed to think the persecution was sent by God for a mysterious purpose.

" 'We must not refuse it,' he said. 'God will give us the strength to bear whatever happens. It's also for you Christians that we suffer.' I'll never forget his face when he said that. I never knew a finer man. He gave Rachel the courage to face up to it too."

Janna sat very still. She hardly recognized her cool, detached teacher. At last Hugo looked up.

"Sorry, Janna, I should not worry you about this." Then, surprised, he said, "I talk to you like a friend, don't I? I have a confession to make. I hated to take this job, but I had to, I was starving. I've come to enjoy it. It's a pleasure teaching a sensitive, honest child."

Janna blushed. "It's been wonderful for me too," she said. "I feel as if I were lost in a jungle and you cut a path for me."

"You did a lot of it yourself," said Hugo. "You've restored some of my faith in human nature. I always believed that there was a compass in the human breast forever pointing to what's true and good . . . or, to make another comparison, that like a root or bulb we cannot be so deeply buried or a green shoot will break its way through to the light. You've proved it, my dear, you've proved it, putting older people to shame." They smiled at each other.

"I think it's . . . it's because lies don't *fit*," said Janna. "Something keeps sticking out."

Hugo laughed. "Very well put," he said. "Where were we with our geometry last time . . . ?"

After the lesson Janna ran up to her room to see whether Sef had arrived, but he was still missing. She felt desperate. She longed for Mina. If only she had someone to talk things over with! She hated to do it . . . things might go wrong again, but she rubbed her ring and wished Mina back. It worked! That very day Mina returned in an ambulance. She had refused to stay in the hospital. Janna's parents were out but she and Corrie settled Mina in her room, after the ambulance men had carried her up five flights of stairs.

As soon as Corrie had left, Mina fixed Janna with a gimlet stare and said, "What have you and Sef been up to? Out with it!"

Janna burst into tears. "We haven't been up to any-thing. . . . He's gone . . ." she sobbed.

"Gone!" Mina hadn't looked exactly rosy, but now she became paler still. "You don't mean . . ."

"No, no," Janna hastened to assure her. "It's not as bad as that. At least, I hope it isn't. He . . . he went to deliver his finished work."

"The fool!" spluttered Mina. "That's what I was afraid of. That's why I insisted they bring me home. Not that I wanted to stay there, the food they served would not have filled a hollow tooth. . . . Why didn't you stop him from going?" she asked suddenly, lifting threatening eyebrows at Janna.

"He didn't tell me," faltered Janna. "He . . . he was gone when I brought him his dinner."

"Ah!" said Mina. "At least he waited till dark. He won't come back in broad daylight either; he's not that kind of an idiot. He may have stayed with a friend . . . he'll have enjoyed that. Poor boy, he's been cooped up for so long."

"You don't think the police will get him?" asked Janna with quivering lips.

"Why think the worst? As the Good Book says, 'Hope maketh not ashamed.' If we didn't trust in a loving providence, how could we get through these days? What I'd like now, my dear, is a nice hot cup of the Baron's tea. What they served in the hospital was bilge water."

Janna went downstairs, greatly relieved to have laid her burden on Mina's broad shoulders.

It had been raining all that day. Her father was suffering from an attack of bronchitis and had gone to bed early with aspirin and a sleeping pill. His understudy had to take over that night.

Janna went to bed early too but could not get to sleep. She was worrying about Sef out in that bad weather. It must have been close to curfew time when she heard the French windows open gently. She whispered, "Is that you, Sef?"

"Yes," he whispered back, shutting the blackout drapes behind him. Janna switched on her bed light and smothered a laugh. Sef was dripping wet and enveloped in a huge old-fashioned cape with a hood that covered most of his face. He threw it off.

"Brrr, what a day," he said, putting down the package he was carrying.

"Didn't you deliver your work?" Janna asked anxiously.

"Yes, I did. I delivered the documents and got some

more to do. Guess what! I've been to see Nella." He had taken a chair and was removing his wet boots.

"You saw Nella?" Janna was taken aback.

"Yes, I heard from friends that she and Eylard, her two-year-old brother, are staying here in the city with an uncle and aunt. Nella has to go on with her schooling. She just entered the Montessori Lyceum, the best high school in Amsterdam; I wish I'd been able to go there. And of course the baby has to be looked after. But she doesn't know where her parents and brothers are. They said goodbye to her and she hasn't heard from them since. Of course, they may be hiding. The boys are getting to the age where they can be picked up for labor . . . or they may have been arrested. She is very brave about it."

Janna blushed. So that lovely, united family was dispersed because her mother had wanted the Osters to be together!

"The uncle put me up last night," Sef went on. "He has a very knobbly sofa. Nella and I talked until late. Nella sends you her thanks for looking after me. I talked to her about the Rembrandt picture, but she said possessions did not matter where lives were at stake, so you can do what you like."

"How nice of her," said Janna, tears filling her eyes. "Couldn't we give some of her things back to her . . . some of her clothes? I have them in my wardrobe."

Sef smiled. "They wouldn't fit her," he said. "She's grown a lot since I saw her last. Her aunt has made her some dresses from spare things of her own. She looked all right."

"How did you escape the police?" asked Janna.

"I didn't meet any. . . . God looked after me."

"An SS man I know says there is no God, or the SS wouldn't be here."

"Hah!" said Sef. "That's arrogance for you, making the existence of Almighty God depend on little twerps like himself."

"You must be starved," said Janna, "I'll go down and get you something."

"You speak a true word," said Sef. "I've been so well fed here I did not want to take what little they had, so I'm hollow. I dreamed all night of Mina's pancakes . . ."

"I don't have Mina's pancakes for you," said Janna. "I'm doing the cooking."

"You?" Sef smiled. "How is Mina?"

"Back," said Janna. "She insisted on leaving the hospital."

"Good for her," said Sef. "Was she mad I went?"

"What do you think?" asked Janna. They both laughed.

"Lock the door after me," said Janna. "I'll knock three times softly when I come back." She went out. As she passed her father's door, she heard him snoring, so the pill had worked. She went upstairs to Mina's room first, to tell her Sef was back. She thought Mina would be sleepless too, worrying about the boy. She was right. Light showed through the cracks of Mina's door. Mina said, "Come in," when Janna knocked.

"Praise be to God from Whom all blessings flow," she exclaimed when Janna told her the news. "Now I can sleep. Did he say anything?"

"Yes, he's seen Nella."

"Nella?" Mina sat upright, revealing a flannel nightgown. Janna repeated to her what Sef had said. "I'm getting

him some food now," she said. "You go to sleep." She
fluffed up Mina's pillow and tucked the blankets around
her. "Is your leg paining you?" she asked.

"A little . . . it doesn't matter. You're a good child . . ."
Mina muttered drowsily. On the way back Janna heard
her father snore again. She went to the kitchen and prepared hot cocoa, fried potatoes, and crackers with caviar.
She was carrying the tray upstairs when she heard a muffled cry from the library. She recognized her mother's
voice. Right after that she heard the Baron say something.
Her mother and the Baron were alone in the library while
her father was sleeping upstairs. It made Janna grow cold
inside. Without reflection Janna rubbed her ring hard and
wished the Baron out of their lives . . .

She had hardly finished her wish when she shrank
back into the shadow of one of the valuable statues. The
library door had opened and the Baron strode out, looking
angry.

"If that's what you think of me," he whispered hoarsely,
"I'll have nothing more to do with you. I am offering you
marriage, I want to make you baroness of my castle—and
you call it an insult!" Her mother had followed him out,
looking every bit as angry as the Baron.

"I'm a married woman," she whispered in concentrated
fury. "Is it not an insult to think I'd make light of my
vows?"

The Baron turned a face to her twisted with conflicting
passions. "Mechtild . . ." he said. It was a cry of pain.

"No, Dietrich, we must not see each other again," murmured Mechtild. "You've spoiled a beautiful friendship
. . ." she ended brokenly.

The Baron left, his cloak swirling after him so that it

got caught in the door and Mechtild had to open it to re-lease him.

Janna stood frozen, not daring to move. She saw her mother rush into the library and heard sounds of wild weeping.

Oh dear, thought Janna as she trudged upstairs with her tray. What have I done! When she arrived at the third floor, her father poked a sleepy face around the bedroom door.

"What's the noise?" he asked thickly. "Was that the front door? Where's your mother?"

"In the kitchen," Janna lied quickly. "We were making a snack. I'm eating mine in my room. Go back to sleep." Her father looked as if there was nothing he'd like better. He withdrew his head and she could hear the springs creak as he went back to his bed.

Janna gave three soft knocks on the door and Sef opened it.

"What happened?" he asked. "You were so long!" He'd been reading Janna's *Nibelungen* book. She could see it lying open on the bed.

"Hush!" she said. She listened at the door; she could hear her mother's footsteps coming up the stairs. Then her parents' bedroom door opened and closed.

"What's the matter?" Sef whispered nervously.

"She's back," said Janna.

"Who?"

"My mother, in her room."

"Where was she then? Did she see you? Has she found out about me?"

"No," said Janna. "She didn't see me. I'm afraid your cocoa is cold," she added.

"Never mind, I'll have it anyway," said Sef. "What happened? You look like a ghost."

"Nothing—at least, nothing about you. I'd rather not talk about it," said Janna.

"All right, Janneke, I won't pry," said Sef cheerfully, gobbling up his fried potatoes.

"What's that?" he asked, pointing to the caviar. Janna told him. Sef said he'd never tasted any.

"Mina must have been holding back on you. The place is full of it," Janna said, smiling. Sef tasted it but said it was too salty for him. He ate the crackers, though. His hair was still wet and clung tightly to his head.

"What did you call me just now?" asked Janna, smiling.

"Janneke, that's a Dutch diminutive of Janna. We have a song about you:

> *"Hupsa Janneke*
> *Stroop in't kanneke*
> *Laat the poppekes dansen!"*

"That means: '*Hupsa Janneke,* syrup in the jug, let the puppets dance,'" translated Janna. "Does it mean anything?"

"Oh, it's probably got some gruesome historical meaning, like most nursery rhymes," said Sef.

"You're cheering me up, Sef. I felt awful."

"I saw it," said Sef. "I've been reading that book of yours. I think Brunhilde is the only decent character in it."

"She caused Siegfried's death," Janna pointed out.

"That mutt," grumbled Sef.

"Oh no," protested Janna. "He's a hero, I love him. You're rather like him," she added shyly.

"Me? A Nordic sap like him? God forbid," said Sef. "I don't believe in that magic potion, you know. That was just a coverup, because he was unfaithful to Brunhilde. She had a right to avenge herself. Except for her, the whole lot are crooked, Wotan most of all, the double-dealing tyrant. As for the ring, I don't think it was magic at all. They only thought it was. The curse came through their own violence, greed, and hatred."

Sef had finished his meal. Gathering up his cloak and boots and the package, he vanished into the wardrobe.

Janna put out the light and lay staring into the darkness. Her mother and the Baron . . . her mother's tears . . . had she done wrong?

✠ FOURTEEN ✠

Betrayal

NOW BEGAN an arduous time for Janna. She and Corrie had to look after the whole household, including Mina up five flights of stairs. The advantage was that Janna did not have to disguise Sef's trays. Whenever she was seen, she blandly pretended they were for Mina. Frau Oster exclaimed over Mina's appetite!

Mechtild was wan and listless these days. The spring seemed to have gone out of her. The Baron did not come any more and even Janna missed him. Something of warmth and refinement had gone from the house.

But though the Baron stayed away, his gifts kept coming. Janna surprised her mother weeping over a brace of pheasants one day that had just been delivered. Janna tiptoed off guiltily, wondering whether she had had the right to interfere with her mother's friendship. But she had her own troubles. Nella haunted her. On one hand she felt sorry for her, without her parents, not knowing where they were . . . but she did not like Sef's interest in her. She was so beautiful . . . and she had known Sef for years. Sef must love her. Janna felt she could not bear it. Sef was her discovery, her Siegfried. She did not want to share him with Nella, even though Nella knew him first. It all came to a head one morning as she brought in Sef's lunch. She almost dropped the tray when she saw what he was doing. He was taping a photograph of Nella on the wall above his bed.

164

"Doesn't she look nice?" he asked, stepping away from it to judge the effect. "She gave it to me the other night."

"Did she," said Janna coldly.

"Don't you like it?" asked Sef, turning around to look at her.

"Does it matter whether I do?" asked Janna.

"Of course." Sef was grinning at her. "I've taped it up to please you. You admire her, don't you?"

"That's not true. You did it to please yourself," Janna retorted. "What do you want with me when you have Nella? Why bother with me at all?"

"Because you're around and she isn't. Anyway, the more the merrier, don't you think?" Sef looked at her in such an irritating way that Janna lost her temper.

"No," she said angrily, slamming the tray on his bed. "I hate being one of a crowd, being a stopgap. You can *have* Nella. If Mina wasn't ill, I'd never, never see you again."

"Ah!" said Sef, who seemed vastly amused. "That would be a pity. I should miss you, Janna." He was leaning with his back against the wall and looked triumphant.

"You . . . you . . ." Janna did not know what word to use to express her fury. Then a word from an old-fashioned novel came to her mind. "You . . . *trifler* . . ." She spat at him, like an angry cat, and turning, she stumbled through the wardrobe, followed by Sef's soft, teasing laughter. When she stepped into her room, she saw Heinz there, rummaging through her desk. She thought she had locked the door! Heinz looked up.

"I know what you're doing in there," he said craftily.

"Oh you do, do you . . ." Janna was still too angry to think. "I suppose you've found out I've a boy friend in there, haven't you?" It was out before she could help herself. When she realized what she had done, she felt sick all over. She'd betrayed Sef! Now Heinz would go looking for him, and if you searched well, you were bound to find the catch and the way into Sef's room. She felt like tearing her hair.

Heinz laughed. "You think you can fool me! That wardrobe isn't big enough. You can't fob me off. You've a radio in there and you're listening to a forbidden station!"

He hadn't believed her! Relief made Janna giddy. Then she realized what Heinz was saying. She must not contradict him; it was better he should believe that than the truth.

"You think you're smart, eh?" she jeered. "Where would I get a radio?"

"How do I know," said Heinz, shrugging his shoulders. "Perhaps you found one in the attic."

"We Germans are allowed radios, aren't we?"

"We're not allowed to listen to enemy propaganda," said Heinz. "If I tell my father . . ."

"Then I'll tell about the statue," Janna said promptly. She saw that had had an effect.

"Well," Heinz conceded, "maybe I won't tell. But then you must let me listen too . . ." He made a movement toward the wardrobe. Janna blocked his way.

"All right," she said glibly, wondering how she was going to do that. Then she asked sternly, "How did you get into my room? I know I locked the door."

"My key fits your lock," said Heinz, grinning evilly. Janna shuddered at the thought of how unsafe she had been all the times she had felt so secure!

As soon as she had got rid of Heinz, she ran up to Mina to confess what had happened. Mina was wearing a knitted bed jacket and her graying hair hung down in plaits. To Janna's surprise, she took the account fairly calmly.

"Is that all you said?" she asked, with a curious expression on her face. "That you had a boy friend in the wardrobe?"

"I said, 'In there.' Heinz thought I meant the wardrobe."

"It's a good thing he didn't believe you, though I must say, it does not sound believable. If he pesters you about the radio, you can let him listen to mine."

"Do you have one?"

"Of course. If you lift up the third floorboard, you'll find it. But it's more important to be able to lock your door. Listen . . ." and Mina gave Janna instructions on where to find a hook and eye to put on her door.

"And make it fit properly." she warned. "Don't leave a crack, so he can slip a knife through and lift the hook. Next time remember that 'he that is slow to anger is better than the mighty; and he that ruleth his spirit better than he that taketh a city.' " Janna hung her head.

"I promise," she said.

"Well, hurry and put up that hook and eye then," said Mina.

On the twenty-ninth of April, 1943, the Wehrmacht Befehlshaber of the Netherlands ordered that the demobilized members of the Dutch Army were to be taken into custody. They would be summoned personally in the newspapers and those who tried to escape could expect the severest retaliation. Announcements to that effect were posted all over the city. The order caused a storm of protest, just as occurred in '41, at the time of the first deportations of the Jews. A general strike broke out spontaneously all over Holland. Herr Frosch noticed first that he could not use the telephone. Then the power failed. Frau Oster had to bring out old-fashioned kerosene lamps. The next morning there was no mail. Janna served canned milk and crackers for breakfast.

"Those stupid Dutch," fumed Herr Frosch. "How do they hope to get away with it? And Seyss-Inquart is in Berchtesgaden! Herr Rauter will have to manage everything."

But Seyss-Inquart was speedily summoned. He was on his way back, bringing more Gestapo and SS troops.

Martial law was declared. There were many executions, of strikers, of prominent Dutchmen. Sef said he feared for the van Arkels, and Janna scanned the lists of victims every day, but so far the van Arkels were not among them.

Heinz had forgotten about the radio. His ambition now was to trap a Dutch officer who had failed to give himself up, and he sat for hours in his spy hole like a cat waiting for a mouse. Janna guessed that his secret wish was to wring praise out of an unappreciative father.

She herself was anxious now to have the Rembrandt safely in her parents' hands. The responsibility of keeping it hidden weighed on her. She discussed it with Mina. At first Mina had vigorously opposed her giving up the family treasure, but when Janna told her what Nella had said, she gave way.

"We'll have to stage a fake discovery, the way we had a fake accident," she said. "Let me think about it."

The theaters were closed. For the first time, as long as Janna could remember, she had her parents' company in the evenings. (Their Monday holidays did not count, for then they had social engagements.)

"Can we sit around the table like a real family?" asked Janna.

"What do you mean, minx, a real family? Aren't we real?" asked her father, pinching her cheek.

"Not like the van Arkels," said Janna.

"What do you know about the van Arkels?" asked her father, frowning.

"I know their picture," said Janna. Her mother understood.

"Let's play a game together, Otto," she said. "We can sit in the library."

Janna found a game in the recreation room, one of those where you throw dice and move little figures along numbered squares. The first player to arrive at a hundred wins the jackpot. Some squares had pictures with special meanings. Janna found some pfeffernuesse in a tin: tiny round spicy cookies. They would serve for the jackpot. She sat down with her parents at Hugo's table. Corrie had made up a fire in the fireplace and Janna's father lit it. It was nice to sit in the familiar room with the light of a kerosene lamp shining on the table while the fire spat and crackled, the draperies closed firmly against the outside world with its dangers. Janna sat between her parents. At last they were a loving family! She glowed.

Unfortunately her parents hadn't played long before they began to argue.

"I'm fed up with this country," her father was grumbling. "All this violence, no decent regard for law and order. It's perfectly reasonable for us to intern the army again, with a probable English invasion in the offing. All this irresponsible striking only makes things worse." He threw the dice so wildly that one of them rolled off the table. Janna picked it up.

"Two sixes, that means twelve," she said, moving her

father's blue figure up twelve points. "Oh, you landed in the grave! Now you're dead, you'll have to wait till someone rescues you."

"That's exactly the way I *feel*," said her father. "It's not only the Dutch, though a colder, unfriendlier people it would be hard to find. But there is that Frosch, suspecting us of stealing the picture! I bet he told his boss, Rauter, about it. The last thing I want is to fall into the hands of the SD. I don't like their methods. Mechtild, I want to accept that invitation we received to play in Paris."

Frau Oster was advancing her yellow figure. "Dear me," she said. "I've got to go back to the beginning."

"Please do," said her husband. "Let's start over again somewhere else, Mechtild. The three of us."

"You must be joking," said Mechtild. "How do you know we'd get permission? We're appreciated here. There now, Janna, you're going to win! You got to ninety-nine."

"Oh no," said Janna. "You can't throw one with two dice. I'll have to move back again."

"I'm not joking," said Herr Oster. "No, Janna, I've got to skip my turn, don't you remember? Of course we'll get permission. It's the same sort of job, but the French are more civilized. Why should we not pull up our stakes here? We don't want to overstay our welcome."

"Twelve," said Janna's mother. "Oh, look, I can advance more, I got a bonus! I'll catch up with you yet, Janna. You forget, Otto, that we have a house here and can have Janna with us. It was hard enough to get."

"There are houses in Paris," said Herr Oster. "I have friends there, don't forget. I come from Alsace. Ah, poor Janna, you threw too much. Now you're back to eighty-nine."

"Why do you want to upset the present arrangement?

We're taken care of here. The Baron sends us food." Mechtild's voice trembled a little. "There now, I'm in prison. I've got to skip a turn."

"You may land in prison if you stay here, Mechtild," warned her husband. "There is a Dutch proverb that says it's bad luck eating cherries with high-placed gentlemen."

"If you mean the Baron, you know he is not coming any more," Mechtild reminded him gently.

"I suppose he's found another man's wife's shoulder to weep on," Otto remarked unfeelingly.

"There now, Janna, you've won," said Mechtild. "All the pfeffernuesse are yours. No, thank you, dear, it's too soon after dinner. And a good dinner it was, even if you had to use canned food. Do you know what Mina said to me? She said you had a real talent for cooking."

"Did she?" Janna blushed with pleasure. Mina's compliments were rare.

"She did. Otto, remember, the devil you know is better than the devil you don't know."

"We may not continue to do well here," predicted her husband gloomily. "They may arrest us about that picture. Frankly, I'm scared. I wish you'd listen to me."

"If we run away now," said Mechtild, "everyone is sure to think we're guilty."

"It's the Baron," said her husband bitterly. "You don't want to leave him." He left abruptly, slamming the door.

Janna stared wide-eyed at her mother. "Do you love the Baron?" she asked.

Her mother laughed the tinkling laugh she reserved for her best roles. "Don't let your father affect you," she said. "The Baron and I are just friends . . ." But there was a misty look about her eyes as they stared into the distance.

✠ FIFTEEN ✠

Hugo

O N MONDAY the strike was still on and Janna wondered whether Hugo would come to teach her. Some people were still going about their business, but the streets were dangerous. Janna and Heinz were not allowed outside; they had to take their exercise in the garden.

Heinz said it was a matter of who was going to win, the Dutch or the Germans.

"We'll win because we're stronger," he said confidently. Janna wondered. Seeing so much of Hugo, Mina, Sef, and Corrie had made her aware of the resistance in the hearts of the Dutch. Could you really win if you did not have the hearts of the people? Could you conquer hearts by force?

Janna had been thinking a lot about Hugo. She felt sorry for him. He had sounded so sad when he said he couldn't lead a normal life. Did that mean he could not marry? In a sudden glow of benevolence she had rubbed her ring and wished him his heart's desire. Now she was waiting impatiently to hear what good fortune had befallen him.

Her father seemed to be thinking of Hugo too. "He might be foolish enough to try and come here today," he said. "The poor fellow, they might do something to him. I'll go and meet him."

"No, no, don't, something might happen to you," cried

Mechtild in a sudden panic. She hung on his arm. "Don't go out."

"Nothing will happen to me," said Otto. "I'm a German, remember?" But Mechtild flung her arms around Otto and would not let him go. Janna watched approvingly.

"Come, Mechtild," Otto said at last, "I'm not going to the end of the world." He disengaged himself and left.

Corrie hadn't come, so Janna was faced with all the work. Meals were simple, just opening cans. Cleaning kerosene lamps was a different matter. She had to run to Mina for advice.

Mechtild helped to get the lunch ready. They were both in the kitchen when Otto returned. He looked white and shaken. There was blood on his hands and his shirt. He fell into a chair.

"Don't get excited now, don't get excited," he warned, waving a hand. This only alarmed the others more.

"You had an accident!" cried his wife. "I knew something would happen! I *knew* it. . . . Why didn't you listen to me?"

"I'm all right," said Otto. "It's not me, it's Hugo, that blasted little idiot, that crazy fool . . ."

"Otto . . . what *happened?*"

"You know people are forbidden to gather in the streets during martial law. A necessary measure. They're shot on sight, without warning, if they do. We've been arming the Dutch National Socialists to help keep order. They're just a lot of trigger-happy louts. A few women were standing in front of an announcement of recent executions. Perfectly innocent. They were probably looking for the names of friends or relatives. One had a small boy by the hand. Along comes that armed scum and starts shooting at them. They scream . . . and who rushes to their rescue? Our little hero, Hugo! He shouts at the Dutchmen not to shoot their own people, or something to that effect, and they laugh at him, call him names in their sweet Dutch way, and start to aim at the little boy to spite him. Hugo moves like lightning and gets the bullet in his own heart."

Janna gave a cry and flung herself into her mother's arms.

"I was still at a distance, but as soon as I got there, I gave those thugs a piece of my mind! I told them I'd inform Herr Rauter of what they had done. That scared them. They were probably already sobered by the harm they had done. Anyway, they went off. The women and the little boy had gone too, leaving Hugo lying there, in his own blood. . . . I lifted him up, he was as light as a child. He smiled at me, moved his lips as if to say something, and he died in my arms. At least he was pronounced dead when I got him to the hospital."

Herr Oster looked at his bloodstained hands. "I liked that little fellow," he said. Janna whimpered in her mother's arms. "It comes from giving guns to ruffians," her father continued. "We Germans have to bear the blame for this. I'm ashamed." There was a silence, broken only by Janna's sobs.

"Well, I suppose it was the way he'd want to die," Otto said heavily after a while. The words pierced Janna's heart. Her wish! Of course! But she hadn't meant anything like that . . . she wanted Hugo to be happily married. She would have rejected this answer if she had known. What kind of queer magic did the ring have? It made no sense. For Hugo wasn't a "little fellow" as her father kept calling him. Hugo was great. His mind and heart could have been of service to Holland for a long time. He himself might think the life of the little boy worth more than his own, but Janna doubted it. People like Hugo were rare. Janna had never met anyone like him, and now she had to learn to live without him. Never again could she ask him questions. . . . She was a murderer like Cain.

"I don't know where to look for another tutor," she heard her father say. "All young men are being called up for labor, or interned as members of the Dutch Army."

Janna tore herself out of her mother's embrace. "I won't have another tutor, I won't!" she screamed. "Never, never!" She collapsed in a storm of tears. Her mother vainly tried to hush her. Her father stroked her hair.

"There, there, darling," he said. "I wish I could take you away from all this. I wish we'd never taken you out of the Black Forest . . ." Janna drew back and looked at her father through drenched eyelashes.

"Left me there?" she asked. "I'd have hated that. I'm glad you sent for me."

"I thought you were happy there," said her father.

"I was then," Janna admitted, wiping her eyes on her sleeve. Her father gave her his handkerchief and she blew her nose.

"But I learned so much here; I'd rather know people like Hugo even if they get killed than never know them at all." Her father looked at her in bewilderment. His face was good and honest and loving, but Janna saw clearly, for the first time, that there would always be a barrier between her and her father because there were things he would never understand. Was that why her mother had turned to the Baron? Yet it did not stop Janna from loving her father.

When she told Sef about Hugo's death, she found sensitive understanding. "Poor Janneke," he said, stroking her hair. "To have made such a friend and to lose him so suddenly! But from what you tell me he seems to have had a great spirit in a very frail shell. Perhaps there wasn't much for him to look forward to in this life. There is another life, you know, Janna, and in that life you may meet again."

"Do you really think so?" Janna looked up at him with wet eyes. In Germany most young people did not believe these things any more. Only older ones. Sef nodded. His eyes seemed wiser than his age. Janna thought he looked as if he had suffered much, young as he was.

She gazed around the little room and noticed how dirty it was beginning to look. "I'm going to clean this place," she announced. She didn't want Mina to see it like this when she was up again. Besides, good hard scrubbing might cure her depression and guilt feelings.

"That's not necessary," said Sef. "I'm very comfortable. You look after me splendidly, little Muff."

"I prefer Janneke," said Janna.

Sef grinned. "That's only for special occasions," he said.

"The room has got to be cleaned," Janna decreed firmly.

"Very well, then, but don't disturb the papers on my table." Janna fetched a pail and other necessary articles and brought them to her room. She fastened the hook on her door and entered Sef's room.

"I'm going to the chapel," said Sef, obviously fearing her domestic armory. Janna did a thorough job. She pulled the sheets from the bed, replacing them with clean ones from the linen closet. She swept and scrubbed the floor. In a corner she found a crumpled piece of yellow cloth. She unfolded it. It was a star with the black word "Jew" across the middle. A Jewish star! How had that got here? Had

the van Arkels been hiding Jews? That was *really* dangerous. That was the worst they could do, worse than making
weapons. If that were found out, they'd be finished, wherever they were. They'd have to share the fate of the
Jews . . . perhaps be sent to a gas chamber. . . . She was
staring at the little yellow cloth when Sef came through
the trapdoor.

"Oh, I see you've found my star," Sef said cheerfully. "I
wondered where it had gone to!"

His star . . . Sef's star . . .

And then she knew! Like an electric shock the knowledge ran through her, making her understand a lot of
things.

Sef was a Jew.

SIXTEEN

The Lost Siegfried

JANNA FELT MISERABLE. She had spoiled everything. She had angered Sef, yet she hadn't been able to help it. She had had an instant revulsion as soon as she had heard from Sef's own lips that he was a Jew. It was a hated, despised word, full of dark associations. Never before had she come face to face with her prejudice, because never before had it touched her personally. But Sef was in her heart now, and it was over her heart as well as over his head that all the evil stories and caricatures she had grown up with had spilled like poison. She felt betrayed, as if Sef had done it on purpose, got her friendship on false pretenses. He said it had never occurred to him that she hadn't guessed.

"Why did you think I was in hiding all the time?"

"Well, you are a Resistance worker, and nearly of age to be sent to Germany . . ."

"Underground workers have papers and passes and can walk around when they are not under immediate suspicion. If I weren't Jewish, I could prove I wasn't the right age yet." Janna saw that she had been stupid.

"But . . . but you're fair and . . ."

"And I haven't got a crooked nose," Sef said. "We don't all look like your caricatures. There are a lot of blond Jews."

"Your name . . ."

"Sef stands for Josef. That's Jewish enough! Anyway,

what did you want me to do? Ring a little bell, like they did in the Middle Ages, to show you're a leper? Or did you want me to wear my star?" He had grown very angry. He went on to say that it was nobody's business what he was. If he wanted to hide that he was Jewish, he had a right to. His ancestry was his own private business, something given him by God. He was himself. If that wasn't enough for people, they could fly to the moon. If Janna felt that way, he was through with her. He'd rather be Jewish than German. Someday Germans would crawl on their bellies trying to hide *their* ancestry.

It had been alarming and Janna had fled in tears. She had to talk to somebody about it and who was there but Mina? But Mina's reaction was almost worse than Sef's. She was like an erupting volcano, spewing out long-suppressed feelings. Her language bristled with Biblical texts.

"So Sef isn't good enough for you, is he?" she spat out with bitter irony. "You have something against him; God's choice does not appeal to you. It's not enough that the poor boy has lost his family and has been cooped up here for years, you must add your little bit to his load! And what are you yourself? Where do you come from? Germans have been laying waste the lands of Europe again and again. What they are now doing to the Jews is unforgivable. We don't know the rights of it yet, but we will know, after we've beaten your country to a pulp. Oh yes, we will. God is on our side, not because we're so good, but because you're so evil. It would be obscene if Hitler won. What we hear from Radio Orange makes our flesh creep . . . gas chambers, mass graves, corpses piled high . . . my God, what are you, devils from hell?

"You may be glad if you get a peep into the heaven

God has prepared for your victims, for truly you have plowed wickedness, you have reaped iniquity. Only when the wicked man turns away from his wickedness that he hath committed and doeth what is lawful and right shall he save his soul alive. But until then your brother's blood crieth to God from the ground. Go, Janna, I don't want to see you. . . . I was beginning to forget you were German, but sooner or later it shows."

Janna slunk off like a whipped dog, appalled at what Mina had said, smarting under her contempt, and bewildered as to how she had earned it. She finally flung herself on her bed and cried herself to sleep.

Then she had a dream. She was trying to find her way through a thick forest. Branches slapped her face, thorns pricked her, but she had to go on. Something was pursuing her. Then she heard singing: "Today we own Germany, tomorrow the world!" She stood still. Why was she running? Those were her friends, the Hitler Youth. Of course! She could see Hildegarde and Kurt. They marched with blood-red banners flaunting black swastikas. She ran to meet them, but they shouted, "Go away, don't come near us, you are wearing a star!" Something was burning her shoulder. She tore it off. It was a yellow star with a black word on it. She threw it down, but another grew, a bigger one. The Hitler Youth laughed and jeered and whistled. She tore this one off too. Blood was flowing down. It hurt.

"She loves the star! She loves the star!" they chanted. Janna trampled on the star and it cried. It cried like a baby! She picked it up. It *was* a baby, a little baby, crying its heart out.

Now the Hitler Youth behind her became a raging mob.

"You're a traitor!" they shouted. "Give us the baby. Give

it up!" Janna knew they would hurt it. She was running again. The baby cried piteously. Its face looked like a monkey's with liquid brown eyes. Her pursuers were very near. Janna's breath was almost gone. The shouting behind her became a howling, a long-drawn-out wolfish howling . . . Just as she thought she could run no more, she saw a house, a Dutch house with a sawtoothed gable. The door opened and there stood Nella. She took the baby and it stopped crying. She shut the door. Outside, the Hitler Youth howled. Nella's mother came down the stairs.

"They are only wolves," she said. "They don't know any better. Oh! You're *hurt* . . ." Janna looked at her breast. She saw a deep, star-shaped wound. Shame overwhelmed her. She ran out of the back of the house into her own village in the Black Forest. She went to Erna's house. She ran in.

"I'm home, I'm home," she cried. But Erna turned her back on her. The old mother was staring at something beyond Janna. Her mouth fell open and her rosary beads rattled to the floor. There was beautiful singing behind Janna. She turned around. It was night. The dark sky shone and twinkled with stars, millions and billions of stars, a whole Milky Way of them, and all the stars were singing and slowly descending to the earth. Half floating, half gliding they came, a long, glittering procession. They stood at the bank of a river, their light reflected in long, liquid streamers. Each star was a shining wound on the breast of a white-robed angel, which bloomed and glowed. Very sweet music came from their voices and their hands reached out to Janna.

"Come, you are one of us."

"No, I'm not." Janna said it with sorrow now, with humility. "It's all a mistake, I belong to the wolves . . . I can't cross the river . . ." The voices faded, the stars melted into a mist. Behind Janna there was a loud howling. As she turned, she saw ferocious jaws with great teeth and lolling tongues . . . Mean little eyes gleamed at her, hungrily . . . There was no escape . . . She was alone . . .

With a cry she woke. Her cheeks were wet with tears. She lay on her back thinking. Sef and Mina were angry with her, and it weighed on her. It had been so wonderful, their friendship. Why had Sef's race come to spoil it? Sef had said that God had given him his race. That was true. He must have been hurt by what she had said. She had not been thinking of Sef, had she? She had only been oc-cupied with her own feelings. For the first time she real-ized the deadly danger Sef was in, had been in for several years. The risk of being an underground worker was bad enough. But an underground worker still had a right to live; he would only be punished for what he did. A Jew was guilty regardless; he was punished just for breathing.

What Sef must have suffered! Was that why he never spoke of his parents? Had his parents been among those faces staring out of the cattle cars? Had those terrible things Mina had mentioned happened to *them?* How could Sef *bear* it! Now she knew why he worked so hard on those forgeries. Janna wept quietly. Mina was right, Janna had been arrogant. Being German was not some-thing to be proud of . . .

Timidly she knocked at the wardrobe panel. A gentle voice said, "Come in." She saw Sef sitting despondently on his chair, his head bowed.

"Oh Sef," she said. What had she done . . . added to all his sufferings! "Oh Sef, I've hurt you . . . I didn't mean to . . ."

"Poor Janna," said Sef. "I understand. I was brutal to

you. I've just been thinking what it must have meant to you to be indoctrinated against Jews all your life and then unknowingly make friends with one. It was hard on you, I admit it."

"No, I was wrong," said Janna. "Can you forgive me? I really like you just as much . . . it's only . . . only . . ."

"You've lost your Siegfried," said Sef, smiling.

"Yes, how did you know?" asked Janna wonderingly. "That's exactly it."

"So I'm just Sef now. That's good. That's what I want to be."

"Oh Sef . . ." Janna smiled through her tears. She felt happy. It was over. Sef and she were together again. She looked at him. Yes, he was Sef, entirely Sef. Not "a Jew." What was "a Jew"? She had no idea. There were Peters and Hildes and Corries and Sefs. There wasn't "a" anything. She'd made a fuss about nothing.

✠ SEVENTEEN ✠

The Picture

JANNA AND MINA made up. They both apologized. "I had no right to go for you like that," Mina said penitently. "The Good Book says: 'Thou shalt not seethe a kid in his mother's milk,' and you're only a child, you can't help what you're taught. Say no more about it."

Despite the strike, Mina had a visit from her brother. Janna opened the door for him: a huge figure of a man who looked as if a little political upheaval was beneath his notice. He left his wooden shoes outside and entered on coarsely knit stocking feet. He looked at Janna with Mina's eyes under Mina's eyebrows. He removed a flat cap.

"I had to see what the old one's gone and done now," he boomed. "What's she been up to, eh? Did you go skipping rope with her? Here, lookit, I brought her some of my best blooms." He was carrying lovely, fragrant hyacinths wrapped in a newspaper.

"Well," he said, wiping his face with a red handkerchief, "I see as you've had a bit of trouble here. Lots of police about. They did not bother me none. I'm too big." With a hearty chuckle he mounted the stairs, his corduroy pants squeaking. He stayed a long time with Mina. When Janna brought them up some coffee and crackers he said, "How would you like it if I took that young man away from you? Would you miss him?" Janna looked questioningly at Mina.

184

"He knows about Sef," said Mina, who was looking younger and pretty in her joy at having her brother there. "He was saying he could use Sef. He keeps several under-divers . . . people in hiding, you know. They help him with his bulb farm. I've told him Sef does more important work here, and it's safe here. No one is going to search the home of an SD official."

Janna gazed at her dumbly, appalled at the idea of los-ing Sef.

"He'd miss you too, I guess," the bulb farmer said with twinkling eyes.

Janna found her tongue. "Oh no, he won't. He likes an-other girl," she said. "He has her picture pinned up."

"Is that so?" said Mina's brother with a quizzical look on his florid face. "My, my, I wonder where his eyes are!"

"Stop teasing the girl, Meindert," said Mina, for Janna was blushing.

After Mina's brother had left, Janna asked her, "Is he your only relative?"

"He is my twin. My parents are dead. When we were small, people said we could have been identical, we were so alike. Of course, now you see the difference." She smiled. "Meindert and Mina, we were a pair, I can tell you!" She looked dreamily back into the past. Then she shook herself. "We must do something about that picture. It has to be hidden where your mother did not look be-fore. The only place I can think of is that old stove in the kitchen, the one we don't use any more."

"And if it doesn't fit?"

"Oh, it will. The lid is large. It used to be a wood stove, burning logs."

"But won't they suspect you of hiding it?" Janna asked anxiously.

"Suspect the cook," asked Mina, eyebrows high, "and risk missing my pastries? Never! Anyway, I've plenty of time to think up an answer if they do. 'In vain is the net spread in sight of the bird.' When will you hide the picture?"

"In the night, that's safest," said Janna.

It was a quiet night, without flak or bombings. People slept deeply. When Janna was sure her parents had gone to bed and she had listened to her father's snores, she put the hook on her door and knocked at the wardrobe panel. Sef was ready for her. He had lit a candle. His face looked weirdly handsome in its glow. Together they crept down the ladder and Sef started the mechanism that made the altar rotate into view. There was the picture, to Janna's relief. She'd had a moment's panic that it might have disappeared. Sef lifted it down and Janna took it in her arms. It was heavy.

"There goes the van Arkel treasure," said Sef. The flickering light set shadows dancing about them.

"You stay here," said Janna. "I'll hide the picture."

"No, I'm coming with you," said Sef. "There's no danger, everyone is asleep." They padded softly through the long room, Sef carrying the picture. As they went down the staircase to the kitchen the stairs creaked. They stopped and listened, but all was still.

Janna lifted the lid of the old stove. It looked very dirty inside and gave out a musty smell.

"You must wrap the picture," whispered Sef. They went looking for paper and string. Janna thought she saw some on top of a cupboard. As she pulled it down, a photograph came with it. It dropped on the floor. Sef gave a cry and picked it up.

"Sh!" warned Janna. "They'll hear you!"

"My photograph . . ." whispered Sef. "My precious, missing picture. How did it get up there? Mina must have stuck it there and forgotten about it. My *picture!*" Janna looked over his shoulder. He had sunk down on a kitchen chair, and in his emotion he had let the candle lean over so that wax was dripping on the floor. Janna took it from him and held it near to light the picture. It was a happy group portrait of a family: a thoughtful father with high forehead and deep, searching eyes; a gentle, blond mother, and two children: one a laughing minx of about four with dancing ringlets, the other obviously Sef, when he was about Janna's age.

"Is that your family?" whispered Janna. Sef nodded. A tear was trickling down his cheek. "It's all I have left of them," he whispered. "I'm so glad I found it."

"What happened to them?" asked Janna.

"Do you have to ask?" Sef's voice was unsteady. His hands had clenched into fists, "They were taken soon after the invasion. My father was a well-known artist, and he had been quite outspoken. He would not tell lies or prevaricate, not even to save our lives. What had to be had to be, he said. He wasn't going to skulk like a criminal when he had done nothing wrong. I only escaped because I was staying with the van Arkels. It was Willem van Arkel's birthday. They kept me with them and treated me like a son."

"And what happened to your parents?"

"I never heard from them. Some people who returned from the concentration camp at Vught said they had been seen there but were sent on to Poland. We know what that means . . ." Sef's cheeks had turned waxen and his forehead was moist as he gave a low groan. "I lie awake thinking of them sometimes . . ." he muttered. "What it was like . . . and my poor little sister . . ." Janna wanted to comfort him but did not dare. It was her people who had done this to him. At last she asked, "Couldn't the Dutch people have protected them?"

"The van Arkels would have sheltered them, but it happened too quickly, long before the regular raids. Anyway, I doubt whether my parents would have accepted their help. The real trouble was that no one really believed such terrible things could happen. I suppose we were too civilized." Sef sighed. "Later we realized that before we surrendered to the Muffs we should have burned all our records, and when stars were prescribed, everyone should have worn them. We should never have let any part of our Dutch people be singled out." Sef was silent. The candle flame sputtered a bit. A moth was trying to warm its wings on it.

"People confuse law with virtue," Sef went on. "The Dutch especially. They think it wrong to oppose a law, even if it is an evil one. Of course it was a strain. We were hoping to be liberated before much harm was done, but now I wonder if any of us Jews will survive."

"Yes, those you're saving with your fake papers," Janna said encouragingly.

Sef shrugged. "So few," he murmured.

Janna began to wrap the Rembrandt in the coarse brown paper she had found. She tied it with some string out of the table drawer. Sef tucked his precious photograph inside his jacket. He helped Janna knot the string tightly. They hid the painting in the old stove. Then, with their stump of candle, they climbed upstairs to their beds.

The next day the strike was over and the house returned to normal, though in the rest of Holland martial law continued and people were executed, even children of thirteen. On the fifth day of May the occupation authorities proclaimed that all students who had refused to sign the loyalty declaration would have to labor in Germany, otherwise their parents would be held responsible.

Janna mourned Hugo. She bitterly missed her lessons.

She and Mina had decided to let Heinz find the picture. They felt sorry for the boy, who was scolded by grownups all day long and beaten by his father at night. Janna could not listen to his screams any more, now that she knew what caused them. She had to put her fingers in her ears and go under the bedclothes. She told Sef about it. He had heard the screams too.

"We in Holland always said the Germans were too strict," he commented. "We think that such harsh, inhuman treatment fitted your people for a dictatorship."

"My parents treat me kindly," Janna said.

"Ah, but you're a girl," Sef answered.

After breakfast, on the morning following the hiding of the picture, Janna did not shoo Heinz out of the kitchen when he wanted to help. She let him dry the dishes. Then she looked at the old stove and said, "I wonder why they keep that useless thing here. It's only taking up room." Heinz needed no further encouragement. He ran to it and looked inside.

"There's something hidden here," he shouted. "Look!" Triumphantly he pulled out the parcel and unwrapped it, tearing at the paper and tugging at the string till Janna cut it with a carving knife. She made suitable noises of astonishment as she wiped her sudsy hands and found a safe place for the picture, leaning against the top half of a dresser. Heinz had guessed immediately that it was the

Rembrandt—he'd probably heard his parents talking about it—and he was so proud and exultant that he ran through the house, banging doors and shouting the good news. Soon everyone was gathered in the kitchen: Herr and Frau Frosch, Herr and Frau Oster (whose rehearsals were starting again that day), and Corrie. Everyone gaped at the painting. Heinz earned his full measure of praise, even from his father, who went so far as to say he was proud of his son. Heinz glowed.

Herr Frosch telephoned Herr Rauter, who came over right away. He was a stocky man with a coarse complexion and a scarred face. He wore the uniform of Höhere SS und Polizeiführer. His thin lips closed, he looked around with gimlet eyes.

"You're lucky you found the picture," he said to Janna's father, looking sideways at him. There was a note of irony in his voice. "We had just got notice to arrest you." Herr Oster was too angry to answer this. He kept still. People did not talk back to the head of police. Herr Rauter was examining the stove that had hidden the picture.

He sniffed suspiciously. "Curious place," he muttered. "Did the cook put it there?"

Herr Frosch took a step forward. His voice trembled as he said, "I vouch for the cook, a loyal soul, above suspicion . . ."

Herr Rauter laughed. "You'd be surprised," he said. "When my men get at her. . . . Where is she? Why doesn't she vouch for herself?"

"Because she sustained an injury in her devoted service to this family, Herr Polizeiführer," gabbled Herr Frosch.

Herr Rauter gave a disagreeable snicker. "You're afraid for your omelettes," he sneered. Then, with a shrug of the shoulders, he abandoned a possible victim. "Very well, the picture is here. We'll spare your cook if you'll lend her to me sometimes when I have a party."

"Oh yes, certainly, Herr Rauter," Herr Frosch said, bowing obsequiously. Janna wondered what Mina would think of that.

Herr Oster cleared his throat. "I want my wife and me relieved of all further responsibility for this picture," he said. "We have been unjustly accused of stealing it."

"There is no proof that you didn't," Herr Rauter answered sharply. "Only that you changed your mind . . . just in time." He gave a sardonic look at the stove.

For a moment Herr Oster was silenced. Then he broke out angrily, "You'd better remove the thing to your office. I see we are still under suspicion."

"Tut, tut," said Herr Rauter, waving his hand. "I did not go as far as that. I merely pointed out that there was no proof."

"It is better for you to take it," Herr Oster insisted. "We have no safe here."

"Impossible," said Herr Rauter. "There are procedures that have to be followed. We have to arrange for proper transportation under armed guard."

"In that case, give it to Herr Frosch. I want nothing further to do with it," Herr Oster insisted.

"Yes, yes," Herr Frosch interrupted eagerly. "I will take good care of it. I will put it in my sitting room and have a second lock made on the door and put a watch in front; no burglar will be able to get at it." He was rubbing his hands with pleasure at the honor of guarding a possession of the Führer's.

"Give it to me in writing," said Herr Oster. "I'm not to be held responsible any more." His voice shook with anger. Herr Rauter looked impatient but sat down at the kitchen table and wrote a few lines on a scrap of paper to the effect that the picture had been removed from the Osters' custody. He signed it with a flourish and gave it to Otto, who pocketed it carefully. Herr Frosch picked up the Rembrandt and bore it reverently upstairs.

Janna ran to tell Mina what had happened, and as soon as it was safe, she visited Sef.

"There won't be any living with Heinz now, he is so proud at having been the one to find the picture," Janna told him, smiling. "It's even better than spying on the neighbors!"

"I'm sorry for him," said Sef. "I'm sorry for all the young people in Germany. What a way to grow up! And they'll bear the brunt of the reaction later, when we've won the war. They'll have to build up the new Germany. Mynheer van Arkel always said that Hitler's greatest crime was what he did to his own people, the way he used the idealism and enthusiasm of youngsters for his own nefarious purposes." Janna nodded, thinking of Kurt. Where was he now, in a training camp?

"Tell me about the van Arkels," she said. "Tell me about Willem. Was he the oldest boy?"

Sef nodded. "He was my best friend. I was in the same class with him at school until the Germans came and threw me out. I had to attend a Jewish school then. Do you know I never realized that being Jewish made me different until the Germans came? My parents were tolerant and liberal. We had our own services, but so had the Protestants and Catholics. My father always said there was but one God and everyone worshipped Him in his own way. What mattered was to be honest and upright and kind. At school we were all equals. Willem and I used to go on Boy Scout trips or we went hunting plover eggs in the fields on a March morning. Plover eggs are a great delicacy —you could get money for them—and we always needed money for our projects. We built huts and made hutches for rabbits. . . . When the invasion came and Holland fell, Willem and Maurits, his younger brother, and I built a boat. It was the queerest tub you ever saw, made out of Heineken's beer barrels. It had a sail and was seaworthy. We managed to reach the open sea in it. We intended to sail to England but we got a head wind which stranded us on one of the northern islands. The coast guard caught us and might have shot us if our boat hadn't looked so wacky. They believed us when we said we'd been accidentally swept out to sea. The hardest thing was to seem grateful for being rescued!" Janna had listened, full of admiration. But she heard Heinz shouting for her, so she could not stay.

Herr Frosch gloried in his custody of the picture. He made a great fuss putting in the extra lock and displayed the key on every possible occasion. Heinz wanted to stand guard over it, he felt a proprietary right in the picture, but his father installed a policeman. Janna had to pass him every time she brought Mina her food. She noticed she was beginning to fear the Gestapo as much as the Dutch did.

During the following days, many friends and acquaintances of Herr Frosch were invited to admire the Rembrandt. Janna met so many strangers on the stairs she took the way through the long room to visit Sef. She was going to him one morning when she heard voices in the anteroom. Herr Frosch's and another somewhat familiar voice. . . . Where had she heard it? She slipped quickly behind the draperies in the long room, vaguely alarmed.

There they were, coming through the glass doors, Herr Frosch and . . . yes! The fat man from the train. Like an enormous ghost from the past, he waddled behind Herr Frosch, who was talking rapidly.

"Great honor, great responsibility," he was saying. "I told Herr Polizeiführer that we'd better have some professional advice about packing the picture. Can't take the chance of having it damaged, you understand. It's going to Berchtesgaden. Herr Rauter said you might cast your eyes over the other pictures. Perhaps there is something else Hitler might fancy."

"Certainly, certainly," the fat man said unctuously. He had his cameras slung over his shoulders and carried a tripod. "Why not have some pictures taken?" His small eyes gleamed.

"Yes, yes, that might be a good idea," Herr Frosch said nervously. "But not today." The fat man was starting to put up his tripod. "I'd have to consult Herr Rauter, you understand, and we'd have to know about prices."

"Oh, our gallery is very reasonable," the fat man assured him.

"Yes, Herr Stolz, but I'm not the one to decide that," said Herr Frosch. "You'll be able to send a man to pack the Rembrandt then?"

"When is the picture going?" asked the fat man, who was peering at the pictures on the walls. "Or hasn't that been decided yet?"

"Oh yes, it's been decided," said Herr Frosch. "These things have to be arranged in advance, you know. Friday at ten the van is coming, under armed guard, of course."

"Very well, our man will be here on Thursday," promised the fat man.

"Do you see anything here that would interest the Führer?" asked Herr Frosch.

"Very good pictures," said the fat man, smacking his

lips. "There's money here all right, genuine Dutch Impressionists. But not for Hitler, no. He considers Impressionism degenerate. You know perhaps that he is an artist himself? No? I thought that was general knowledge. . . . If he had been accepted at the Viennese Academy, who knows? We might not have a new order in Germany now. On such trifles hangs the world. Now, Göring is another kettle of fish. A real connoisseur of art. Bought a Vermeer here, you know, from a collector called Vermeegheren. An astonishing piece of work . . . and no one knew it existed. A real find. Hitler was angry not to have been told of such an important picture. Vermeers are very rare, you know. Adolf and Hermann have—what shall I say—a friendly rivalry. They try to snatch pictures away in front of each other's nose and they smash crockery in anger when they do not succeed. The little ways of the mighty! But Göring pays well and Hitler does not. You would not consider giving the Rembrandt to Göring? It would be much more profitable, I assure you."

"It has nothing to do with me," said Herr Frosch stiffly. "I am merely the custodian. I do what I'm told."

"Ah yes, the loyal servant," said Herr Stolz with profound admiration. "What would our Reich do without them! Never thinking of gain, dutifully anchored to their desks, signing documents that bring life or death to others. Admirable. Ah, look at that. A genuine Israels! Göring would covet that."

"It's painted by a Jew," said Herr Frosch contemptuously. "He wouldn't want that."

"You don't mean it." Herr Stolz sounded astonished.

"It's a Jewish name," Herr Frosch pointed out.

"Yes, but I'm surprised you'd reject the picture, which is worth a lot of money, for that reason. I did not think that there was anything valuable the Jews possessed that you could not use. Live and learn, I say."

"I don't know what you mean," Herr Frosch said stiffly.

"Ah, I see. If you only rob on a sufficiently large scale, it becomes invisible. You're sure you don't want a photograph?" He sighed. "A pity, the light is excellent today."

"Shall I show you the Rembrandt now?" asked Herr Frosch, who had been unable to follow the twists and turns of the fat man's conversation. He preceded Herr Stolz into the anteroom. "If your man will come Thursday night with the necessary material, I'll make sure . . ." His voice faded.

Janna emerged from her hiding place. She had a cramp in her leg and rubbed it. She wondered what the fat man was up to. He had been much too polite. She went to tell Sef about it. As she recounted the story of her train journey, she found at last a perfect listener.

"You backed the wrong horse there," Sef told her, smiling. "The fat man was right, the little one was obviously a Jew. I hope he got away, poor fellow."

"Oh!" said Janna. How stupid she had been! It all came from having such a distorted idea of Jews, she hadn't been able to recognize one when she saw him. She had half believed the story that they had cloven hoofs.

"I don't like your fat man," Sef went on. "I'll keep the door of the chapel locked from now on. He is quite capable of stealing the big picture and exposing this place."

That was true; Janna hadn't thought of that.

"He was more interested in the Israels, though," she said.

On Thursday the man from the art dealer came to pack the painting. Herr Frosch was taking no chances. He supervised the work and never let the picture out of his sight. On Friday the van arrived under armed Gestapo guards, looking formidable. Herr Frosch put his valuable parcel in their keeping and signed a paper they gave him.

"Aren't you supposed to give me a receipt?" he asked.

"That won't be necessary," they said. "Goodbye, Herr Frosch." The van roared off.

A day later, at breakfast, there was a telephone call for Herr Frosch. The phone was just outside the dining room. They all heard Herr Frosch's anguished cries.

"No, no! Impossible! I signed for it. . . . They were armed guards of the SD. What do you mean, gagged and bound? They were SD men, I saw their insignia. . . . Switched uniforms? How is it possible? What do you mean, you don't believe me? Of course I signed, they told me to. . . . Everything was in order. A declaration that the picture was to go to Göring? No, no, I did not sign that. It was a release . . . well, they said it was. I did not read the whole thing, there was no time. It was all correct, in order, I tell you. . . . Well, why not get the picture back from Göring? Surely the Führer can command what he wants? Well, ask Herr Stolz from the art gallery. He said something about Göring and I told him I was not authorized. You heard he's gone? Herr Stolz has vanished? My God, I should have known he was a scoundrel! Herr Rauter . . . Herr Rauter. . . . He's hung up!"

The family at the breakfast table had listened spellbound. Herr Frosch staggered to his seat, looking ten years older. Frau Oster quickly poured him more coffee.

"What's wrong?" she asked.

"The picture!" he groaned, placing his elbows on the table and holding his head. "There's been foul play! The real guards were found bound and gagged in a shed and the people I handed the picture to were agents of Göring. It has been sent to Göring, not Hitler, and Hitler is furious."

"It's not possible!" exclaimed Frau Oster. Frau Frosch was trembling. She spilled her coffee. She's afraid Herr Frosch will take it out on her, thought Janna. Heinz stared fixedly at his father, forgetting to eat.

"The trouble is, Herr Rauter won't believe I had nothing to do with it," Herr Frosch continued, gulping his food. "Herr Stolz has disappeared. Of course he did it."

"Why doesn't Hitler tell Göring to give back the picture?" asked Frau Frosch.

"He'd have to buy it back," explained her husband. "Hitler would have got it for nothing, but Göring paid a considerable sum. Besides, he can't afford to offend Göring, who is very popular and the head of the air force. Hitler took a lot of trouble to get that picture and now it's all coming to nothing. Of course he is angry."

"What will he do to you, Father?" asked Heinz.

"Nothing, son. To me he can do nothing. I'm innocent," his father answered. But his optimism was misplaced. Someone had to suffer for Hitler's displeasure and Herr Rauter was determined that it should not be himself. Having signed that paper, Herr Frosch was the obvious scapegoat. The Osters were out of it, thanks to Herr Rauter's scribble. The fact that Herr Frosch had acted in perfect good faith did not matter. As he himself had often asserted, his government was ruthless. He was clapped into prison.

Heinz was furious. Janna caught him tearing the pictures from the walls of his room and rending the flag into shreds. He stamped and spat on them.

"I'll never be a Hitler Youth," he shouted. "I hate Hitler. My father is innocent!"

Janna marveled. Heinz was destroying what he had admired and believed in for the sake of a father who had beaten him almost every night. But she liked him better than she ever had.

Frau Frosch, after weeping in her room for several days, cheered up when she got a letter from her parents inviting her and Heinz to make their home with them. Frau Frosch explained to the Osters that her parents had a farm not far from Hamburg. "Heinz will be able to go to school and make friends," she exulted. The next week Frau Frosch and Heinz left, on a beautiful May morning, while the birds were twittering and the canals reflected the blue sky. Heinz and Janna shook hands solemnly. Heinz had grown up. He was no longer the little monkey who had stuck his tongue out at Janna. Janna was different too. Now she had respect for Heinz. Beside him, his mother looked like a schoolgirl going home.

When Janna and Corrie were cleaning out the Frosches' apartment, Janna found a crumpled letter stuck in a drawer. It was signed "Erich Stolz." She could not resist reading it.

Honored Sir [it said],
I'm writing this just before boarding a plane—to South America—which Göring has obligingly lent me. I want to apologize for any inconvenience I may have caused you, and to thank you for your cooperation in supplying the details concerning the removal of the picture. I also want to point out to you that I was willing to go halves with you. We could have cleaned up the Impressionists at the same

time. However, I did not wish to sully what you obviously regarded as your honor; I am glad I am not hampered that way. Meanwhile, I forgive you for any unkind thoughts you may have had about me. I have obtained enough money to enable me to forgive my worst enemies. Hoping that you'll be able to talk yourself out of an awkward situation, I remain

Yours sincerely,
Erich Stolz

(My future address, for obvious reasons, will remain a secret, so you need not answer this.)

Janna laughed aloud. She realized with surprise that you could like and dislike someone at the same time.

✠ EIGHTEEN ✠

The Ball

GERMANY WAS LOSING heavily on all fronts. In the kitchen Mina and Corrie rejoiced. Mina was on her feet again, though she still had to take it easy. She was full of Biblical predictions.

"Who sheddeth man's blood, by man shall his blood be shed" and "They have no rest day or night who worship the Beast and his image. But they that wait upon the Lord shall renew their strength: they shall mount up with wings as eagles, they shall run and not be weary, they shall walk and not faint."

Sef also gloried in the Allied victories. Janna was happy for them, but sobered by the thought that it was her own country that was losing and might be laid waste. She had seen the destruction of Cologne while Hitler's armies were still advancing. What would happen when vengeful soldiers trampled the fertile valleys and entered the little villages, she shuddered to think.

She could not wish for Germany's victory. She knew by now that even the Baron did not wish for that. But she hoped that Germany might rise again and become happy and prosperous with a new, merciful government.

There was a general feeling that the Allied invasion was not far off. The German Army was gathering around the coastline, studying maps, guessing what the enemy was going to do.

Visitors coming to the house seemed nervous and reckless. Janna wondered about the Baron. What was he thinking now? The house was dull without Heinz's shrill voice and his pranks.

But the worst was her mother's depression. Mechtild seemed to have lost interest in everything. She drifted vaguely through the days, rather like Frau Frosch. Otto said her acting wasn't up to standard.

"What's the matter?" he asked her one evening after dinner. "Worried about the war? Never fear, Hitler will make a comeback. The man is a genius."

"A genius," said Mechtild listlessly. "Fine genius! Look where he landed us. Dietrich says all he had was beginner's luck."

"Dietrich? Have you seen him?"

"You know I haven't."

Otto looked lovingly at her. He put a hand on her shoulder. "Poor Mechtild, lost her playmate," he said. "You need a diversion. Let's give a party . . . a ball. The long room is perfect for it!"

Janna's mother cheered up at once. "A fancy-dress ball!" she cried. "A marvelous idea!" She started to make arrangements right away. Janna had to help address invitations. It would be held on a Monday, the actors' night off.

"Are we going to send an invitation to the Baron?" asked Janna. Her mother looked startled and blushed.

"Why not?" she said, brightening. "It would be wrong to leave him out after all he's done for us." Then she said despondently, "Of course he won't come."

Janna could not bear to see her so sad. She surreptitiously rubbed her ring. Let the Baron come to the ball, she wished. After all, what harm could it do, just for one evening, to make her mother happy?

The Baron received his invitation, for he sent cases of champagne, baskets of game, truffles, and pastries. It made her mother weep again.

Mechtild took a lot of trouble repairing her costume, an old-fashioned wedding dress she had found in the attic, dating from the Napoleonic era. Some of the silver beads had fallen off and there were tears in the satin and lace. Janna wanted to be dressed as Brunhilde, so her mother borrowed a costume from the stage wardrobe: flowing white robe, silver breastplates, sandals, shield, helmet, and spear—just as Janna had visualized it for Hildegarde's play. It would be a warm costume to wear in June, but when she saw herself in the mirror, she knew she wouldn't mind the heat.

The costume had to be taken in only a little. "You aren't the little tyke who came here in February," Mechtild said approvingly. "What a difference! You look almost like a young lady."

The evening of the party was warm and sultry. In the long room Janna excitedly slid up and down the golden parquet floor, shining with wax. She'd never been to a ball before. If only Sef could have been with her—but he'd be looking through the peephole in the picture. It made her feel less alone.

It was still light when people began to arrive. Corrie, wearing a new black dress with frilly cap and apron, was kept busy opening the door and taking guests' wraps. She wasn't going to stay late; her father was going to fetch her and take her home after supper had been served.

As people came in, Janna saw one lovely costume after another: a comical Red Ridinghood with a ferocious wolf, a Satan in scarlet with a cow's tail and horns, a Neptune with a three-pronged fork. There were also a lot of Wotans and Freyas and Siegfrieds. The room was filled with chatter and the clinking of glasses. As dusk fell, drapes were pulled across the open windows and the chandeliers were lit. The air became more oppressive and the ladies twirled their fans. Janna had put her shield and spear on a window seat while she handed around appetizers and crackers.

She saw Herr Schmidt and Herr Wolff. They were dressed as wizards, and their beards kept parting from their chins. Otto, who had refused to dress up—he said it was no fun for an actor—stood behind the serving table and poured drinks. Mechtild, in her bridal dress, a wreath of white roses on her head over a diaphanous veil, was, as usual, surrounded by admirers. She had never looked lovelier, thought Janna.

People were beginning to dance to the music of a small band around the piano. Janna watched them, enchanted by the colors, the music, the whirl of movement. A shepherdess lost her crook, a clumsy Tarzan trod on a queen's train; little incidents happened all the time to amuse her. Then her father asked her to dance and she became part of the scene.

"You dance very well," he said. "Where did you learn it?"

"At our Youth meetings," said Janna. "But the boys were always so clumsy. I prefer to dance with you." After a while the atmosphere became stifling and her father put out the lights so he could open the blackout drapes. The orchestra managed with small, shaded lamps behind a screen. Now they were dancing by the moonlight, which was pouring through the open windows along with a smell of honeysuckle and jasmine.

Then Corrie announced, "Supper is served." Janna's father closed the drapes again and the lights went on. People exclaimed over the delicacies on the buffet table in the anteroom. They shoved and jostled to get to it. A beautiful Chinese vase was smashed to bits. They ate carelessly, dropping food on the Turkish carpet, marking polished tables with their glasses, spilling sauce . . .

"It sounds like thunder," someone said, "and I left my windows open at home."

Janna thought of Sef. She went to the kitchen, but before she had reached the stairs there was a ring at the door. She opened it and there was the Baron, in his ordinary uniform. He didn't seem to see her, didn't answer her greeting. There was a wild look on his face as he gazed beyond her. When Janna turned, she saw her mother, whom some instinct had sent into the hall. Janna stepped back, helpless, and watched what happened with a sinking heart.

"Dietrich . . ." her mother's voice sang.

"Mechtild . . . I couldn't stay away . . ." They met in the hall and went downstairs . . . and there was nothing Janna could do about it. She saw them go into the garden, the romantic garden, where water tinkled in the marble fountain, flowing over the arms and heads of the Rhine maidens; where the moon silvered everything and flowers scented the air. . . . And it was all her own fault.

Unhappily she went into the kitchen and found Mina sitting in a rocking chair, reading the Bible. She started when Janna entered.

"Have you some food for Sef?" Janna asked. "I want to bring it to him. He's missing everything."

"I saved some for him. It's on that plate," said Mina dourly. She started to read out in a sepulchral voice: " 'And there was a great earthquake: and the sun became black as sackcloth of hair and the moon became blood and the stars of Heaven fell into the earth even as a fig tree casteth her untimely figs, when she is shaken of a mighty wind. And the Heaven departed as a scroll when it is rolled together; and every fountain and island were moved out of their places. And the kings of the earth, and the great men, and the rich men, and the chief captains and the mighty men and every bondsman and freed man hid themselves in the dens and in the rocks of the mountains: and said to the mountains and rocks: fall on us and hide us from the Face of Him that sitteth on the throne, and from the wrath of the Lamb; for the great day of His Wrath is come and who shall be able to stand?' "

Janna listened with dismay. "What's that?" she said. She hadn't got further than Moses in her Bible reading.

"It's the vision of St. John," said Mina gloomily. "And I think it's going to happen soon. I feel it in my bones. All this godless cavorting about when people are starving or dying in agony. . . . God will spit out his creatures like saliva."

"You're feeling like that because it's going to storm," said Janna. "Even animals feel queer then."

"I'm not an animal," said Mina. "I know something bad is going to happen. Mark my words, don't say I didn't warn you!"

Janna ran upstairs with the tray, passing some amorous couples on the stairs. Ladies were giggling and fixing their hair in the bathroom.

"Look at Brunhilde. She's got herself a private little feast," they mocked.

"Isn't it nice to be young and not have to mind your manners!"

Janna put the hook on her door and turned the key as

well. She crawled through the wardrobe and found Sef at work.

"I thought you were watching," she said.

"I was, until the lights went out," said Sef. He sounded as depressed as Mina.

"Look what I have for you," said Janna. "That's real champagne, and there's a partridge leg, and those pastries are scrumptious."

Sef cheered up. "I'm glad you came," he said. "It's so stuffy in here and I was wondering whether the time would ever come when I could go to parties and dances."

"How old are you?" asked Janna.

"Nearly seventeen," said Sef. "I wish I'd been old enough to be in the army. I wish I'd died fighting the invasion . . ."

"Oh, please, Sef, you're as bad as Mina," said Janna.

"How bad is Mina?" asked Sef, his eyes twinkling. He finished the fowl and bit into one of the pastries. His face cleared. "They're great," he said. "The Baron's, I suppose. I wonder whose supplies he looted. . . . Thanks for bringing them, little Muff."

"Mina was reading awful bits out of the Bible," said Janna, answering his question. "About the sun falling and the moon bleeding and people covering themselves with rocks."

Sef laughed. "You've really cheered me up, Janna," he said. "I think what was bothering me was that I'd never had a chance to dance, being in hiding all the time. I'll probably die without having learned it."

"I'll teach you now," said Janna.

"Where?"

"In the chapel. You can hear the orchestra there and no one will hear us in all the noise."

"What a good idea!" said Sef. "You're a real friend, Janna." (But not such a friend as Nella, thought Janna with a glance at the photo on the wall.)

As soon as the orchestra started again, Janna and Sef were ready. The music came through clearly. Moonbeams strayed through the ivy and threw weird patterns on the floor. Sef had a good sense of rhythm, and after a few awkward moments they accommodated their movements to each other. When the band struck up a waltz, he seemed to catch on right away. As they whirled around, Janna felt so happy she wished it could go on forever. She marveled at how different it felt to dance with Sef when her father really was the better dancer. This was much more exciting . . .

"How old are you?" asked Sef in her ear.

"Thirteen," she said. "Fourteen next April."

"A baby," sighed Sef. Janna wanted to protest, but she didn't want to interrupt the dancing. She wanted to go on turning and whirling and gliding in Sef's arms forever and ever. We must do this again, she thought. We must do it often . . . but how to get the music? How could they keep it secret? Oh, she'd find a way . . .

It was Sef who broke the magic. "You'd better go back," he said. "They might get suspicious if you stay away too long. Remember, we don't have the protection of the SD any more, now that the Frosches are gone." That was true. Janna had not thought of that. She clung to Sef, unwilling to go. He pushed her away, but gently and reluctantly.

"I'll watch you through the peephole," he promised.

"No, no," warned Janna. "A lot of people have been drinking steadily. It isn't safe. Keep the door locked. Promise." She remembered Mina's dire predictions.

"Promise . . ." she repeated anxiously.

"All right, all right," Sef said, laughing. "You're as moody as a weathercock. I'll go back to work. I feel a lot better than before you came in." They looked at each other, and in the dim light Sef's eyes seemed like a sea, a greenish sea into which she was slipping, deeper and deeper . . . till the waves washed over her head . . .

Sef abruptly turned away his face. "You're quite a girl," he said. "Off you go now."

"All right," Janna said meekly.

She stopped by her balcony and stepped out on it. It was good to breathe the cool, fragrant air. The moon was still shining, but big clouds were massing in opposite directions, proceeding like armies in battle formation. It was completely still. Only the fountain tinkled gently, glittering in the moonlight. And then Janna heard whispers and soft laughter, followed by the deep tones of a man's voice. Her mother and the Baron! They were in the summerhouse, now a bower of flowering honeysuckle and wild roses. She could see her mother's white dress glimmering between the tendrils. Janna stood rigid, full of dark forebodings. Mina was right, something terrible was going to happen. The Baron would take her mother away, far away, to his castle in Bavaria. They would probably offer to take her too, but she couldn't go. She couldn't leave her father alone, it wouldn't be fair. But to live without her mother! They had become so close lately, ever since Janna knew they shared the horror at what Germany was doing. They had that in common with the Baron as well. Her father would not see it. He was too loyal. To him it was unthinkable that Germany could do wrong.

The clouds had been moving nearer and nearer. Now they enveloped and conquered the moon. Lightning split the sky and for an instant Janna saw her mother and the

Baron sitting close together, their arms entwined. Then thunder threw its boulders heavily across the sky and gusts of wind began to shake the trees. Her mother squealed. Another whiplash of lightning showed her getting up, the Baron helping her. Then the rain pelted down, drenching them. Mechtild and the Baron ran. The slanting spears of water pursued them, lashed them like furies.

Janna hurried inside and closed her windows. Leaving the room, she locked it on the outside, pocketing her key. There were too many strangers about. She passed couples on the stairs, smoking cigarettes and scattering ashes. As she got to the second floor, she saw her mother and the Baron coming up from the first. Her mother's wreath hung crooked, but she looked like a queen. Raindrops were scattered over her like pearls. The Baron had a triumphant air.

She hoped this was going to happen. She dressed like a bride on purpose, thought Janna bitterly.

Her mother floated into the ballroom to the strain of a languorous waltz. The Baron followed her, Janna at his heels. She looked for her father. He was telling a funny story in a corner of the room, surrounded by admiring women. When he looked up and saw his wife with the Baron, telltale rain on their heads and shoulders, he stopped in the middle of a sentence, rose and strode toward them, his face glowering. Janna had never seen him look so ugly, except when he was playing Hunding. The play came forcibly to her mind. Something about his red face also suggested that he had been drinking too freely of the Baron's champagne.

"Where have you been?" he shouted at his wife. "Is that a way for a hostess to behave?" He grabbed her roughly by the arm and shook her.

"Let go, you're hurting me," cried Mechtild, all the glow washed from her face.

"I won't let you go," growled her husband. "You're mine, do you hear? Mine!" Janna remembered with horror that those were the very words her father had said in the play. He was shaking Mechtild so roughly that her wreath fell off, scattering petals all over the floor. People had stopped dancing and were gathering to look at this new entertainment. They thought it was a comedy to amuse the guests and clapped. The Baron had been watching, his eyes flashing. As the wreath fell, he could contain himself no longer.

"Let go, Otto," he said ominously. "Let go." This seemed to enrage Otto more. He grabbed Mechtild by the neck as if to strangle her. The Baron's fist flashed out and hit Otto on the chin. Otto loosened his hold on Mechtild and fell backward. There was a cry from the guests, who began to understand that this was a real fight. The orchestra stopped playing. Mechtild sank to the floor with a moan. Several of her admirers darted forward and picked her up. She was borne off to a quiet corner where she sat down, sobbing.

Otto scrambled up, his face contorted. He sprang at the Baron like a tiger, but the Baron hit him again. Now Otto began to roar as he punched the Baron in the nose. Blood spouted out. Janna covered her eyes with her hands. It was terrible to see them behaving like wild beasts. And the ring was no use to her. If she let her father win, her mother might feel so sorry for the Baron that she would go off with him anyway, and if she let the Baron win, her mother might think he was the better man. Meanwhile, the fight was going on, punctuated by flashes of lightning, which penetrated even the blackout curtains, and deep growling thunder. Suddenly the electric lights went out and the men struggled in the darkness at the end of the room. Janna could hear pants and groans, and the sound of the piano when they fell against it. Then there was a terrific rattle of thunder and simultaneously a blinding flash of lightning, which showed everyone what was happening. The struggling men staggered against the van Arkel picture. Its cord broke. The painting dropped, wobbled, and fell flat on the floor. The lights went on again as suddenly as they had gone out, showing two panting, bedraggled, blood-smeared men gazing stupidly at the wall space the picture had covered. The secret door stood revealed to all.

✠ NINETEEN ✠

Twilight of the Gods

JANNA DID NOT await further developments. Sef had to be warned at once. She pushed through the crowd of guests, who were exclaiming and commenting on the surprising discovery, and sped up the stairs to her room. She met Mina in the hall and whispered to her what had happened. Mina needed no long explanations. With trembling fingers Janna unlocked her door. She shut it and fastened the hook. They both rushed into Sef's room.

"You must fly," cried Mina. "They've discovered the door!"

"It's locked," said Sef.

"Good, that'll give us some time. Help me, Janna, we'll pull up the ladder." Janna and Mina opened the trapdoor and pulled up the ladder. It would be some time before Sef's hideout could be reached now. Sef meanwhile was gathering his most needed possessions and putting on the cloak Nella had given him.

"I'll go to Nella," he said.

"No you won't," said Mina, who was gathering up Sef's papers and documents and stuffing them into the fireplace. "You're coming with me, to my brother. I've a bike in the cellar and I'll get you there. Go by the balcony and meet me in the back alley. I have to get my coat and purse and the bike. Be as quick as you can. Janna, you burn the evidence. Don't be too hasty about it; without the ladder they won't get here that quickly. There's kerosene in that can there and matches on the shelf. It's a good thing it's raining so hard, that will keep policemen away. Sef, I give you five minutes. . . . I still have to get that bike out. 'Gird up now thy loins like a man and go and the Lord be with thee.' Don't say I didn't tell you we'd have bad luck, Janna."

As soon as Mina was gone, Sef took Janna in his arms and kissed her.

"My Janneke," he whispered. "If we both get out of this alive, I'll search for you the world over."

Janna could hardly breathe. "For me?" she asked incredulously. "Not for Nella?"

"No, for you." He gave her a mischievous smile. "I only hung up that picture to tease you . . . and because you look like her." He gave her one more kiss, and then the wardrobe swallowed him up. Janna stared after him, unable to think, trembling all over. But she had no time to brood. If she didn't destroy that evidence . . .

Feverishly she searched for incriminating scraps, adding them to the papers in the fireplace. She even found the yellow star! But when she tried to light the pile she found it wasn't easy. The paper caught fire, but smoldered around the edges, a red worm creeping from one blackened surface to another without appetite. Downstairs Janna heard people forcing the door and bursting into the chapel. She poked at the papers but only raised a half hearted flame here and there that vanished as soon as she stopped. She began to panic. The evidence had to burn, it *had* to. Too much was at stake—the van Arkels' lives as well as Sef's and Mina's, not to speak of her parents'. Herr Rauter might not believe in their innocence!

Then she remembered the kerosene. She seized the can

and poured the fuel on the papers. The flames leaped to meet it with a roar, the can exploded . . . but Janna had flung it away in time to save herself. The flames were raging on the floor now. Janna grabbed Sef's jug of drinking water and poured it on the flames, but that made them worse. The kerosene floated on the water and spread the fire all over the room, attacking all Sef's books and magazines. Thick black smoke was billowing up . . . the fire was uncontrollable. Janna ran for her life. The flames followed her, and so did the smoke. The whole room was a roaring furnace; black smoke poured through the wardrobe into Janna's bedroom. Janna ran down the stairs crying, "Fire! Fire!" The smoke pouring after her attracted more attention than her cries. People jostled and fought to get out of the house. Herr Oster, his face swollen and one eye closed, struggled to the phone and called the fire department.

"Our house has been struck by lightning," Janna heard him say. "Yes, it's burning . . ." The roar of devouring flames became louder and louder.

"Janna, Janna," cried Frau Oster.

"Here I am," shouted Janna, pushing through the mob. "Otto!"

"Here I am!" Her father was carrying out wraps and umbrellas for the guests.

"Dietrich!" But there was no answer. The Baron was nowhere to be seen. The motley company fled into the street, into the pouring rain. By the flickering firelight they looked like a scene from an opera, only more bedraggled. The noise of people shouting and calling, the roaring of the flames, covered the sounds of the approaching fireboats. Neighbors on either side were also fleeing their houses. One of the old ladies stood by the canal, wringing her hands and crying, "My sister! My sister!" The other one seemed to be missing. People scurried about like ants. The firemen jumped ashore and roared through megaphones that everyone had to move to the other side of the canal.

"We need the space on this side," they shouted. Dutch policemen hustled people along. The old lady would not go.

"My sister is in there," she shrieked, pointing to the house. Tongues of flame were licking out of the windows. Mechtild was pushing and shoving to get nearer.

"Dietrich, Dietrich!" she cried.

Otto grabbed Janna's arm. "Mina. Have you seen Mina?"

"She went out the back way," said Janna. She was also looking for the Baron. And then she saw him, staggering out of the neighboring half-house, his face black with smoke, carrying the other old lady. She was alive; Janna could see her move and clutch at the Baron. He carried her to her sister, who cried, "Alida," and folded her in trembling arms. Neighbors immediately offered them shelter and they tottered off, supported by their friends. The Baron was wiping the soot from his face.

"Dietrich!" cried Mechtild. The Baron went to her. The heat was so intense by now that the last stragglers were running across the bridge, guarded by police. Janna and her father joined the crowd collecting on the other side of the canal, watching the spectacle. Even there they could feel the glow of the fire. Janna heard snatches of conversation.

"So disappointing. I thought it would at least be an arsenal, but it was only a gym. I wonder why they hid the door."

"Well, it wasn't pretty . . ."

"They must be insured for millions . . ."

"I said to Bruno, I said, pay up the premium, you never know, and I was right. This could have happened to us."

"I remember another curious case of lightning striking when I was in Wiesbaden . . ."

"What do you think of that marriage?"

"I always thought they were devoted, but it seems . . ."

Janna watched the powerful motors of the fireboats pump water from the canal through hoses onto the burning houses. The flames, mirrored in increasing brilliance in the water, splattered when the spray hit them. Clouds of steam hissed up into the dark sky. The firemen gave up trying to save the burning houses and concentrated on the adjacent ones. The house which had shared the chimney in Sef's room was beginning to burn, but the firemen were able to control the flames. The house on the other side, where the children lived, was saved completely.

Janna could not keep her eyes from the glorious and awing spectacle. As she watched, tears dripped down her cheeks, mingling with the rain. She remembered the sleety day she had arrived, the comfortable dining room, her own room with its mysteries, the beautiful golden long room, the hidden altar. . . . Oh, she hoped Sef and Mina were safe!

I've been Brunhilde all right, she thought. I really *have* lit a funeral pyre!

But no one suspected her. Everyone blamed the lightning. As Janna looked at the pulsing flames which twisted and reached for the sky, she remembered the paintings, especially the big one of the family . . . the rugs, the dollhouse . . . all, all gone. The light of the fire lit up the mournful group standing in the drizzle, scantily covered with wraps, holding umbrellas, unable to tear themselves away.

Janna saw the houses collapse in a shower of sparks. Built together, they perished together. As she watched the fire raging at a lower level, she realized that all traces of Sef and his work were now gone, erased more securely than by any other method she could have devised. She hoped that if the van Arkels knew, they'd forgive her.

Sef and Mina would read about the fire in the paper and have the sense to stay away. Mina would probably guess what had happened. She would probably stay with her brother now and keep house for him.

The glow faded and Janna felt forlorn. All she had learned to love these past months was being taken from her. Mina and Sef . . . would she ever see them again? Only her parents were left . . . or were they?

Janna saw her mother and the Baron standing close together under the shelter of a tree, deep in conversation. The Baron was pleading. Her mother looked as if she was crying. They would go off together, of course, like Siegmund and Sieglinde. That was what her father and the Baron had been fighting about. How could her mother do anything else? What would she do in her mother's place? The Baron was a hero . . . he was rich, handsome, owned a castle in Bavaria. . . . How could that compare with her father, amiably distributing wraps and umbrellas? Janna's lips tightened.

"I won't have it," she muttered angrily. "I'll stop it . . ." But as she grabbed her ring, a feeling of shame overwhelmed her. What was she doing? With the flaming results of her last intervention before her eyes, she was ready to meddle again! She loved her mother, of course, and wanted to keep her . . . but what if her mother wanted to go? She was playing with forces she did not understand, with what the Baron called the wrong kind of power . . .

tyranny and violence. Yes, because she was trying to force her mother—with what? With magic? Sef had said there was no magic; he'd said she was imagining it. But wasn't imagination itself a kind of magic? Hugo had said that thoughts could do harm.

The real trouble was that Janna didn't trust her mother. If she loved her mother enough, wouldn't she leave her free, as God had set Cain free? Even though it was risky, because people did such awful things when they were free! But Janna supposed it was the only way they could learn . . . hadn't her mother said that? Janna saw suddenly that she had been imagining magic to make things go the way she wanted, but it hadn't worked. She didn't like what had happened; everything had gone wrong. It was silly to think a girl like herself could guide events. She didn't have the power—and, what was more, she did not have the wisdom. Only God had that. Her mother was right to believe in God. It was much better than believing in a ring. Perhaps Brunhilde had seen that too, in the end. . . . Pulling the ring from her finger, Janna threw it into the canal. For a moment it winked in the afterglow of the fire; then it was gone. Janna would never play Brunhilde again. She would be just Janna, as Sef was just Sef.

The fireboats were still spraying water on the glowing ashes and blackened woodwork. Janna turned her head sadly. She was sure the Baron would now carry off her mother to his beautiful castle. That's where she belonged, her glamorous mother. She and her father would have to make the best of it. But how would they manage without a house, clothes, possessions? Janna realized suddenly that all she had to wear was her sopping wet Brunhilde costume . . . like those poor Jews . . . Only Janna wasn't going to a gas chamber.

And then someone brushed past her: the Baron in his swirling cloak. He looked tragic, defeated. Her mother stood alone by the canal, wrapped in the raincloak Otto had found for her. Janna watched the Baron as he strode out of her life. She knew she would never see him again and her eyes filled with tears. She could have loved him so much!

"Mother!" cried Janna, flying into her arms. "Mother, are you going to stay with us?"

Her mother kissed her. "Darling," she said. "Is that what you've been worrying about? As if I could leave you! My goodness, what would you do without me, with no house to go to, no clothes to wear—and Papa sure to come down with bronchitis! Here, crawl under my cape, poor child, you're drenched . . ." Janna let herself be snuggled under her mother's open cloak.

"What will happen to us?" she sobbed. "Are you going to send me back to Erna?"

"Of course not," came her father's voice reassuringly from her other side, while a sheltering umbrella appeared above her. "I've already booked a hotel room and friends are lending us clothes. Am I glad I had my wallet with me and wasn't caught in fancy dress! No matter what happens, you'll stay with us. We won't do without her again, will we, Mechtild?"

"No, indeed," said Mechtild. "She wants to be an actress and she might as well start playing small parts. I did at her age. She can be a member of our company. She is really quite good, Otto, and we could use a child. We'll take her with us to Paris."

"To Paris? Do you mean it?" cried Otto joyfully.

"To Paris. I mean it."

The rain was still pouring down. The street was emptying as the spectators wandered off. The show was over. The houses had been reduced to ashes. The fireboats made ready to go.

But in Janna new hope flickered. She was going to act in real plays! She was going to be a member of her parents' company! She would stay with her parents, who were no longer ideal phantoms, existing only to make her happy, but real, imperfect people whom she had learned to love. They were a real family after all, for being a real family didn't mean playing games around a table: it meant sticking together through thick and thin, being loyal to each other. And someday, when all danger was over and the war a thing of the past, Janna would tell her parents the true story of the borrowed house.

About the Author

Hilda van Stockum wrote twenty of her own books and illustrated numerous others between the years 1934 and 1976. Born in 1908 in Holland of Dutch and Irish heritage she met her American husband, E.R. Marlin, in Ireland at the outset of her portrait painting career. After her marriage she put her classical art training to excellent use in her books for children. Her works not only reflect the various countries and cultures of which she has been a part, but are often lively representations of life with her own six children.

Hilda van Stockum wrote in a recent letter that she considered *The Borrowed House* her best "historically and pyschologically, but of course it is for slightly older children."

She also said in an interview that this last title was the most challenging to write of all her books—"it took an enormous amount of research. . . . I spent hours [at the Library of Congress], and the Baron in that book is modeled on the descriptions of the Junker class, the professional officers, a wonderful type of people who hated Hitler and all he stood for. I was also helped by my Dutch relatives, who'd lived through it all." These, and others who went through the Nazi occupation of Holland, confirmed the book's authentic atmosphere and realistic recounting of advents.

When later asked about the significance of the Nordic theme, Hilda van Stockum replied that she could not "write about Hitler if I had not something of beauty to concentrate on." This consideration adds further depth to a many-layered depiction of war and of those caught up in it.

Now in her nineties, the author lives in England amidst family and friends—still active and interested in all that is going on in the world.